2008
Nature's Sunshine Products
The person-to-person
Natural Health Business

Starting out in 1972 as a modest, kitchen-table enterprise in Provo, Utah, Nature's Sunshine Products has matured into one of the fastest growing businesses in the health industry.

There are many reasons for Nature's Sunshine's success. Cutting-edge quality assurance guarantees that NSP's herbal products are the standard of the industry. A highly motivated sales force proudly presents these top-quality products to the world, which in general has become increasingly receptive toward natural health philosophies that incorporate a program of nutritional supplementation.

NSP's success can also be directly attributed to a company-wide philosophy of putting personalized customer service above all other concerns.

In keeping with that spirit, NSP from A to Z is designed to be an easy reference for all 600 or so Nature's Sunshine products (listed in alphabetical order). We've also included a glossary of terms and a section that contains a comprehensive listing of NSP's sales aids and supplies that will help you better display and market these products. It's an invaluable tool in any Nature's Sunshine-based natural health business.

Finally, you'll find a section that explains the body-systems approach to natural health.

A&D, Vitamin *(see Vitamin A&D)*

Acidophilus, Milk-Free

[*Digestive, Intestinal*] is a strain of *Lactobacillus acidophilus*, a symbiotic homo-fermentative, lactic acid-producing microorganism. Acidophilus helps regulate the intestinal tract. Since many people are vegetarian or cannot tolerate dairy products, our acidophilus is dairy-free. Each capsule contains a minimum of 100 million organisms, freeze-dried to maintain viability. Each capsule is also coated with a "modified release" coating so that the contents will be released in the intestinal tract and not in the stomach. Best if stored in a freezer or refrigerator.

Take 1–2 capsules daily with a meal.
Stock No. 1666-7 (90)

Acne

[*Skin*] is a natural homeopathic medicine for the treatment and prevention of pimples due to acne. Use it to clear and heal skin, dry up pimples and prevent future outbreaks. For use internally.

Take 10–15 drops under tongue four–six times daily, decreasing to three times daily upon improvement. For children under 12, consult your health care professional.
Stock No. 8890-9 (1 fl. oz.)

Activated Charcoal

(see Charcoal, Activated)

AdaptaMax®

[*Immune*] is an exclusive combination that combines powerful adaptogens with other nutrient-rich, immune-supporting herbs for a complete, energizing formula. AdaptaMax's adaptogenic strength comes from *Rhodiola rosea*, *Eleutherococcus senticosus*, Korean ginseng, ashwaganda, rosemary, *Gynostemma pentaphyllum* and schizandra. Together these herbs help the body cope with a variety of stressful conditions, including stress on the immune system, fatigue and aging. They fight oxidative cellular damage, energize the body, support positive mood and stimulate the immune system. Other ingredients in this formula include astragalus, reishi mushroom, suma and *Ginkgo biloba* concentrate—to fortify the immune system and help protect the body from the consequences of stress. Alfalfa, kelp, chromium and a fruit-and-vegetable base provide additional nutrients to nourish the body's cells.

NOTE: Pregnant or lactating women should consult their health care professional prior to taking this supplement.

Take 2 capsules with a meal two to three times daily.
Stock No. 872-9 (100)

Adrenal Support

[*Glandular, Nervous*] is a synergistic blend of vitamins, minerals, enzymes and adaptogenic herbs designed to support the adrenal glands. Adrenal Support is formulated with powdered bovine adrenal gland from New Zealand. The ingredients in Adrenal Support may offer help in supporting and maintaining adrenal gland health. The B vitamins, for example, support many of the biochemical processes in the adrenals. Vitamins B1 and B2 help the body cope with stress. Adrenal Support combines the most bioavailable and biological-terrain-friendly forms of these vital nutrients. Each capsule contains powdered bovine adrenal gland, generous amounts of vitamins B1, B2, B6, pantothenic acid and vitamin C, plus zinc, protease, borage oil powder, licorice root and schizandra fruit.

Take 1 capsule with a meal twice daily.

Stock No. 1507-0 (60)

Alfalfa [*Vital Nutrition*]. Arabs called it the "father of herbs." Alfalfa's roots grow 20 feet deep or more, providing the plant with a rich source of nutrients not always found at the ground's surface. Each capsule contains 340 mg alfalfa.

Take 2 capsules with a meal three times daily.

Stock No. 30-2 (100) Ko
Stock No. 32-7 (270) Ko

Algin [*Intestinal*]. Sodium alginate, an important part of the kelp plant, is mucilaginous and gels in water. Many people use it as a nutritional supplement supportive of the intestinal system. Its bulking action encourages normal eliminative function. Alginates have been widely used as food additives and in the cosmetic industry.

Take 2 capsules three times daily between meals. Drink two glasses of juice or water with each serving.

Stock No. 675-1 (100)

ALJ® [*Respiratory*] is the key product for the respiratory system. Airborne particles are everywhere. When particles enter the respiratory system via the nose or the mouth, the body turns on its cleansing mechanisms, and the immune system is put on active duty. Herbal nourishment supports a healthy respiratory system that can be challenged by inhaled irritants. ALJ combines selected herbal ingredients to nourish the immune and respiratory systems. This formula supports healthy lung function and helps support the body during seasonal changes. It also encourages the entire respiratory tract to gently cleanse itself and helps promote respiratory tissue health. It contains:

    Boneset aerial parts
    Fennel seeds
    Fenugreek seeds
    Horseradish root extract
    Mullein leaves extract

Each of these herbs has been used traditionally as a dietary supplement. ALJ combines them in a balanced formula. ALJ liquid extract provides all the benefits of its powdered counterpart in an easily absorbable liquid form, preserved in a glycerin base.

Take 2–4 capsules/tablets with a meal three times daily; liquid, take 20–30 drops (1–2 ml) with water every two–four hours; children take 10–20 drops (0.5–1 ml) with water every two–four hours. One ml is equal to 2 ALJ Vegitabs.

Stock No. 774-3 (100) capsules Ko
Stock No. 767-4 (100) Vegitabs Ko
Stock No. 768-6 (270) Vegitabs Ko
Stock No. 3166-5 (2 fl. oz.)
Liquid Herb (4 Kids Too!) Ko

All Cell Detox [*Digestive, Intestinal*]

contains 17 herbs that support proper bowel function. It contains:

Gentian root
Irish moss plant
Cascara sagrada bark
Fenugreek seeds
Golden seal root and rhizome
Slippery elm bark
Safflower flowers
Black walnut hulls
Myrrh gum
Parthenium root
Yellow dock root
Dandelion root
Oregon grape root and rhizome
Uva ursi leaf extract
Chickweed aerial parts
Catnip leaves

NOTE: This product contains cascara sagrada. See your health care provider prior to use if: pregnant or nursing, any medical condition exists, or when taking any medication. Read and follow recommendation carefully. Do not use if diarrhea, loose stools or abdominal pain are present or develop. Not intended for prolonged use. Use of this product may worsen these conditions and be harmful to your health. Chronic diarrhea can result in serious illness.

Take 2 capsules with a meal three times daily.

Stock No. 1072-4 (100) Ko

Allergy [*Respiratory*]

is a natural homeopathic medicine for the relief of common allergy symptoms, including runny nose, watery eyes, cough and itching associated with hay fever, certain foods, poison ivy and insect bites.

Adults and children age 12 and above, take 10–15 drops under the tongue every 10–15 minutes or as needed until symptoms improve; then decrease to every one to two hours, then to four times daily until symptoms are relieved. For children under 12, consult your health care professional.

Stock No. 8714-3 (1 fl. oz.)

Allergies—Hayfever/Pollen

[*Respiratory*] is a natural homeopathic medicine for the relief of minor hay fever/pollen allergy symptoms of runny nose, sneezing, itchy eyes, watery eyes and respiratory congestion.

Take 10–15 drops under the tongue every three hours for acute symptoms. For chronic allergies, take 10–15 drops three times daily for at least 30 days. For children under 12, consult your health care professional.

Stock No. 8925-0 (1 fl. oz.)

Allergies—Mold, Yeast & Dust

[*Respiratory*] is a natural homeopathic medicine for the

relief of minor symptoms of congestion, headaches, sore throat, watery eyes, sneezing and itching related to mold, dust and yeast allergies.

Take 10–15 drops under the tongue every three hours for acute symptoms. For chronic allergies, take 10–15 drops three times a day for at least 30 days. For children under 12, consult your health care professional.

Stock No. 8920-8 (1 fl. oz.)

Aloe Vera [*Intestinal, Skin*] is a nutritional storehouse, naturally containing several vitamins plus 18 amino acids, in addition to many other dietary factors. It soothes the skin and the tissues lining the digestive tract. It contains many biologically active compounds that support the digestion and absorption of food and nourish the intestinal system.

Many companies manufacture aloe vera, but most products on the market have lost much of the plant's original benefits due to over-processing. Beware of aloe vera juice that claims to have no disagreeable taste. Removing this taste can leave you with a product that is only 10–15 percent aloe vera at best.

NSP aloe vera is processed in a special way to avoid the loss of essential vitamins, minerals and other constituents. The leaf is filleted; then the green outer portion that contains aloin is removed, leaving the gel that remains in the leaf. The gel remains thick when the leaf is first cut, but after a few minutes, an enzymatic reaction causes it to become liquid and freely run out. It is this 100 percent pure liquid that NSP collects. To prevent bacterial contamination, we add sodium benzoate as a preservative. Sodium benzoate is effective in very small quantities, and it properly and safely preserves aloe vera juice.

NSP Whole Leaf Aloe Vera provides a higher level of mucopolysaccharides than regular filleted aloe vera. Only the intense cleansing components have been removed, leaving a high level of mucopolysaccharides (7,000 mg per liter). Used externally, aloe is known for its hydrating and moisturizing properties. Shake well before using and refrigerate after opening.

For external use, try Aloe Vera Gel. The gel is created by adding a gelling agent, Irish moss extract, to the juice. Aloe vera gel spreads on quickly and moisturizes, leaving no stickiness.

For best results, drink 2–6 oz. Aloe Vera Juice daily as is or mixed with water or juice. Or, drink 1 oz. Whole Leaf Aloe Vera Juice mixed with 8 oz. of water or juice 4 times daily. Apply Aloe Vera Gel to the skin as desired for its moisturizing and toning properties.

Stock No. 1680-4 (32 fl. oz.)
Aloe Vera Juice Ko
Stock No. 1693-4 (32 fl. oz.)
Whole Leaf Aloe Vera
Stock No. 1679-2 (8 fl. oz.)
Aloe Vera Gel

Aloe Vera, Freeze Dried

[*Immune*]. Provides the same benefits as liquid Aloe Vera Juice but in capsulated form. Freeze-drying removes water content while maintaining the full botanical value of Aloe Vera. Each capsule contains 150 mg freeze-dried aloe vera and is equivalent to 1 fluid ounce of 100% Aloe Vera juice.

Take 1 or 2 capsules with a meal three times daily.

Stock No. 1686-1 (64) Ko

Alpha Lipoic Acid [*Nervous, Glandular*]

is often called the universal antioxidant. It has both fat- and water-soluble properties and can cross any membrane in the body. Consequently, alpha lipoic acid can protect the integrity of the cell membrane as well as offset cell stress. Alpha lipoic acid also promotes mitochondrial activity to help keep your body and its tissues vibrant. It also enhances the efforts of other antioxidants and helps support the body's natural removal of toxins. In addition to its antioxidant properties, alpha lipoic acid directs calories away from fat production and toward energy production, supports blood sugar levels already within the normal range and enhances the nervous and cardiovascular systems. NSP Alpha Lipoic Acid is formulated with turmeric, a liver-protecting antioxidant. Each capsule provides 250 mg alpha lipoic acid.

Take 1 capsule with a meal twice daily.

Stock No. 1505-6 (60) Ko

Amino Acids, Free

(*see Free Amino Acids with Magnesium & l-Carnitine*)

Anamú [*Immune, Structural*].

Folk use suggests that people who wish to target their immune systems may benefit from the immune-enhancing properties of the anamú leaf. Historically, the leaf powder has been used to support the structural system, particularly the joints.

Anamú has many active constituents, including tannins, polyphenols, senfols and benzyl-2-hydroxyethyl-trisulfide. Some of these constituents appear to provide protection to cells. Each capsule of NSP Anamú contains 400 mg of anamú leaf powder, scientifically identified and certified as mucura hembra anamú.

NOTE: Pregnant women or women considering pregnancy should not use this product.

Take 1 capsule with a meal three times daily.

Stock No. 39-8 (100) Ko

Anti-Gas, Chinese [*Digestive, Intestinal*]

is a Chinese formula combining 15 herbs. It is considered "earth-reducing" in Chinese herbology. Its Chinese name *xiao dao* can be translated as "clear the congestion." It supports both the digestive and detoxifying functions of the body, including the urinary system. The primary herbs in Anti-Gas are gastrodia, agastache, crataegus and hoelen. Under Chinese philosophy, this formula is

designed to move energy (chi) to the head and support the natural elimination of excess moisture and toxins. Anti-Gas contains:
  Agastache tops
  Crataegus fruit
  Hoelen sclerotium
  Magnolia bark
  Oryza fruit
  Shen-chu whole plant
  Citrus peel
  Gastrodia rhizome
  Panax ginseng root
  Typhonium rhizome
  Atractylodes rhizome
  Cardamon fruit
  Platycodon root
  Ginger rhizome
  Licorice root
  Take 3 capsules with a meal three times daily.
Stock No. 1869-9 (100)

Anti-Gas TCM Concentrate, Chinese [*Digestive, Intestinal*]

contains the same 15 herbs found in Chinese Anti-Gas but in a highly concentrated blend. It is considered "earth-reducing" in Chinese herbology. Its Chinese name *xiao dao* can be translated as "clear the congestion." This formula supports both the digestive and detoxifying functions of the body, including the urinary system. Key herbs in this formula include gastrodia, agastache, crataegus and hoelen. Under Chinese philosophy, this formula is designed to move energy (chi) to the head and support the natural elimination of excess moisture and toxins. Anti-Gas contains:
  Agastache tops
  Crataegus fruit
  Hoelen sclerotium
  Magnolia bark
  Oryza fruit
  Shen-chu whole plant
  Citrus peel
  Gastrodia rhizome
  Panax ginseng root
  Typhonium rhizome
  Atractylodes rhizome
  Cardamon fruit
  Platycodon root
  Ginger rhizome
  Licorice root
NOTE: Pregnant or lactating women should consult with a health care provider prior to taking this supplement.
  Take 1 or 2 capsules with a meal daily. Each capsule is equivalent to 6 capsules of regular Chinese Anti-Gas.
Stock No. 1018-9 (30)

Anti-Gas Formula [*Digestive*]

contains a special blend of herbs that support digestion, assisting the body's efforts to expel intestinal gas and calm occasional nausea. This formula contains:
  Papaya fruit extract
  Ginger rhizome
  Peppermint leaves
  Wild yam root
  Fennel seed
  Dong quai root
  Lobelia aerial parts
  Spearmint leaves
  Catnip leaves and flowers
  Take 2 capsules after meals three times daily.
Stock No. 1198-4 (100) Ko

Appetite Control [*Weight Management*] is a natural

homeopathic medicine that assists in the control of appetite as an aid to weight loss.

Take 10–15 drops under the tongue 30 minutes prior to meals. This medicine is not recommended for children under 12.

Stock No. 8722-4 (1 fl. oz.)

APS II® with White Willow Bark

[*Nervous*] provides nutrients that aid proper nervous system function. White willow bark contains salicin, a compound chemically similar to salicylic acid. Salicin appears to help prevent the production of prostaglandins. Valerian root provides additional nervous system support, including promoting feelings of relaxation. APS II with White Willow Bark is a source of trace amounts of calcium and magnesium. Its ingredients include:

White willow bark
Lettuce leaves
Valerian root
Capsicum fruit

Take 2 capsules with a meal three times daily.

Stock No. 780-8 (100) Ko

Artemisia Combination

[*Intestinal*] combines all the herbal components of NSP's former Elecampane Combination with two species of artemisia—wormwood (*Artemisia annua*) and mugwort (*Artemisia vulgaris*). These herbs contribute to a friendly environment for intestinal flora. Add to them elecampane root, clove flower buds, garlic bulb root, ginger root, spearmint herb and turmeric root, and you have a more powerful product. Artemisia is used widely for intestinal support.

CAUTION: Not recommended during pregnancy.

Take 2 capsules with a meal three times daily for 10 days, then discontinue use for 5 days. Repeat this cycle (10 days on, 5 days off) for up to 60 days. For best results, use with Para-Cleanse.

Stock No. 787-6 (100) Ko

Arthritis

[*Structural*] is a natural homeopathic medicine for the relief of minor arthritis symptoms: pain, stiffness and inflammation of joints.

Take 10–15 drops under the tongue every 10–15 minutes or as needed until symptoms improve; then decrease to every one or two hours, then to four times daily until symptoms are relieved. This medicine is not recommended for children under 12.

Stock No. 8800-4 (1 fl. oz.)

Ascorbates, Vitamin C

(*see Vitamin C Ascorbates*)

Asthma

[*Respiratory*] is a natural homeopathic medicine for control of the symptoms of asthma and bronchitis, including difficulty in breathing, shortness of breath, tightness of chest, wheezing or coughing. Contains 20 percent USP Alcohol.

CAUTION: For asthma sufferers only. Seek medical assistance immediately if symptoms do not improve within 1 hour or become worse. Do not use this product unless you have been diagnosed by a doctor as having asthma. If you have ever been hospitalized for asthma, or if you currently take any prescription drugs for asthma, use only when directed by a doctor. *Take 10–15 drops under the tongue every 10–15 minutes or as needed until symptoms improve; then decrease to every one or two hours, then to four times daily until symptoms are relieved. For children under 12, consult your health care professional.*

Stock No. 8704-4
(1 fl. oz.) 4 Kids Too!

Astragalus [*Immune, Circulatory*] root has been used to promote immune function and as a tonic to build stamina. Ancient Chinese texts record the use of astragalus for tonifying the spleen, blood and chi.

Astragalus contains saponins, sterols, flavonoids, isoflavones and polysaccharides that have health-promoting benefits. Astragalus root may stimulate the immune system in many ways. It promotes the production of stem cells in bone marrow and lymph tissue and encourages their development into active immune cells. It appears to help trigger immune cells from a "resting" state into heightened activity.

One study showed that astragalus root helps promote and maintain respiratory function. It also enhances the body's production of immunoglobulin and stimulates macrophages. Astragalus can help activate T cells and natural killer cells. Several studies also show that astragalus demonstrates heart benefits, including protection against oxidative cellular damage.

The flavonoids, saponins and polysaccharides found in astragalus root help minimize free radical damage to membranes. Each capsule contains 420 mg of astragalus root. *Take 2 capsules with a meal three times daily.*

Stock No. 40-1 (100) Ko

Ayurvedic Blood Sugar Formula [*Glandular*].

This formula, developed by Indian Ayurvedic masters, provides nutrients necessary for glandular system function. It supports the liver, pancreas and intestines in promoting blood sugar levels already within the normal range. Each preservative-free capsule contains a 570 mg blend of concentrated extracts of these herbs:

Gymnema sylvestre leaf extract
Momordica charantia fruit bark extract
Pterocarpus marsupium gum extract
Aegle marmelos leaf extract
Enicostemma littorale herb extract
Andrographis paniculata herb extract
Curcuma longa rhizome extract
Syzygium cumini seed extract
Azadirachta indica leaf extract
Picrorhiza kurroa root extract
Trigonella foenum-graecum seed extract
Cyperus rotundus tuber extract
Take 2 capsules with a meal three times daily.

Stock No. 1298-8 (100)

Ayurvedic Bronchial Formula

[*Respiratory*] is designed to offer support to the respiratory system. This system regularly encounters airborne particles such as microorganisms, pollutants, pollens and dust, and protects delicate body tissues. As a result, the functions of the lungs and bronchi can be affected.

This formula nourishes the lungs and bronchi and helps support the respiratory system. Its Western counterparts are ALJ and Sinus Support EF®. Ayurvedic Bronchial Formula is composed primarily of traditional herbs used in Ayurveda, the ancient health science of India. It includes:

Adhatoda vasica leaf extract
Glycyrrhiza glabra root extract
Alpinia galanga rhizome extract
Clerodendrum indicum root
Inula racemosa root extract
Myrica nagi bark extract
Verbascum thapsus leaves
Phyllanthus emblica fruit
Hedychium spicatum root
Picrorhiza kurroa root extract
Pimpinella anisum fruit
Pistacia integerrima gall
Zingiber officinale rhizome
Ocimum sanctum leaf extract
Tylophora asthmatica leaf
Abies webbina leaf
Elettaria cardamomum seed
Ferula assafoetida gum
Take 2 capsules with a meal three times daily.

Stock No. 1297-2 (100)

Ayurvedic Joint Health

[*Structural*] provides nutritional support for the skeletal system. This system takes a lot of punishment: from heavy lifting, to sedentary living, to getting a less-than-optimal level of necessary nutrients. Exercise and nutrition play very important roles in the development and strengthening of the skeletal system. It is of the utmost importance to seek a balanced environment that will contribute to skeletal health.

Ayurvedic Joint Health's Western counterpart is Joint Support. This formula contains the following:

Withania somnifera root
Commiphora mukul gum extract
Smilax china root
Boswellia serrata gum
Holarrhena antidysenterica bark
Paederia foetida leaf extract
Vitex negundo leaf extract
Apium graveolens seed
Boerhaavia diffusa root
Trachyspermum ammi fruit
Tribulus terrestris fruit
Cyperus rotundus tuber
Tinospora cordifolia stem
Trigonella foenum-graeceum seed
Take 2 capsules with a meal three times daily.

Stock No. 1296-1 (100)

Ayurvedic Skin Detox

[*Skin*]. As the largest organ of the body and one that has continuous contact with the environment, the skin needs proper care and nourishment to remain healthy. Since the skin is a primary detoxifying organ, the state of the skin often reflects our general state of internal health.

As with all NSP Ayurvedic formulas, Skin Detox is designed to maintain a balanced state of well-being. Its Western counterpart is HSN-W®. This formula contains:

Dandelion root
Acacia catechu bark extract
Azadirachta indica bark extract
Smilax china root
Picrorhiza kurroa root
Hemidesmus indicus root
Holarrhena antidysenterica bark
Rubia cordifolia root
Swertia chirata herb extract
Caesalpinia crista seed extract
Fumaria parviflora herb
Alstonia scholaris bark extract
Tinospora cordifolia stem
Curcuma longa rhizome
Phylilanthus emblica fruit
Terminalia belerica fruit
Terminalia chebula fruit

Take 2 capsules with a meal three times daily. For best results, use with BP-X® (blood purifier formula) and Irish Moss Hand & Body Lotion.

Stock No. 1299-6 (100)

B

B12 Complete, Liquid *(see Liquid B12 Complete)*

B-Complex *(see Vitamin B-Complex, Vitamin B6, Liquid B12 Complete, Niacin and Pantothenic Acid)*

Balanced B-Complex
(see Vitamin B-Complex, Balanced)

Barley Juice Powder Concentrate *[Vital Nutrition]* is derived from young barley plants, which have strong enhancing functions. Barley greens (dry weight) are also a superior source of chlorophyll, the nutrient-rich byproduct of photosynthesis that makes plants green and is chemically similar to human blood. Barley greens (dry weight) provide 30 times more vitamin B1 than milk, 9–10 times more calcium than milk, seven times more vitamin C than oranges, and nearly five times the iron of spinach. Each capsule contains 480 mg barley juice powder.

Take 8 capsules daily with water on an empty stomach.

Stock No. 55-1 (100) Ko

Bayberry *[Glandular, Immune]*.
The dried bark of the bayberry root has astringent properties. It has been used traditionally for a variety of systems and organs, including the female reproductive system, the liver, the immune system, oral health and more. Each capsule contains 440 mg bayberry root bark (*Myrica cerifera*).

NOTE: Pregnant or lactating women should consult their health care professional prior to taking this supplement.

Take 1 capsule with a meal twice daily.

Stock No. 60-6 (100) Ko

Bedwetting *(see Herbasaurs® Bedwetting)*

Bee Pollen [*Vital Nutrition*], a true gift from Mother Nature, contains many essential nutrients. As bees forage, the pollen mixes with nectar and accumulates in yellow granules on the bees' legs. Pollen has a strong nutritional profile. It contains up to 35 percent complete protein, 22 amino acids, B vitamins, 27 mineral salts, trace elements and several enzymes. Greeks called it the "nectar of the gods." NSP Bee Pollen is naturally dried to preserve vital enzymes. Each capsule contains 450 mg bee pollen.

Take 2 capsules with meals twice daily.

Stock No. 70-9 (100) Ko

Bentonite, Hydrated [*Intestinal*] is a natural clay that comes from volcanic ash. Taken internally, it supports the intestinal system in the elimination of toxins. This product is made by suspending microfine USP-grade bentonite in purified water.

Take 1 tablespoon with a glass of water twice daily as an aid for detoxification via the alimentary canal. Shake well before use.

Stock No. 1725-9 (32 fl. oz.)

Bergamot BIO Pure Essential Oil (*see Essential Oils*)

Berry Healthy® Drink Mix [*Immune, Circulatory*] combines natural berry powders and antioxidant flavonoids. It contains no artificial flavors and provides an excellent source of vitamin C (100% DV). Antioxidants support the immune system and help maintain optimum circulatory health. They also nutritionally support the brain, eyes and urinary tract. For remarkable health benefits in a great-tasting drink mix, get Berry Healthy today!

Mix 1 slightly rounded scoop with 6 oz. of cold water.

Stock No. 3206-8 (9.8 oz.)

30 Servings

Bifidophilus Flora Force® [*Digestive, Intestinal*]. The healthy human intestinal tract contains billions of intestinal flora that live in a delicate balance with each other and in symbiosis with us. We provide them with a home, and in turn they break down our food into easily absorbed nutrients. They also aid digestion in a variety of ways and promote immunity. Factors such as stress, environmental conditions or the use of certain substances can affect their vitality.

Bifidophilus Flora Force provides billions of beneficial intestinal microorganisms that offer a whole range of health benefits. This product contains *Lactobacillus acidophilus* and *Bifidobacterium longum* plus two additional strains, *L. casei* and *L. rhamnosus* for a more complete probiotic formula and added support for the immune system. NSP added fructo-oligosaccharides (short- and long-chain), which support the growth of these beneficial organisms to ensure the potency of this product. Each capsule provides a good balance of 4 billion beneficial microorganisms.

This product is recommended for daily use to help maintain a healthy balance of friendly flora in the intestinal tract and to support the immune system. Refrigerate or freeze to maintain freshness. Each capsule is coated with a "modified release" coating so that the contents will be released in the intestinal tract.

Adults: Take 1–2 capsules with meals daily. Children: Take 1 capsule daily with a meal.

Stock No. 4080-4 (90) Ko

Bilberry Fruit Concentrate [*Vital Nutrition*].

Bilberry (*Vaccinium myrtillus*) is also known in some parts of the U.S. as huckleberry. During World War II, British pilots ate bilberries before their night flights to nutritionally support their vision. Bilberry also supports the circulatory system. Its active constituents include anthocyanins, which are strong antioxidants. Nature's Sunshine uses 40 mg of bilberry fruit standardized to 25 percent anthocyanins. Bilberry should be used over time in order for the body to best assimilate its unique nutritional properties. Each tablet contains 40 mg bilberry fruit concentrate.

Take 2 tablets with a meal three times daily.

Stock No. 74-8 (60) Ko

Black Cohosh [*Glandular*]

has been valued by many societies for its nutritional support of the female reproductive system. Many women have found that black cohosh provides nutritional support during menopause. Black cohosh contains phytoestrogens. Each capsule contains 525 mg of black cohosh.

Take 1 capsule with a meal twice daily. For best results, use with Vitamin E.

Stock No. 80-3 (100) Ko

Black Currant Oil [*Immune*]

contains gamma-linolenic acid (GLA) along with other important polyunsaturated fatty acids. Fatty acids are involved in many bodily functions, such as maintaining body temperature, insulating nerves, cushioning and protecting tissues and creating energy. These essential fatty acids are precursors of prostaglandins, which must be present for functions involved with blood vessels, maintaining arterial pressure already within the normal range, metabolizing dietary cholesterol, activating T-lymphocytes, protecting against platelet aggregation and other functions. Before the discovery of black currant oil, the only other known sources of GLA were mother's milk and evening primrose oil. Each black currant oil capsule provides 40–45 mg GLA per serving, that's 16–18 percent GLA (more than evening primrose oil). It contains two essential fatty acids—linoleic acid and alpha-linolenic acid—and the unique stearidonic acid.

Take 1 capsule with a meal three times daily.

Stock No. 1810-9 (90)

Black Ointment [*Skin*] is

designed for topical use. Historically, many of the herbs in this ointment were used to help soothe the skin. Black Ointment contains extracts of chaparral herb, lobelia herb, comfrey leaf, golden seal root, plantain root, red clover herb, mullein herb, marshmallow root, chickweed herb and myrrh gum in a base of olive oil, beeswax, pine tar and vitamin E oil. Mixed with Bone/Skin Poultice, Black Ointment makes an excellent poultice.

Apply liberally as often as needed.
Stock No. 1696-9 (1 oz.)

Black Walnut [*Intestinal*]. The

ancient Greeks used the hulls of black walnut to support the intestinal system and the skin. Herbalists classify black walnut as an astringent because it is rich in tannins, which have toning properties. Black walnut's fame in folk herbology is due to its cleansing properties. The unripe hulls of the black walnut contain vitamin C and the trace minerals chromium and iodine. Available in capsules and in an alcohol-base liquid form. Each regular capsule contains 500 mg black walnut. Each ATC concentrated capsule contains 480 mg black walnut concentrate.

Take 2 capsules with a meal twice daily. ATC concentrated: Take 1 capsule with a meal twice daily. Liquid: Take approximately 20–25 drops (1 ml) with water twice daily. One ml is equal to 2 capsules of black walnut.

Stock No. 90-8 (100) capsules Ko
Stock No. 93-3 (50)
ATC Concentrated Ko
Stock No. 1755-7 (2 fl. oz.)
Liquid Herb Ko

Blessed Thistle [*Glandular*]

historically has been used to support the female reproductive system, improve digestion and support liver function. It contains sesquiterpene lactones (support digestion) and lignans. Each capsule contains 325 mg blessed thistle aerial parts.

Take 2 capsules with a meal twice daily.
Stock No. 100-1 (100) Ko

Blood Build, Chinese

[*Circulatory*] is a Chinese combination of 18 herbs designed to nutritionally support the blood, liver, glands and general circulation. The Chinese call this formula *bu xue*, which translates as "to nurture the blood." It is designed to strengthen a weakened wood constitution. This formula may improve blood quality and purity and help strengthen the immune system. Primary herbs include dang gui, alisma, peony, ganoderma and atractylodes. The combination includes:

Ganoderma mushroom
Lycium fruit

Peony root without bark
Tang-kuei root
Bupleurum root
Cornus fruit without seeds
Curcuma root tuber
Salvia root and rhizome
Achyranthes root
Alisma rhizome
Astragalus root
Atractylodes rhizome
Cnidium rhizome
He shou wu root tuber
Ligustrum fruit
Rehmannia root tuber
Cyperus rhizome
Panax ginseng root

Take 3 capsules with a meal three times daily. For best results, use with I-X and Skeletal Strength.

Stock No. 1881-9 (100)

Blood Build TCM Concentrate, Chinese [*Circulatory*] contains

the same herbs found in Chinese Blood Build but in a highly concentrated blend. This combination of 18 Chinese herbs is designed to nutritionally support the blood, liver, glands and general circulation. The Chinese call this formula *bu xue*, which translates as "to nurture the blood." It is designed to strengthen a weakened wood constitution. This formula may improve blood quality and purity and help strengthen the immune system. Primary herbs include dang gui, alisma, peony, ganoderma and atractylodes. The combination includes:

Dang gui root
Ganoderma plant
Lycium fruit

Peony root without bark
Bupleurum root
Cornus fruit without seeds
Curcuma root tuber
Salvia root and rhizome
Achyranthes root
Alisma rhizome
Astragalus root
Atractylodes rhizome
He shou wu root tuber
Ligustrum fruit
Cnidium rhizome
Rehmannia root tuber
Cyperus rhizome
Panax ginseng root

NOTE: Pregnant or lactating women should consult their health care provider prior to taking this supplement.

Take 2 capsules with a meal daily. For best results, use with I-X and Skeletal Strength. Each capsule is equivalent to 5 capsules of regular Chinese Blood Build.

Stock No. 1005-9 (30)

Blood Pressurex [*Circulatory*].

Blood Pressurex is a blend of essential and natural ingredients that may help the body maintain blood pressure levels already within the normal range. The main ingredients of this formula are the powerful herbs *Coleus forskohlii*, olive leaf extract, hawthorn berries extract and golden rod; the amino acid l-arginine; and the potent antioxidants vitamin E and grape seed extract. Grape seed extract contains an array of bioflavonoids, antioxidants and polyphenols, including resveratrol. Studies suggest that grape seed extract may be beneficial for maintaining blood pressure levels and may contribute to overall cardiovascular health.

All of these nutrients combine to help protect blood vessels, promote blood flow in the peripheral arteries and inhibit cell damage. These benefits are made possible due to their potent antioxidant properties.

CAUTION: Consult your health care provider before using this product if you are currently taking prescription medication(s) for high blood pressure or if your blood pressure is above normal (diastolic reading above 90). Do not discontinue use of your prescription medication(s) without your doctor's approval.

Take 1 capsule with a meal three times daily. **Stock No. 554-8 (60)**

Blue Cohosh [*Glandular*]. Also
called papoose root or squaw root, this herb is known to women as a mild alternative to black cohosh. It is traditionally used for female glandular support. Each capsule contains 450 mg blue cohosh root (*Caulophyllum thalictroides*).

Take 1 capsule with a meal twice daily. **Stock No. 110-0 (100)** Ko

Blue Vervain [*Nervous*] is also
known as wild hyssop or traveler's joy. It is considered a bitter and a tonic by herbalists who use the plant's leaves and flowers. The plant contains glycosides, volatile oils, tannins, alkaloids and bitter substances. Nature's Sunshine

offers blue vervain in a highly concentrated liquid form. The active substances are extracted and suspended in a base of pure vegetable glycerin. This liquid extract contains no preservatives or additives.

Adults: Take 1/2 to 1 teaspoon (2.5 to 5 ml) three times daily. Children: Take 1/4 to 1/2 teaspoon (1.25 to 2.5 ml) three times daily.

Stock No. 3160-8 (2 fl. oz.)

4 Kids Too! Ko

Bone/Skin Poultice [*Structural*]
is an ideal herbal substitute for encapsulated comfrey leaf. It contains plantain leaves, rehmannia root, mullein leaves and yarrow aerial parts.

Take 2 capsules with a meal three times daily, or use with Golden Salve and Black Ointment as a poultice.

Stock No. 1248-2 (100) Ko

Bowel Detox [*Intestinal*] is a
key product that supports proper digestive and intestinal function. It promotes healthy, regular elimination of waste from the colon. This formula provides digestive enzymes to aid digestion in the upper gastrointestinal tract along with ingredients to provide needed bulk, and to encourage proper flow of waste through the colon.

	Amount per capsule	Amount per 3 capsules	% DV
Vitamin A	300 IU	900 IU	15
(beta-carotene, contains soy)			
Vitamin C	10 mg	30 mg	50

Vitamin E (d-alpha tocopherol from soy)	2 IU	6 IU	20
Zinc (gluconate)	1 mg	3 mg	20
Selenium (amino acid chelate)	5 mcg	15 mcg	25

Bowel Detox contains betaine HCl (24 mg), bile salts (24 mg), pancreatin (108 mg) and pepsin (24 mg, contains lactose from milk). These nutrients come in a base of psyllium hulls, algin, cascara sagrada bark, ginger rhizome, apple pectin, parthenium root, charcoal, marshmallow root extract, sodium copper chlorophyllin and bentonite clay.

NOTE: This product contains cascara sagrada. See your health care provider prior to use if you are pregnant or nursing, any medical condition exists or when taking any medication. Read and follow recommendation carefully.

Do not use if diarrhea, loose stools or abdominal pain are present or develop. Not intended for prolonged use. Use of this product may worsen these conditions and be harmful to your health. Chronic diarrhea can result in serious illness. May cause allergic reaction in persons sensitive to inhaled or ingested psyllium.

Take 2 capsules with morning meal and 3 capsules with evening meal daily.

Stock No. 3020-8 (120)

BP-X® [*Circulatory*] combines herbs traditionally used to support blood and kidney health. This formula helps maintain healthy bowel function and supports digestion, which may support blood quality. It contains:

Burdock root
Pau d'arco bark
Red clover tops
Dandelion root
Sarsaparilla root
Yellow dock root
Buckthorn bark
Cascara sagrada bark
Yarrow flowers
Oregon grape root
Prickly ash bark

NOTE: This product contains cascara sagrada and buckthorn. See your health care provider prior to use if: pregnant or nursing, any medical condition exists, or when taking any medication. Read and follow recommendation carefully. Do not use if diarrhea, loose stools or abdominal pain are present or develop. Use of this product may worsen these conditions and be harmful to your health. Chronic diarrhea can result in serious illness.

Take 2 capsules with a meal twice daily.

Stock No. 803-2 (100) Ko

Brain-Protex with Huperzine A

[*Nervous*], a perfect supplement for longevity and health, is designed to give the brain protection against free radical damage. It is especially helpful for those who desire extra support for brain health, nerve function and alertness. Brain-Protex combines protective herbs, antioxidants and phospholipids that favorably impact age-related memory loss, boost mental acuity and curb free radical damage to the brain.

This formula features the celebrated herb *Ginkgo biloba*, which improves cerebral blood circulation to help promote memory and concentration. Huperzine A, from an extract of Chinese club moss, may play a role in aiding memory. Brain-Protex also contains a blend of phosphatidyl serine, choline, ethanolamine and inositol—substances that may help support memory and brain function. It also includes *Rhododendron caucasicum*, a potent free radical quencher used for decades in Russia by longevity enthusiasts. It also contains the powerful antioxidants lycopene and alpha lipoic acid.

Take 2 capsules with a meal twice daily.

Stock No. 3114-1 (60)

Breast Assured® [*Glandular*] is a

blend of herbs and nutrients that support and protect the female reproductive system, including the breasts. The active compounds and the metabolites that compose Breast Assured act as antioxidants, bind estrogen receptors and boost immune stimulation.

Breast Assured is a combination of flax meal, ellagic acid from pomegranate extract powder, genistein from kudzu extract, maitake mushroom, lutein beads and calcium d-glucarate. Maitake mushroom stimulates immune system activity. Ellagic acid has been shown to have chemo-protective properties. Flax promotes a healthy balance of estrogen levels in the body.

Take 2 or 3 capsules once daily with a meal.

Stock No. 1122-4 (60)

Breast Enhance [*Glandular*].

Breast Enhance is an all-natural herbal combination that helps support female reproductive health and breast tissue. The postovulatory and premenstrual experience of breast enlargement, when both estrogen and progesterone secretions are higher, suggest that hormone levels may affect breast appearance and shape. Isoflavones may mimic the hormones principally responsible for the growth of breast tissue. Breast Enhance contains isoflavones, vitamins and some phytosterols. Ingredients include kudzu root extract, alfalfa aerial parts, dong quai root extract and saw palmetto fruit extract.

Take 1 capsule with a meal three times daily.

Stock No. 1107-3 (90) Ko

Breathe EZ TCM Concentrate, Chinese [*Respiratory*]. This

combination of 14 Chinese herbs provides nutrients for the respiratory system. The Chinese would consider this a formula for a stressed metal constitution. Its Chinese name *xuan fei* can be translated to mean "ventilate the lungs." This formula supports the body in the battle to remove toxins from the entire respiratory tract, especially the lungs.

Its primary herbs— citrus peel and schizandra—support the body's efforts to clear waste from the respiratory system and enhance energy in the lungs. Chinese Breathe EZ contains:

Citrus peel
Typhonium rhizome
Bamboo sap
Bupleurum root
Fritillaria bulb
Hoelen sclerotium
Perilla leaves
Platycodon root
Xingren apricot seed
Ophiopogon root tuber
Tussilago flower buds
Ginger rhizome
Schizandra fruit
Licorice root

NOTE: Pregnant or lactating women should consult their health care provider prior to taking this supplement.

Take 2 capsules with a meal daily.

Stock No. 1036-3 (30)

Breathe Free Pure Essential Oil Blend (*see Essential Oils*)

Burdock [*Digestive, Immune*] is a common weed with giant leaves, and seeds (burrs) that cling tenaciously to clothing. Its active constituents give burdock immune and digestive system-supporting properties. Each capsule contains 360 mg burdock. In herbology, the dried, powdered root is used.

Take 2 capsules with a meal twice daily.

Stock No. 140-2 (100) Ko

Butcher's Broom [*Circulatory*]. Traditionally, the herb was taken to support the circulatory system. Butcher's Broom contains important flavonoids (natural substances that strengthen capillary walls) such as rutin. It also contains saponins, which offer a variety of circulatory benefits. Each capsule contains 400 mg of the dried, powdered root.

Take 2 capsules with a meal twice daily.

Stock No. 135-5 (100) Ko

C

C, Vitamin (*see Vitamin C*)

C-X [*Glandular*] is designed to provide herbal support for the reproductive glands of mature women. The formula consists of:

Dong quai root
Blessed thistle aerial parts
Licorice root
Eleuthero root
Sarsaparilla root extract
Black cohosh root extract
Squaw vine whole plant
False unicorn root

NOTE: Pregnant or lactating women should consult their health care provider prior to taking this supplement.

Take 2 capsules with a meal three times daily.

Stock No. 1230-6 (100) Ko

CA, Herbal [*Structural*] provides the body with natural sources of important minerals. Magnesium works synergistically with calcium, and silicon strengthens body tissues, including the sheath surrounding the nerves. The formula consists of:

Alfalfa herb
Horsetail herb
Oatstraw stem
Plantain herb
Marshmallow root
Wheat grass herb
Hops flowers

These herbs are traditionally used to support the structural system.

The ATC formula contains:

Alfalfa herb
Marshmallow root
Slippery elm bark
Oatstraw stem
Irish Moss plant
Horsetail herb
Passion flower herb

Take 1 capsule with a meal three times daily. ATC: Take 1 capsule with a meal twice daily.

Stock No. 823-5 (100) Ko
Stock No. 826-3 (50) Ko
ATC Concentrate

Caffeine Detox [*Nervous*] is a natural homeopathic medicine for relief of minor symptoms of caffeine withdrawal, such as irritability, impatience, anger, headache, sleeplessness, upset stomach, heartburn and nausea.

Adults and children 12 and older, take 20–30 drops under the tongue every two hours on the first day; the second day, 15 drops every two hours; the third day, 15 drops every three hours; thereafter, 20–30 drops every four–six hours, or as often as necessary. For children under 12,

consult your health care professional.

Stock No. 8727-8 (1 fl. oz.)

Calcium, Liquid (*see Liquid Calcium*)

Calcium–Magnesium, SynerPro® [*Vital Nutrition*]

combination recognizes that each of these minerals depends on the other for proper assimilation in the body. Calcium is essential to the health of bones, teeth and muscles, and it plays an essential role in blood clotting, nerve conduction and many cellular functions. Magnesium is an integral part of more than 300 enzymes in the body and, with calcium, affects nerve and muscle functions. More than 80 percent of the natural magnesium in grains is lost by removal of the germ and outer layers during food processing.

This product provides nutrients that support and maintain the structural system, supports the maintenance of a balanced pH and supports the circulatory system.

This combination also includes vitamin D, known to facilitate the absorption of calcium, as well as phosphorus, zinc, copper and boron. Two tablets contain the following nutrients in the SynerPro concentrate base:

	Amount per 2 tablets	% DV	Amount per 4 tablets	% DV
Vitamin D	100 IU	25	200 IU	50
Calcium	400 mg	40	800 mg	80
Phosphorus	250 mg	25	500 mg	50
Magnesium	200 mg	50	400 mg	100

Zinc	7.5 mg	50	15 mg	100
Copper	1 mg	50	2 mg	100
Boron	0.5 mg	*	1 mg	*

*Daily Value not established.

Take 2 tablets with a meal twice daily.

Stock No. 3194-9 (240)

Calcium Plus Vitamin D

[*Structural*] supplies nutrients required for both the structural and nervous systems. Derived from bone meal and combined with other trace minerals needed by the body, NSP Calcium helps replenish bone tissue that is constantly being replaced. Calcium comprises half of all the minerals in the body. This formula also contains phosphorus, the second most abundant mineral in the body. It works with calcium.

This formulation provides calcium and phosphorus at a 2:1 ratio. Magnesium is also added in the same 2:1 ratio with calcium. Without these important ratios, the body begins to lose one or more minerals before it can utilize them.

Calcium is needed by the immune system and is critical to muscle contractions. Phosphorus works synergistically with B vitamins to help maintain a proper fluid balance in the body. Vitamin D is added to help calcium do its job. At least 400 IU of vitamin D is needed on a daily basis, especially for those not getting enough sunshine (D is the "sunshine vitamin").

	Amount per 1 tablets	% DV	Amount per 3 tablets	% DV
Vitamin D	133 IU	30	399	90
Calcium	250 mg	25	750	75

Phosphorus	140 mg	10	420	30
Magnesium	125 mg	30	375	90

These nutrients come in a base of bone meal and alfalfa herb and contain no sugar, starch, artificial coloring or flavoring.

Take 1 tablet with a meal three times daily.

Stock No. 1675-0 (200) Ko

Calming [*Nervous*] is a natural homeopathic medicine for children experiencing restless sleep, fussiness and irritability accompanying minor illness and teething.

For children and infants over 4 months, take 3–5 drops under the tongue every 15–20 minutes until symptoms improve, then decrease to every two–four hours until symptoms are relieved. Administer to children under 4 months old only on the advice of a health care professional.

Stock No. 8870-5 (1 fl. oz.)

Candida [*Immune*] is a natural homeopathic medicine for relief from itching, burning and other symptoms associated with candida yeast infections.

Take 10–15 drops under the tongue four times daily for at least one month, then take half the dosage for an additional three months as maintenance. For children under 12, consult your health care professional.

Stock No. 8713-7 (1 fl. oz.)

Caprylic Acid Combination

[*Intestinal*] is designed to

nutritionally support the needs of those who want to maintain optimal balance in their friendly flora. Caprylic acid has anti-fungal properties. Each capsule contains:

Caprylic acid (100 mg)
Elecampane root
Black walnut hulls
Red raspberry leaves

Each capsule is coated with a "modified release" coating so that the contents will be released in the intestinal tract.

Take 2 capsules with a meal twice daily.

Stock No. 1808-2 (90)

Caprylimune [*Immune*] is a Dr. Jack Ritchason formula designed to nutritionally support the immune system.

	Amount per 2 tablets	% DV	Amount per 6 tablets	% DV
Caprylic Acid	100 mg	*	300 mg	*
Vitamin A	3667 IU	73	11,000 IU	220
Vitamin C	333 mg	556	1,000 mg	1,667
Vitamin E	107 IU	356	320 IU	1,067
Calcium	185 mg	15	555 mg	45
Phosphorus	144 mg	10	432 mg	30
Biotin	0.13 mg	44	0.4 mg	133
Pantothenic Acid	123 mg	1233	370 mg	3,700
Zinc	13.3 mg	89	40 mg	267
Selenium	0.13 mg	*	0.4 mg	*

*Daily Value not established

These are combined in a yeast-free, sugar-free, wheat-free base of:

Pau d'arco bark
Garlic bulb
Golden seal root
Yucca root
Lemon grass herb

Rose hips concentrate
Hesperidin complex
Citrus bioflavonoids

Take 2 tablets with a meal three times daily.

Stock No. 2808-5 (150)

Capsicum [*Digestive, Circulatory*]

is added to many herbal formulas as a catalyst for the other herbs. It also stimulates digestion and enhances blood flow. It became NSP's first product back in 1972 after Gene Hughes took it by the spoonful to help his stomach. Each capsule contains 520 mg capsicum. The capsicum used in this product contains 35,000–45,000 Scoville Heat Units.

Capsicum Liquid Herb is a natural and pure extract composed of the finest capsicum fruit with water and 15–20 percent alcohol.

Take 1 capsule four times daily with food. Liquid herb: Take approximately 10–15 drops (0.5 ml) in water with food four times daily. One ml is equal to 2 capsules of capsicum.

Stock No. 160-5 (100) Ko
Stock No. 1782-0 (2 fl. oz.) Ko
Capsicum Shaker Stock No. 166-7

Capsicum & Garlic with Parsley [*Digestive, Circulatory, Immune*]. This combination offers botanical sources of several important trace minerals. Capsicum stimulates digestion and may enhance blood flow. Garlic may provide enhanced support to the immune and circulatory systems, and parsley is added to the

formula for its chlorophyll content because chlorophyll has been used as a deodorizer for the body. In combination, this formula helps maintain blood pressure levels that are already within the normal range.

Take 2 capsules with food three times daily.

Stock No. 832-3 (100) Ko

Carbo Grabbers® [*Weight Management*].

Now you can partially interfere with the enzymatic digestion of dietary starches with all-natural Carbo Grabbers. Carbo Grabbers contains an amylase inhibitor derived from *Phaseolus vulgaris*, northern white kidney beans. It naturally and safely interferes with the digestion of starchy carbohydrates and may help reduce the calories that may be available to your body. Carbo Grabbers may help prevent weight gain from starch intake. Because the enzymatic breakdown of some dietary starch may be inhibited, these undigested starches can be carried through the intestinal tract where the body can eliminate them.

Take 1–2 capsules up to three times daily before a meal high in carbohydrates. Do not take in combination with any product containing protease enzymes.

Stock No. 2954-6 (60) Ko
Stock No. 2789-9
(20 retail sample packets) Ko

Cardio Assurance [*Circulatory*]

blends heart-benefiting ingredients that are designed to support your heart and cardiovascular system, including hawthorn berries extract, vitamin K2 (MK7), resveratrol, folic acid and vitamins B6 and B12. Hawthorn is one of the most thoroughly researched herbs for heart and circulatory support. Hawthorn contains flavonoids, which are packed with antioxidant protection and help maintain blood vessels and promote blood flow in the heart arteries. Hawthorn also aids in reducing cholesterol synthesis as well as facilitating the metabolism of cholesterol in the liver.

Research shows that Vitamin K2, a menaquinone, may support bone mineral density. Recent studies show that osteocalcin, a vitamin K-dependant protein, improves insulin synthesis while directing cells to store less fat; this process plays an important role in the regulation of fat cells and glucose metabolism, which may result in more effective weight management. Vitamin K2 is extracted from soy.

Resveratrol is a polyphenolic phytoalexin, a chemical compound that acts to support plants that are under attack by foreign organisms. Studies indicate that resveratrol has promising heart-healthy benefits and may be the answer to the French Paradox. (Despite their high intake of fat, the French have a low incidence of heart issues.)

Folic acid, vitamin B6 and vitamin B12 work synergistically to metabolize homocysteine, an amino acid that can damage blood vessel linings. Vitamin B6 also aids the synthesis of coenzyme-Q10, a heart-protecting compound.

Take 1 capsule with a meal twice daily.

Stock No. 553-2 (60)

Carotenoid Blend [*Vital Nutrition*]. Natural health enthusiasts have focused for years on beta-carotene, a carotenoid found naturally in carrots and other sources. Its antioxidant properties make it important to overall health. Many members of the carotenoid family have been shown to have a positive influence on health. For example, lycopene (responsible for the red color of tomatoes) may support prostate health; lutein (found in dark green vegetables) offers a variety of health benefits, particularly to the eyes; and zeaxanthin (also found in dark green veggies) may support immune function as an antioxidant.

Although individual carotenoids offer distinctive health advantages, their combined effects may enhance their influence and range of benefits. These include powerful free-radical quenching ability, heart and circulatory system support and support of healthy vision. This blend may also provide some protection from ultraviolet light damage to the eyes and skin, in addition to supporting the glandular system and offering a host of immunosupportive benefits.

Each capsule contains a specially formulated 75 mg blend of beta-carotene, alpha-carotene, lutein, lycopene, zeaxanthin, cryptoxanthin, phytoene, phytofluene and astaxanthin.

Take 1 capsule three times daily with a meal.

Stock No. 4073-3 (60) Ko

Cascara Sagrada [*Intestinal*], known as sacred bark, is one of Nature's Sunshine's most popular herbal products. The bark has been used by cultures around the world. Historically cascara sagrada has been used as an herbal laxative. Scientists are now investigating its potential for supporting gastrointestinal health. Nature's Sunshine offers the herb individually or in many combinations. Each capsule contains 390 mg cascara sagrada (Vegitabs 410 mg).

NOTE: See your health care provider prior to use if: pregnant or nursing, any medical condition exists, or when taking any medication. Read and follow recommendation carefully. Not intended for prolonged use. Do not use if diarrhea, loose stools or abdominal pain are present or develop. Use of this product may worsen these conditions and be harmful to your health. Chronic diarrhea can result in serious illness.

Take 2 capsules/tablets with a meal twice daily.

Stock No. 170-8 (100) capsules Ko
Stock No. 172-1 (100) Vegitabs®

Catnip [*Nervous*]. A member of the mint family, catnip supports both the nervous and immune systems. Catnip contains natural trace minerals and vitamins. Each capsule contains 300 mg catnip.

Take 2 capsules with a meal three times daily.

Stock No. 180-4 (100) Ko

Catnip & Fennel [*Digestive, Nervous*] liquid is a combination of two time-honored botanicals that primarily support the digestive and nervous systems. Catnip contains natural trace minerals and vitamins. Fennel also contains important trace minerals. NSP's method of extraction produces herbs that are easily assimilated, highly concentrated and preservative-free. Liquid herbs can be taken straight from the dropper or used in tea.

Adults: Take 1/2 to 1 teaspoon in water with a meal three times daily. Children: Take 1/4 teaspoon in water with a meal three times daily. Shake well before using. One ml is equal to 1 capsule of catnip and 1 capsule of fennel.

Stock No. 3195-3
(2 fl. oz.) 4 Kids Too!

Cat's Claw (*see Uña de Gato*)

CBG Extract (*see Combination CBG Extract*)

CC-A [*Circulatory, Immune*] provides nutrients that may support several body systems. It contains trace minerals and vitamins from plant sources. The formula includes:
Rose hips
Chamomile flowers
Slippery elm bark
Yarrow aerial parts
Capsicum fruit
Golden seal root and rhizome
Myrrh gum
Peppermint leaves
Sage leaves

Lemon grass aerial parts
Take 2 capsules with a meal twice daily. Children: Take 1 capsule with a meal twice daily.

Stock No. 840-5 (100) Ko
4 Kids Too!

CC-A with Yerba Santa
[*Immune, Respiratory*]. This longtime favorite contains rose hips, chamomile flowers, mullein leaves, yarrow flowers, yerba santa leaves, golden seal root, myrrh gum, peppermint leaves, sage flowers, astragalus root, slippery elm bark, lemon grass herb and capsicum fruit.

Take 20–25 drops in 2 oz. of warm water with a meal twice daily. Children: Take approximately 10–15 drops in 2 oz. warm water with a meal twice daily.

Stock No. 3165-0 (2 fl. oz.) Ko
4 Kids Too!

Cellular Build [*Immune, Intestinal*] provides the body with dietary sources of nucleotides— the building blocks of DNA and RNA, which store our genetic information. Whenever a cell divides, the body needs nucleotides to make a complete copy of DNA for the new cell. In times of stress, the need for new cells increases, which requires millions of nucleotides. The synthesis of new nucleotides requires considerable time and energy for an already-stressed body. Dietary nucleotides support cell multiplication and optimal health. Nucelotides are especially important in areas of the body where rapid cell division occurs, such as in the intestinal system, where the lining of the gastrointestinal tract renews itself about once a week. Here, Cellular Build may enhance digestion, improve the uptake of nutrients, promote the growth of beneficial flora, support enzyme activity, and in general, support the intestinal system. Cellular Build also contains the immune-enhancing and intestinal tract-supporting nutrients astragalus and fructo-oligosaccharides, plus milk thistle.

Take 1 capsule twice daily with a meal.
Stock No. 1400-3 (60)

Cellular Energy [*Vital Nutrition, Glandular*] contains vitamins, minerals, amino acids and other co-factors involved in vital processes that are important for normal energy production and cellular metabolism. In addition to their nutritional value, the ingredients in Cellular Energy exert reasonable antioxidant effects that may help address some of the metabolic issues that affect energy production. The B vitamins in Cellular Energy perform important biochemical functions in cellular energy metabolism. Manganese and magnesium support muscular and skeletal systems, while zinc universally supports all body systems either as an integral part or as a component of enzymes and hormones.

People who experience fatigue, reduced stamina, feelings of weakness or who need an energy boost for prolonged physical activity could benefit from supplementing their diets with Cellular Energy. It provides highly absorbable forms of the vitamins and minerals needed to boost cellular metabolism. Cellular Energy contains generous amounts of vitamins B1, B2, E, niacin, pantothenic acid, zinc and manganese, plus ferulic acid, alpha lipoic acid, alpha-ketoglutaric acid, L-carnitine, coenzyme Q10 and dimethyl glycine.

Take 1 capsule twice daily with a meal.
Stock No. 1879-6 (60)

Cellu-Smooth® with Coleus
[*Weight Loss, Circulatory*] provides nutrients that may support circulation; help mobilize fat for better distribution; and protect against free radical damage to structural skin proteins. One ingredient, *Coleus forskohlii* root extract, may cause a shift from a more fatty body mass to a more lean body mass, which may benefit overall health. Cellu-Smooth also includes bladderwrack, which contains minerals essential for thyroid function, thereby supporting metabolism; milk thistle, which acts as an antioxidant, supporting the liver cells' detoxifying function; ginkgo, a known free radical scavenger; rhodiola root extract, which may improve strength and stamina; and rhododendron root, an antioxidant that may promote microcirculation.

Take 1 capsule with a meal two or three times daily. Drink at least

eight glasses of water a day. Not recommended for pregnant or nursing women, or children.
Stock No. 926-0 (90)

Cellu-Tone Pure Essential Oil Blend (*see Essential Oils*)

Chamomile [*Nervous*] may
be best known as a popular late-night herbal tea. The herb contains flavonoids, coumarin and volatile oil. Contemporary herbalists recommend chamomile for its ability to soothe the nerves and promote more restful sleep. Each capsule provides 250 mg chamomile.

Take 1 capsule with a meal twice daily.
Stock No. 190-7 (100) Ko

Chamomile, Roman Pure Essential Oil (*see Essential Oils*)

Charcoal, Activated [*Digestive*]
has been used for at least 2,000 years and is well-known for its adsorptive ability. It is often used to support the body's cleansing and detoxification mechanisms as it helps bind toxins in the digestive tract. It may also help the body's efforts to expel intestinal gas. Each capsule contains 260 mg activated charcoal.

Take 4–8 capsules daily with water at least two hours after or one hour before eating a meal.
Stock No. 366-2 (100) Ko

Chickweed [*Urinary, Glandular*],
a mild herb, has been used

traditionally to support the urinary system. Some use it to provide nutrients that must be present for the body's metabolism-balancing functions. It contains natural amounts of some vitamins and minerals. Each capsule contains 375 mg chickweed.

Take 2 capsules with a meal twice daily.
Stock No. 220-2 (100) Ko

Chlorophyll [*Intestinal*] is the
green pigment in plants that harnesses the sun's energy in photosynthesis. Chlorophyll performs metabolic functions in plants such as respiration and growth. Interestingly, the chlorophyll molecule is chemically similar to human blood, except that its central atom is magnesium, whereas that of human blood is iron. Liquid Chlorophyll may help improve immune response and deodorize the body. The alfalfa plant, from which Nature's Sunshine's chlorophyll comes, is an excellent source of chlorophyll. Nature's Sunshine offers chlorophyll in both liquid and capsules for varying needs.

For liquid, take 1 teaspoon in water twice daily. For capsules, take 1–2 capsules daily with a meal.
Stock No. 1683-7 (16 fl. oz.) Ko
Stock No. 1689-6 (32 fl. oz.) Ko
Stock No. 1690-7 (60)

Cholester-Reg® II [*Circulatory*].
This combination of policosanol, phytosterol (plant sterols), inositol nicotinate (a form of niacin),

resveratrol and artichoke powder offers a host of benefits to the heart and the circulatory system. These include maintaining cholesterol levels that are already in the normal range, protection of the heart, antioxidant properties, maintaining already-normal platelet aggregation levels and more.

Policosanol appears to perform a similar action in the body as Chinese red yeast rice extract. Human studies show that policosanol can effectively play a role in maintaining cholesterol levels already in the normal range and that it can help maintain already-normal platelet aggregation (clotting).

The chemical structure of plant sterols is similar to that of cholesterol, so plant sterols compete with the absorption of cholesterol in the body. Excess plant sterols are not absorbed by the body but are eliminated.

Inositol nicotinate helps relax smooth muscles and improves microcirculation. It is particularly effective in maintaining triglyceride levels that are already in the normal range.

Resveratrol has been in the news in recent years for its antioxidant abilities. It may help promote general good health through its antioxidant activity.

Finally, artichoke powder (*Cynara scolymus*) contains components that benefit the liver and promote digestion. Artichoke is popular in Europe for its ability to maintain cholesterol levels already in the normal range.

CAUTION: Do not take this product if: pregnant, lactating or planning to become pregnant. Consult your health care professional before using if you are currently taking any cholesterol-lowering agents. Cholesterol levels should be checked regularly. For adults 20 years or older only. Keep out of the reach of children.

Take 1 capsule with a meal three times daily.

Stock No. 557-7 (90)

Chondroitin [*Structural*] helps bond connective tissue to maintain strength and inhibits enzymes that can deplete cartilage nutrition. (Cartilage functions to protect bones from moving against each other and to reduce friction.) Chondroitin helps retain moisture in the joints, allowing for flexibility and resiliency, and cushioning against activities like jumping and lifting. In addition, chondroitin works with other nutrients like glucosamine to stimulate the rebuilding and maintenance of cartilage. The body produces chondroitin, but that production decreases as we grow older. Chondroitin is found in foods, but usually only in small amounts. Fortunately, the body absorbs chondroitin well, making supplementation a viable alternative. Each capsule contains 300 mg of chondroitin sulfate.

Take 2 capsules with a meal twice daily. Drink 8 oz. water along with the capsules.

Stock No. 1811-5 (60)

Chromium, GTF [*Glandular*] is a trace mineral that plays a role in maintaining blood sugar levels that are already within the normal range. Each "glucose tolerance factor"(GTF) molecule, a hormone-like compound, requires chromium as its central atom. GTF is thought to work with insulin to transport glucose from the blood into the cells. The liver also needs chromium to manufacture fatty acids, lecithin, cholesterol and lipoproteins. Chromium may positively affect blood fat levels and the liver filtration process. Processing destroys much of the chromium content in foods. Each tablet of GTF chromium contains 500 mcg of chromium amino acid chelate and chromium nicotinate in a base of horsetail stems and strobilus, red clover flowers and yarrow aerial parts.

Take 1 tablet daily with a meal.

Stock No. 1801-6 (90) Ko

Citrus Bioflavonoids
(*see Vitamin C*)

CLA [*Weight Management, Vital Nutrition*], or Conjugated Linoleic Acid, is a mixture of essential fatty acids that are important to the body. It can help modify body composition by sustaining lean muscle tissue and enhancing lipolysis (the burning of fat), resulting in a number of health and weight benefits. CLA is a patented ingredient for fat reduction. It has also been shown to be effective for maintaining cholesterol levels already within the normal range.

NSP's patented formula is of the highest quality and delivers all of the benefits of CLA in a softgel capsule. Each CLA softgel supplies 750 mg CLA in a base of safflower oil.

Take 1 capsule with a meal three times daily.

Stock No. 3010-1 (75)

Clary Sage Pure Essential Oil
(*see Essential Oils*)

CleanStart® [*Intestinal*] helps protect your body from common colon toxins that affect your overall health. This two-week program supports natural waste elimination to provide a sense of improved energy and well-being. CleanStart is easy to take and is balanced for more complete results. Each program contains 28 daily drink packets and 28 capsule packets.

Each drink packet contains:
Psyllium hulls
Bentonite clay
Aloe vera juice
Chlorophyll
Potassium
Stevia
Natural apple-cinnamon or wild berry (black currant and raspberry) flavoring.

Each capsule packet contains 1 capsule of Enviro-Detox and 2 capsules of LBS II® to enhance waste elimination. The program delivers 10 grams of fiber per day to promote waste removal. Plus you get the additional cleansing benefits of bentonite, aloe vera and chlorophyll.

NOTICE: This product contains

cascara sagrada, buckthorn and Turkey rhubarb. See your health care provider prior to use if: pregnant or nursing, any medical condition exists, or when taking any medication. Read and follow recommendation carefully. Do not use if diarrhea, loose stools or abdominal pain are present or develop. Use of this product may worsen these conditions and be harmful to your health. Chronic diarrhea can result in serious illness. May cause allergic reaction in persons sensitive to inhaled or ingested psyllium.

Take the contents of one cleanse drink packet 15–30 minutes before breakfast and again 15–30 minutes before dinner. Take the contents of 1 capsule packet with breakfast and dinner (twice daily). Mix cleanse packet powder in 8 oz. juice or water. Shake, blend or stir vigorously. Drink immediately. Drink an additional glass of water immediately following this. Drink plenty of water throughout the day.

Clove Bud BIO Pure Essential Oil (*see Essential Oils*)

CLT-X [*Intestinal*] nutritionally supports the stomach and intestinal system, providing relief of occasional intestinal distress. CLT-X consists of:
Slippery elm bark
Marshmallow root
Ginger rhizome
Dong quai root
Wild yam root
Lobelia aerial parts
Take 2 capsules with a meal three times daily. For best results, use in conjunction with Anti-Gas Formula.

Co-Q10 Plus [*Circulatory, Vital Nutrition*] is a unique product containing a vitamin-like substance called coenzyme Q10. An enzyme can induce chemical changes in other substances without being changed itself. Enzymes are made up of two parts—a protein portion and a cofactor portion consisting of minerals or vitamins. Each capsule contains 10 mg of coenzyme Q10 in combination with the following minerals:

	Amount per Capsule	Amount per 3 capsules	% DV
Iron	2 mg	6 mg	30
Magnesium	25 mg	75 mg	18
Zinc	5 mg	15 mg	105
Copper	2.5 mg	7.5 mg	375

These minerals are organically chelated to the amino acids leucine, histidine and glycine for better absorption, and they are combined in a base of capsicum fruit and hawthorn berries.
Take 1 capsule with a meal three times daily.

Co-Q10 30 [*Circulatory, Vital Nutrition*] contains 30 mg of Co-Q10 per capsule, along with zinc (10 mg), copper (1.3 mg), magnesium (100 mg), capsicum fruit, hawthorn berries and concentrated ginkgo leaf.

Take 1 capsule with a meal three times daily.

Stock No. 4089-6 (60)

Co-Q10 75 [*Circulatory, Vital Nutrition*] helps produce cellular energy and acts as an antioxidant. It also supports already-normal-range blood pressure levels. Many studies suggest that Co-Q10 supports cardiac function. As an antioxidant, Co-Q10 scavenges free radicals, protects cardiac cells and promotes the regeneration of vitamin E, another heart-healthy antioxidant. Co-Q10 75 has an oil-base delivery system, which improves bioavailability (about three times as bioavailable as Co-Q10 in the powdered form). You get 75 mg Co-Q10 with each easy-to-swallow softgel. Rice bran oil, beeswax and beta-carotene are added to support membrane fluidity and antioxidant activity.

Take 1 softgel with a meal three times daily.

Stock No. 1895-5 (60)

Cold [*Respiratory*] is a natural homeopathic medicine for relief from the symptoms of the common cold, including runny nose, sneezing, headache, sore throat and difficult breathing.

CAUTION: If sore throat pain is severe, persists for more than two days, or is accompanied or followed by fever, headache, rash, nausea or vomiting, consult your health care professional.

Take 10–15 drops under the tongue every 10–15 minutes or as needed until symptoms improve; then decrease to hourly, then to four times daily until symptoms are relieved. For children under 12, consult your health care professional.

Stock No. 8765-2 (1 fl. oz.)

Cold, Herbasaurs®
(*see Herbasaurs Cold*)

Collatrim Plus capsules
[*Weight Management, Structural*] is composed mainly of bovine collagen—the fibrous protein in bones, tendons and connective tissues. It provides the building blocks of protein and amino acids. Your body may utilize the amino acids in Collatrim to rebuild muscles and strengthen lean muscle mass.

For weight management, take 6 to 9 capsules daily before bedtime with one glass (8 oz.) water on an empty stomach. For structural benefits and skin support, take 2 to 3 capsules with a meal three times daily.

Stock No. 3065-4 (180) Ko

Collatrim Plus Powder
[*Weight Management, Structural*] is designed to support weight management by utilizing high levels of protein and important amino acids contained in our premier source of collagen. Collatrim provides the building blocks of protein and amino acids, which the body utilizes to build and stengthen lean muscle tissue. Collagen is also important for

healthy skin and strong joints. Each serving of Collatrim powder provides 4.6 grams of protein and 5.0 grams of premier quality, hydrolyzed collagen.

For weight management: Mix one rounded scoop (10.8 grams) with 4 oz. water and take before bedtime on an empty stomach. For joint and skin support: Mix 1/3 scoop (3.6 grams) in 4 oz. of water three times daily.

Stock No. 3062-0 (30 servings, 326.5 g)

Colloidal Minerals [*Vital Nutrition*] provide structural integrity for many body systems, support enzyme function, play a role in protein synthesis, and support the immune system. NSP Colloidal Minerals is made with high-quality, inorganic-based colloids that can be easily assimilated into the body, providing enhanced mineral supplementation in an economical, great-tasting lemon-lime liquid. These colloidal minerals come from ancient plant deposits and provide a natural balance of minerals. It contains a full spectrum of macro and trace minerals, many of which are required for daily cell function and structure. Colloidal Minerals is pH-balanced for maximum benefit.

Take 1 tablespoon with a meal twice daily. May be mixed with juice or water.

Stock No. 4013-6 (32 fl. oz.)

Colostrum [*Immune*] is a super-nutritional substance secreted by the mammary glands of nursing mammals. It contains immuno-globulins and broad-based immune enhancers. Colostrum supports the immune system and may impart passive immunity. Mother Nature designed colostrum to stimulate and support a newborn's immune system. NSP Colostrum comes from bovine sources and contains transfer factors from milk.

Take 1 capsule four times daily, one hour before meals and bedtime with 8 oz. water.

Stock No. 1828-7 (90)

Colostrum with Immune Factors [*Immune*] is a combination of nutritional and herbal elements designed to nourish and support the immune system. The immune factors in this product are known to stimulate cytokines and strengthen the intestinal lining. This unique formula contains colostrum (the foremilk produced by mammals before the onset of lactation), astragalus (enhances the production of immunoglobulin and helps stimulate macrophages), inositol hexaphosphate ([IP6], has immunostimulatory actions), maitake mushroom (contains powerful beta-glucan) and shiitake mushroom (stimulates macrophages).

Take 1 capsule with a meal three times daily.

Stock No. 1587-3 (60)

Combination CBG Extract

[*Immune*] is used to support the immune system nutritionally. The herbs' key ingredients are extracted in alcohol using the spagyric process.

This word is from two Greek words that mean to extract and to reunite. This involves soaking the raw herb materials in natural solutions. Then plant fiber is removed and reduced to ash. Later the ash and liquids are recombined and mixed with alcohol to preserve the active ingredients. Combination CBG Extract contains:

Black cohosh root
Chickweed aerial parts
Golden seal root
Passion flower aerial parts
Licorice root
Valerian root

Extracts are rapidly absorbed by the body and are an excellent alternative for those who have difficulty swallowing tablets. CBG can be taken under the tongue or mixed in water.

Adults: Take 1/2 teaspoon three times daily with water. Children: Take 1/4 teaspoon three times daily with water. This product may also be used as a mouthwash; mix 1 teaspoon (5 ml) with water.

Stock No. 1751-2 (2 fl. oz.) Ko
4 Kids Too!

Coral Calcium [*Vital Nutrition*]
is designed especially for those who desire to keep their acidity levels within a normal range. Because coral calcium is naturally alkaline, it can be of great support to those who need to maintain normal-ranged pH levels. Plus, it provides essential calcium to help maintain bone integrity and health.

Each serving of Coral Calcium provides the body with 325 mg of readily available calcium, plus 163 mg of magnesium. We've also included montmorillonite clay, a full-spectrum trace mineral source that helps adsorb toxins from the digestive tract.

Many people—especially elderly men and women, middle-aged women, persons with a family history of osteoporosis and white and Asian women ages 11 to 35—can benefit from proper calcium intake. Scientific studies show that regular exercise and a healthy diet with adequate dietary minerals, such as those contained in Coral Calcium, can promote bone health.

Coral Calcium capsules offer the same benefits as the powder. The capsules contain 110 mg of readily available calcium plus 55 mg of magnesium for bone mineralization.

Powder: Mix one rounded scoop (included) in 8 oz. of water or other beverage. Capsules: Take 1 capsule with a meal three times daily.

Stock No. 1873-7 (75 g/50 servings)
Stock No. 1899-7 (90)

Cordyceps [*Circulatory, Immune, Respiratory, Glandular*]
is perhaps best known as the supplement that members of the Chinese women's track and field team used in training before they broke several records in 1993 and 1994. Team members tested negative for using illegal substances, and their coach revealed that the athletes' diets were supplemented with a Chinese "caterpillar fungus."

Fungi supplements—like reishi and shiitake mushrooms—are growing in popularity in the

U.S. Another important species, *Cordyceps sinensis*, is also gaining recognition. Cordyceps has properties similar to those of ginseng and is traditionally used to help the body build strength and endurance. In traditional Chinese medicine, cordyceps has been used to benefit the glandular system in both women and men. In addition, cordyceps supports the kidneys, aids the upper respiratory tract and helps the body maintain proper blood viscosity.

CAUTION: Cordyceps is safe for adults, but people using immune-suppressing drugs, anticoagulant drugs or bronchodilators should consult their health care practitioners before using this product. Pregnant or lactating women should avoid using this product. Store in a cool, dry place.

Take 2–3 capsules with a meal three times daily.

Stock No. 1240-5 (90) Ko

Cornsilk [*Urinary*]. The silky tassel inside the corn husk is used in herbology as a support to the urinary system. Cornsilk is very popular in Chinese herbology. Each capsule contains 400 mg cornsilk.

Take 2 capsules with a meal three times daily.

Stock No. 235-3 (100) Ko

Cough Syrup, Herbasaurs®
(*see Herbasaurs Cough Syrup*)

Cough Syrup DH [*Respiratory*] is a natural homeopathic medicine for the relief of dry, hoarse coughs accompanying minor illness, allergies and throat irritations.

Adults: Take 2–4 teaspoons as required. Children 4–12: Take 1–3 teaspoons. Repeat as necessary to relieve symptoms. For children under 4, consult a health care professional.

Stock No. 8780-3 (4 fl. oz.)

Cough Syrup LP [*Respiratory*] is a natural homeopathic medicine for the relief of congested coughs with loose phlegm and difficult expectoration.

Adults: Take 2–4 teaspoons as required. Children 4–12: Take 1–3 teaspoons. Repeat as necessary to relieve symptoms. For children under 4, consult a health care professional.

Stock No. 8785-5 (4 fl. oz.)

Cough Syrup NT [*Respiratory*] is a natural homeopathic medicine for the relief of a persistent nighttime cough that disturbs sleep and is due to minor illness.

Adults: Take 2–4 teaspoons as required. Children 4–12: Take 1–3 teaspoons. Repeat as necessary to relieve symptoms. For children under 4, consult a health care professional.

Stock No. 8790-8 (4 fl. oz.)

Cramp Relief [*Glandular*]. For some women, menstrual cramps can interfere with everyday activities. Cramp Relief contains herbs that have been used traditionally to help the body relax contracted muscles and ease cramping. This formula contains several herbs that support various body systems to help in the management of minor menstrual discomfort. Traditionally, wild yam supports the female reproductive system, while black cohosh may help lift mild mood changes (so-called dark moods) that often accompany female discomfort. Cramp Relief herbal formula contains cramp bark, black cohosh root, lobelia aerial parts, plantain leaves and wild yam root.

Take 2 capsules with a meal two or three times daily.

Stock No. 1124-9 (100) Ko

Cranberry/Buchu Concentrate

[*Urinary*]. Scientific studies have concluded that cranberry juice contains substances that affect the urinary tract by interfering with the adhesion of potentially dangerous microbes to the urinary tract lining. NSP combines cranberry juice concentrate with buchu herb concentrate. Buchu helps nourish the urinary tract. Its powerful, penetrating aroma is akin to peppermint. Careful processing reduces the liquid to a concentrated powder before encapsulation.

NOTE: Do not take this concentrated formula in conjunction with uva ursi.

Take 1–2 capsules with a meal three times daily. Children: Take 1 capsule with a meal twice daily. Use daily to help maintain a healthy urinary tract.

Stock No. 834-5 (100) Ko
4 Kids Too!

D

Damiana [*Glandular*] is an aromatic shrub that grows abundantly in dry, rocky soils. It is believed to have mildly stimulating qualities. Damiana supports glandular health and is traditionally sought to support sexual health. The Aztecs used it as an aphrodisiac. Damiana also contains alkaloids, flavonoids, cyanogenic glycosides, tannins and resins, which add to its healthful benefits. Each capsule contains 350 mg damiana.

Take 2 capsules with a meal twice daily.

Stock No. 240-9 (100) Ko

Dandelion [*Urinary, Digestive*] is a member of the sunflower family. Its name is a corruption of the French *dents de lion*, meaning "teeth of the lion." Herbalists consider this plant one of the most nutrient-rich in the plant kingdom. The whole plant is edible—the flowers, the leaves and the roots. Dandelion supports digestion and nourishes the liver. The herb is a source of many important minerals and vitamins. Each capsule contains 460 mg dandelion root.

Take 2 capsules with a meal twice daily.

Stock No. 250-4 (100) Ko

Deep Relief Pure Essential Oil Blend (*see Essential Oils*)

Defense Maintenance®

[*Immune*] provides nutrients that support the immune system.

The formulation contains many antioxidants, beneficial cruciferous vegetable powders and extra vitamins and minerals that support immune functions.

	Amount per 2 Capsules	% DV	Amount per 4 Capsules	% DV
Vitamin A	10,000 IU	200	20,000 IU	400
Vitamin C	240 mg	2400	480 mg	4800
Vitamin E	120 IU	400	240 IU	800
Zinc (gluconate, oxide)	10 mg	70	20 mg	140
Selenium	50 mcg	70	100 mg	140

These nutrients are in a base of:
  Barley grass juice powder
  Asparagus powder
  Astragalus root
  Broccoli powder
  Cabbage powder
  Ganoderma herb
  Parthenium root
  Pau d'arco bark
  Schizandra fruit
  Eleuthero root
  Wheat grass juice powder
  Myrrh gum
Take 2 capsules with a meal twice daily.

Stock No. 1654-5 (120)

Depressaquel® [*Nervous*] is a

natural homeopathic medicine to assist in the alleviation of melancholy, apathy and listlessness by lifting the mood and mental outlook.

Adults and children age 12 and above, take 10–15 drops under the tongue every hour until symptoms improve, then take four times daily until symptoms are relieved. Do not give to children under the age of 12.

Stock No. 8755-1 (1 fl. oz.)

Detoxification [*Immune*] is a

natural homeopathic medicine for the relief of minor symptoms of headache, vomiting, nausea, aches and joint discomfort associated with exposure to mercury, arsenic and other pollutants and toxins.

Take 10–15 drops under the tongue three times daily for 60 days. For children under 12, consult your health care professional. It is helpful to drink 1–2 quarts of water daily and eat a high-fiber diet while taking this remedy.

Stock No. 8940-3 (1 fl. oz.)

Devil's Claw [*Structural, Immune*]

is named for its blossoms that turn into thorny pods with hook-like projections, resembling claws. It is found in the harsh Kalahari Desert of southern Africa and is used by natives for many purposes. Herbalists consider devil's claw a nutritional aid for the structural and immune systems. For best results, Nature's Sunshine uses only the plant's secondary roots or tubers. Each capsule contains 450 mg devil's claw root (*Harpagophytum procumbens*).

Take 2 capsules with a meal three times daily.

Stock No. 255-9 (100)

DHA [*Circulatory, Nervous*]. DHA

(docosahexaenoic acid) is an omega-3 fatty acid that is absorbed into the fatty perimeter of cells. There it exerts its biochemical properties. DHA is one of the most abundant fatty acids in the brain. It is also highly concentrated in

D

the retinal neural tissues. DHA is required for brain development and is important in maintaining and protecting the neural tissues. NSP DHA supports brain and nervous system function. It can also benefit ocular health by supporting and protecting retinal cells. Each softgel contains 250 mg DHA and 50 mg EPA in a base of fish oil and natural lemon oil to significantly reduce the aftertaste from fish oil.

Take 1 softgel with a meal three times daily.

Stock No. 1513-5 (60)

DHEA-F [*Glandular*] contains 25 mg DHEA per capsule in a synergistic herbal base of wild yam, false unicorn and chaste tree. (The "F" indicates that this formula is for females.) DHEA-dehydroepiandrosterone— is a hormone precursor produced by the adrenal glands. It is converted to essential hormones in the body. After about age 25, the body's production of DHEA declines, leading many experts to believe that DHEA plays a role in the aging process. Wild yam, false unicorn root and chaste tree berry concentrate are recognized by health-conscious women throughout the world and are prized for their ability to help the body maintain overall balance.

Take 1 capsule daily with a meal or as directed by your health care provider following DHEA level assessment.

Stock No. 4202-2 (100)

DHEA-M [*Glandular*] contains 25 mg dehydroepiandrosterone (DHEA) per capsule in a synergistic herbal base of sarsaparilla, damiana leaves, saw palmetto fruit, pumpkin seed and Korean ginseng extract. (The "M" indicates that this formula is for males.) The herbal base provides dietary factors that are uniquely valuable to men. Saw palmetto supports healthy prostate function. Pumpkin seeds contain nutrients, and fatty acids and are used to support male reproductive health. Sarsaparilla and damiana have been used by men for centuries, and the unique, energizing herb *Panax ginseng* is known the world over for its contribution to optimal well-being. DHEA is a hormone precursor produced by the adrenal glands. After about age 25, the body's production of DHEA declines, leading many experts to believe that DHEA plays a role in the aging process.

Take 1 capsule daily with a meal, or as directed by your health care provider following DHEA level assessment.

Stock No. 4200-7 (100)

Dieter's Cleanse® [*Weight Management*]. Proper cleansing of the digestive tract allows for better elimination of waste and improved absorption of nutrients from the food you eat. Dieter's Cleanse is a safe, simple, convenient cleansing program. Product elements provide dietary fiber, support the production of digestive enzymes and bile, nourish the liver and glandular system, promote detoxi-fication and support the body's weight-management mechanisms.

Each box of Dieter's Cleanse contains 14 AM packets, 14 NOON packets and 14 PM packets. The following NSP products are elements of Dieter's Cleanse:
• Bowel Detox (2 capsules in AM and NOON packets)
• Master Gland Formula (2 capsules in AM and NOON packets)
• Enviro-Detox (1 capsule in AM and NOON packets)
• Liver Cleanse Formula (1 capsule in AM and NOON packets)
• LBS II® (3 capsules in PM packet)
• SF® (2 capsules in PM packet)
• Chromium (1 capsule in PM packet)

NOTE: This product contains cascara sagrada, buckthorn and Turkey rhubarb. See your health care provider prior to use if: pregnant or nursing, any medical condition exists, or when taking any medication. Read and follow recommendation carefully. Not intended for prolonged use. Do not use if diarrhea, loose stools, or abdominal pain are present or develop. Use of this product may worsen these conditions and be harmful to your health. Chronic diarrhea can result in serious illness.

Kick off your weight-loss program by using Dieter's Cleanse for one week. Take 1 AM packet with breakfast. Take 1 NOON packet with lunch. Take 1 PM packet with dinner. Then begin your weight-management program. The second-week supply of Dieter's Cleanse can be used during recommended rest periods of other NSP weight-loss programs. This product may also be used by any adult desiring a two-week cleanse. This product could produce bowel movements during the night or in the morning.

Stock No. 3220-4 (14-day supply)

Digestive Bitters Tonic [*Digestive, Intestinal*] enhances the secretion of digestive juices in the body, improves digestion, stimulates appetite, and stimulates and cleanses the liver and gallbladder. Includes stevia and glycerin.

This liquid formula includes:
Gentian root
Cardamom tincture
Orange peel tincture
Dandelion root
Red raspberry syrup
Potassium sorbate
Adults: Take 1 teaspoon 15 minutes before each meal. Children: Take 1/2 teaspoon 15 minutes before each meal.

Stock No. 3113-9 (4 fl. oz.) Ko

Distress Remedy [*Nervous*] is a homeopathic flower medicine that provides relief for minor accidents, injuries and bruises; pain and inflammation; and emotional upset due to physical trauma. It contains the same ingredients of other flower remedies on the market, plus the added benefits of comfrey,

arnica and calendula. It features leopard's bane, garden marigold, rock rose, traveler's joy, impatiens, cherry plum, star of Bethlehem and nightshade. It also contains purified water, glycerin and potassium benzoate. Use before, after and/or during times of physical and associated mental stress.

Take 10–15 drops under the tongue every 10–15 minutes, or as needed until symptoms improve. Then decrease to every one to two hours, then to four times daily until symptoms are relieved. For children under 12, consult your health care professional.

Stock No. 8975-1 (1 fl. oz.)
4 Kids Too!

Dong Quai [*Glandular*],

pro-nounced "don kwy," is considered the queen of herbs by the Chinese and is China's most popular herb for women. Chinese physicians use the herb to enrich the blood, promote circulation, regulate menstruation, calm nerves and soothe the intestines. Each capsule contains 520 mg dong quai root.

Take 1–2 capsules with a meal three times daily.

Stock No. 258-8 (100) Ko

Dulse Liquid [*Glandular, Immune, Vital Nutrition*].

Dulse, *Rhodymenia palmata*, is a type of red seaweed that grows on rocks at the low tide line in the North Atlantic and Northwest Pacific oceans where currents are strong and the bottom is clean. Dulse is a natural source of iodine, an essential trace mineral that is important to the health of the thyroid gland. It also helps provide building blocks for the hormones secreted by the thyroid.

Alcohol-free Dulse Liquid comes in a glycerin base and is palatable to the taste. Each 1 ml serving provides 225 mcg of natural iodine.

Take 1 ml (approximately 15–20 drops [1/4 teaspoon]) in water once daily.

Stock No. 3156-6 (2 fl. oz.) Ko

E

E, Vitamin (*see Vitamin E*)

E-Tea® [*Immune*]

is NSP's easy-to-use, encapsulated form of traditional Essiac Tea. Essiac tea is an herbal formula used since 1922 by Canadian nurse Rene Caisse. The formula originated from a native Ojibwa medicine man.

Due to the complexity of the preparation process, it would take hours for you to make this tea at home. Thanks to NSP, it is possible to provide the same herbal combination in convenient capsule form. E-Tea contains burdock root, sheep sorrel aerial parts, slippery elm bark and Turkey rhubarb root. It is traditionally used to support immunity and help detoxify and purify the blood.

NOTE: This product contains Turkey rhubarb. See your health care provider prior to use if: pregnant or nursing, any medical condition exists, or when taking any medication.

Read and follow recommendation carefully. Not intended for prolonged use. Do not use if diarrhea, loose stools or abdominal pain are present or develop. Use of this product may worsen these conditions and be harmful to your health. Chronic diarrhea can result in serious illness.

To drink as a tea, empty the contents of 2 capsules into 4 oz. hot water. Or, take 2 capsules three times daily on an empty stomach. Two capsules of E-Tea are equivalent to 2 oz. traditionally brewed Essiac Tea.

Stock No. 1360-4 (100) Ko

Echinacea/Golden Seal

[*Immune*] combines two popular immune system-supporting herbs. Echinacea may influence the immune system in a positive way. This product combines the qualities of *Echinacea purpurea* aerial parts and root and *E. angustifolia* root.

Golden seal root and rhizome (*Hydrastis canadensis*) contains the powerful alkaloids berberine and hydrastine that help the body maintain strong immunity. It has become one of the most popular herbs in America today. Golden seal's constituents also benefit the digestive and circulatory systems.

NOTE: Pregnant or lactating women should not take golden seal.

Take 2 capsules with a meal three times daily.

Stock No. 835-2 (100) Ko

Echinacea/Golden Seal Liquid Herb

[*Immune*] includes roots of two species of echinacea—*Echinacea purpurea* and *E. angustifolia*. Each 5 ml serving provides 125 mg of the echinacea combination and 125 mg of golden seal root—a powerful blend that supports the immune system and helps the body maintain health. This combination comes in a glycerin base and is appropriate for use by both adults and children.

NOTE: Pregnant or lactating women should not take products that contain golden seal.

Adults: Take 15–20 drops (1 ml) in water with a meal three times daily. Children: Take approximately 5–10 drops (.5 ml) in water with a meal three times daily.

Stock No. 3180-1 (2 fl. oz.) Ko
4 Kids Too!

Echinacea Purpurea

[*Immune*] bears purple flowers that resemble black-eyed Susans. Active compounds in echinacea include polysaccharides, glycoproteins, alkamides, volatile oils and flavonoids. Several laboratory and animal studies suggest that echinacea contains active substances that enhance the activity of the immune system and have antimicrobial, anti-inflammatory and antioxidant activity. Each capsule contains 400 mg *Echinacea purpurea* herb and root.

Take 2 capsules with a meal three times daily.

Stock No. 263-8 (180) Ko

Echinacea, Ultimate

[*Immune*] combines the synergistic benefits of the three most popular echinacea species into a powerful immune system combination. We carefully process *Echinacea purpurea, E. angustifolia* and *E. pallida* into a concentrate that preserves the maximum potential of the three species' roots. This alcohol-free tincture is sweetened with natural vegetable glycerin and provides excellent assimilation. This unique combination contains echinacosides, glycoproteins, isobutylamides and polysaccharides found selectively in each species.

Adults: Take 15–20 drops (1 ml) in water with a meal three times daily. Children age 6 or older: Take approximately 5–10 drops in water with a meal three times daily. Pregnant or lactating women should consult their health care provider before use.

Stock No. 3181-2 (2 fl. oz.) Ko

Eczema/Psoriasis [*Skin*] is a

natural homeopathic remedy for the treatment of eczema, dermatitis and psoriasis when the skin is dry, scaly and inflamed.

Take 10–15 drops under the tongue every two–four hours or as needed for pain and discomfort. Decrease to three or four times daily upon improvement and continue until skin clears. For children under 12, consult your health care professional.

Stock No. 8900-2 (1 fl. oz.)

Elderberry Defense® [*Immune*]

is great to have on hand during the cold weather season as it promotes immune system function and provides essential nutrients for health. Elderberry contains naturally occurring fruit acids, volatile oils and anthocyanins. Scientific studies confirm elderberry's immunostimulatory activity.

Echinacea is the most popular herb in America for the immune system; it is mild and suitable for all ages. Olive leaf extract provides antimicrobial activity. Royal jelly is another remarkable nutritive food, produced by young nurse bees from honey and pollen to feed the queen bee. Each capsule contains a special blend of elderberry extract, *Echinacea purpurea* aerial parts, olive leaf extract and royal jelly.

Take 2 capsules with a meal three times daily, plus 2 capsules at bedtime.

Stock No. 868-5 (100)

Eleuthero [*Glandular*]. Eleuthero

is considered to be an adaptogen. Adaptogens support energy and help to maintain balance in the body. Eleuthero belongs to the Araliaceae family and is a distant relative of Korean and American ginsengs. The root is not harvested until it is two or more years old; the older the root, the higher its value. It is held in high esteem in China, where it has been valued for thousands of years, sometimes commanding a higher price than gold. Eleuthero is found in the Siberian province of Russia. Each capsule contains 410 mg eleuthero root.

Take 2 capsules with a meal three times daily.

Stock No. 660-9 (100) Ko

Energ-V® [*Circulatory, Glandular, Nervous*] was designed to support the body's own energy-building system. It works with the glandular, nervous and circulatory systems to help relieve stress and support energy production. It provides a variety of nutrients to support vitality—some that nourish the glands (kelp and licorice) and some that nourish the brain and nervous system (gotu kola), better enabling the body to cope with stress.

Energ-V also provides support from adaptogenic herbs (schizandra and eleuthero) that help the body under environmental stress. It contains:

Bee pollen
Eleuthero root
Gotu kola aerial parts
Licorice root
Rose hips
Yellow dock root
Barley grass aerial parts
Schizandra fruit
Kelp leaves and stems
Capsicum fruit

Energ-V is commonly used in conjunction with vitamin C, B complex, bee pollen and iron supplements.

Take 2 capsules with a meal twice daily.

Stock No. 875-8 (100) Ko

Enviro-Detox [*Vital Nutrition*]. Environmental pollutants and toxins can build up in the body, slowing the body's natural cleansing processes. Enviro-Detox is a combination of 13 nutrients selected for their ability to provide ongoing support to the body's organs that may play roles in detoxification: the liver, kidneys, lungs, bowels and skin. It contains:

Burdock root
Dandelion root
Fenugreek seed
Ginger rhizome
Pepsin (contains lactose from milk)
Red clover flowers
Yellow dock root
Marshmallow root
Sarsaparilla root
Lactospores
Cascara sagrada bark
Echinacea purpurea root
Milk thistle fruit concentrate

All have a long history of folk use. Each nutrient in this exclusive formula has been carefully selected to provide maximum nutrition for individual body systems and the body as a whole. The beneficial intestinal flora *Lactobacillus sporogenes* helps populate the intestinal tract as cleansing may cause a flushing of friendly flora. Unlike other strains of the organism, it does not need to be refrigerated to maintain viability.

NOTE: This product contains cascara sagrada. See your health care provider prior to use if: pregnant or nursing, any medical condition exists, or when taking any medication. Read and follow recommendation carefully. Not intended for prolonged use. Do not use if diarrhea, loose stools or abdominal pain are present or develop. Use of this product may worsen these conditions and be harmful to your health. Chronic diarrhea can result in serious illness.

Take 1 capsule with a meal three

times daily. Drink one glass (8 oz.) of Nature's Spring water with capsules.
Stock No. 874-1 (100)

ESSENTIAL OILS

Essential oils are an important part of any aromatherapy program. Using aromas that remind us of different moods, aromatherapy can help elicit feelings and help us experience harmony, balance and stability in our lives. NSP Essential Oils are versatile, effective, calming, soothing, revitalizing and balancing. Pure, genuine and complete, they are the best you can buy. Essential oils will strengthen any holistic program and can be used in conjunction with herbal and other nutritional supplements. Their amazing benefits can be enjoyed not only through massage and inhalation, but in the bath, shower, vaporizer, humidifier, in gargles, skin care and even household jobs. All oils should be diluted prior to topical use. Do not use essential oils near the eyes or mucous membranes.

Aromaball Plug-in Diffuser.
Use the Aromaball to get the scent of your favorite essential oil into a room quickly. Simply place a few drops of oil onto the diffuser scent card and insert the card into the Aromaball. Then plug it in and enjoy the fresh scent of your oil or blend for many hours.
Stock No. 3895-7

Aromaball Diffuser Scent Cards.
For use with the Aromaball Plug-in Diffuser. Pack of 10.
Stock No. 3951-3 (10)

Bergamot BIO Pure Essential Oil
(*Citrus bergamia, cold pressed, organic*) has balancing, cooling, refreshing, stimulating and uplifting properties that are welcome in any stress-filled life. Bergamot is useful for oily skin and other skin conditions. Do not use topically prior to sun exposure or during pregnancy.
Stock No. 3900-5 (5 ml)

Bottle with Sprayer.
Mix your favorite oil or blend with distilled water in this convenient spray bottle so you can spray linens or freshen the air.
Stock No. 3936-9 (2 fl. oz.)

Breathe Free Pure Essential Oil Blend
(*Geranium, Niaouli BIO, Peppermint and Rosemary*). Lightly apply this clearing and stimulating blend to the forehead and behind the ears and neck. Do not use during pregnancy or with high blood pressure or epilepsy. Not for use on children under 2.
Stock No. 3919-1 (5 ml)

Cellu-Tone Pure Essential Oil Blend
(*Cypress, Geranium, Juniper, Niaouli BIO, Pink Grapefruit BIO, Rosemary, Thyme Linalol BIO, Vetiver*) is a stimulating combination that provides powerful, beneficial properties for the skin. Massage well into desired area. Do not use topically prior to sun exposure. Do not administer to

people with kidney disorders.

Stock No. 3927-3 (5 ml)

Chamomile, Roman Pure Essential Oil (*Chamaemelum nobile, steam-distilled*)

has traditionally been used for its refreshing yet calming and soothing properties. Roman Chamomile is widely used in shampoos and is particularly useful for sensitive skin and other skin types and is appropriate for children. Not for use during pregnancy.

Stock No. 3901-6 (5 ml)

Cinnamon Pure Essential Oil

(*Cinnamonum zeylanicum, steam-distilled*) has warming properties that comfort and soothe the mind and spirit. Cinnamon has a pungent, spicy aroma, and its warming properties make it excellent for massage when well diluted. Do not use in cases of hemophilia or severe kidney or liver disease. Always use well diluted.

Stock No. 3898-6 (5 ml)

Citrus Fresh Diffuser Kit.

Fragrance your home with the refreshing smell of pure citrus oils. Lemon, Mandarin and Pink Grapefruit are included with this easy-to-use, refillable plug-in diffuser. To change the fragrance, simply replace the diffuser scent card (includes 10 replacement cards).

Stock No. 3949-4

Clary Sage Pure Essential Oil

(*Salvia sclarea, steam-distilled*) has an inspiring, regenerating aroma that is balancing and relaxing. It is especially helpful for women and beneficial for dry skin. Its powerful aroma can seem almost intoxicating and should be used in small amounts. Not for use during pregnancy.

Stock No. 3902-4 (5 ml)

Clear Roll-on Bottle.

For those who need a roll-on application of essential oils, you can mix oils with massage oil in this bottle and pinpoint where you want it.

Stock No. 3950-2 (.5 fl. oz.)

Clove Bud BIO Pure Essential Oil (*Eugenia caryophyllata, steam-distilled, organic*)

has traditionally been used for its powerful and penetrating properties. It is useful for those who want to inspire feelings of rest and relaxation. Not for use during pregnancy or on children under 2. Strong skin irritant.

Stock No. 3903-1 (5 ml)

Deep Relief Pure Essential Oil Blend (*Clove Bud BIO, Ginger, Nutmeg*).

This is a penetrating combination. Apply to ankles, knees and arms. Do not use during pregnancy or on children under 2.

Stock No. 3926-2 (5 ml)

Empty Amber Bottle.

Store your own blended creations in dark amber bottles for best shelf life.

Stock No. 3894-0

E

Eucalyptus BIO Essential Oil

(*Eucalyptus globulus, steam-distilled, organic*) is cooling, stimulating and penetrating and inspires feelings of emotional balance. It is useful during the changing seasons. It contains strong compounds and can be used for all skin types. For external use only. Not for use during pregnancy, on children under the age of 2 or by asthmatics.

Stock No. 3904-9 (5 ml)

Fragrance Testing Papers.

These papers come in handy when sharing aromatherapy with others, as they allow customers to sample different fragrances without opening and closing bottles.

Stock No. 2799-0 (100)

Frankincense Pure Essential Oil

(*Boswellia carterii, steam-distilled, wildcrafted*), popular since ancient times, has an aroma that is centering, comforting and elevating. For ages, it has been associated with meditation and spirituality. It is useful for the skin, especially mature or dry skin. Not for use during pregnancy.

Stock No. 3899-9 (5 ml)

Funnel.

Pour your custom-made oils and blends into an amber bottle with the help of a funnel. Specially made to fit the amber bottle and roll-on bottle.

Stock No. 3956-4

Geranium Pure Essential Oil

(*Pelargonium graveolens, steam-distilled*) has a sweet aroma that is balancing, calming and uplifting. It is widely used in skin care because of its ability to restore balance to oily or dry hair and skin. It is helpful for patchy skin and is gentle enough for sensitive skin. Not for use during pregnancy.

Stock No. 3905-3 (5 ml)

Grapefruit, Pink BIO Pure Essential Oil

(*Citrus paradisi, cold-pressed, organic*) has traditionally been used for its toning and stimulating properties. Pink Grapefruit is astringent, uplifting, soothing and refreshing. Its aroma can uplift the spirit. It is beneficial for oily skin and hair. Do not use topically prior to sun exposure; can irritate skin. Not for use during pregnancy.

Stock No. 3906-7 (5 ml)

Guardian Pure Essential Oil Blend

(*Lavender Fine BIO, Ravensara BIO, Roman Chamomile, Tea Tree*). This combination is spiritually "strengthening." Not for use during pregnancy.

Stock No. 3922-9 (5 ml)

Health, Home and Beauty Kit.

This kit contains Lavender, Bergamot, Cinnamon leaf, Lemon, Grapefruit, Geranium, Frankincense, Pine Needle, Mandarin and Peppermint. This versatile collection of oils can be used to create hundreds of blends for everything from women's concerns to cleaning your bathroom tiles.

Available while supplies last.
Stock No. 3954-1

Helichrysum Pure Essential Oil

Helichrysum Pure Essential Oil (*Helichrysum italicum, steam-distilled*) is 100 percent genuine and complete, wild crafted in the natural humus of Yugoslavia or in Corsica in the Mediterranean. A sharply scented oil, helichrysum contains beneficial compounds. For external use only. Not for use during pregnancy.

Stock No. 3943-0 (5 ml)

Jasmine Pure Essential Oil

Jasmine Pure Essential Oil (*Jasminum officinalis, hexane*). This sensually sweet floral aroma has been used in human sexuality for centuries. Jasmine is especially helpful for those with dry, sensitive skin.

Stock No. 3890-1 (2 ml)

Lavender Fine Pure Essential Oil

Lavender Fine Pure Essential Oil (*Lavandula angustifolia, steam-distilled, AOC*) has long been considered the wonder oil of essential oils because of its versatility. Lavender's cool, mellow, peaceful fragrance has traditionally been used for its balancing effects and soothing properties. Lavender is good for all skin types, even sensitive skin, and can be used undiluted topically. Not for use during pregnancy.

Stock No. 3907-8 (5 ml)

Lemon BIO Pure Essential Oil

Lemon BIO Pure Essential Oil (*Citrus limon, cold-pressed, organic*) has a bright aroma that is stimulating, refreshing and clean. Its toning and soothing actions are helpful to condition the skin, including oily skin. Do not apply topically prior to sun exposure; can irritate skin. Not for use during pregnancy.

Stock No. 3908-2 (5 ml)

Mandarin Pure Essential Oil

Mandarin Pure Essential Oil (*Citrus reticulata, cold-pressed*). Mandarin's fruity, cheerful aroma is invigorating and uplifting. Its astringent properties make it beneficial for skin tone, while natural antioxidants help protect the skin. Do not use topically prior to sun exposure; can irritate skin.

Stock No. 3897-4 (5 ml)

Marjoram Pure Essential Oil

Marjoram Pure Essential Oil (*Origanum majorana, steam-distilled*) has a warm, soothing fragrance that calms yet strengthens. Marjoram makes an excellent massage oil. Not for use during pregnancy.

Stock No. 3896-3 (5 ml)

Myrrh Pure Essential Oil

Myrrh Pure Essential Oil (*Commiphora myrrha, steam-distilled, wildcrafted*). This ancient aroma is centering and peaceful. It has long been associated with inspiration, strength and endurance. Not for use during pregnancy.

Stock No. 3939-3 (5 ml)

Neroli Pure Essential Oil

Neroli Pure Essential Oil (*Citrus aurantium, steam-distilled*) has a fresh, floral aroma that brightens the spirits and clears the mind. Neroli's soothing properties enhance skin tone. Not for use during pregnancy.

Stock No. 3891-2 (2 ml)

Oregano, Wild Pure Essential Oil
(*Origanum campactum, steam-distilled*) is stimulating and warming. It contains compounds useful for conditioning the skin. Do not use during pregnancy or on children under 5. Always dilute well before topical application. Use a concentration of less than 2 percent (15 drops per tablespoon of NSP massage oil). Blend Wild Oregano oil with other essential oils before diffusing. For external use only.

Stock No. 3934-6 (5 ml)

Patchouli Pure Essential Oil
(*Pogostemon patchouli, steam-distilled*) is soothing, calming and exotic. This sensuous oil should be used sparingly. It is beneficial to the skin—particularly dry skin. It also has toning properties.

Stock No. 3909-0 (5 ml)

Peppermint Pure Essential Oil
(*Mentha piperita, steam-distilled*) is both warming and cooling as well as refreshing, uplifting and invigorating. Its properties are especially soothing to the skin and are balancing to oily skin and hair. Not for use during pregnancy or on children under 2. May irritate skin.

Stock No. 3910-9 (5 ml)

Pine Needle Pure Essential Oil
(*Pinus sylvestris, steam-distilled, wildcrafted*) has traditionally been used for its warm, stimulating and revitalizing properties. Its aroma acts as a household deodorizer. Do not use on children under 2 or on those with kidney disorders. Can irritate skin.

Stock No. 3911-5 (5 ml)

Rose Bulgaria Pure Essential Oil
(*Rosa damascena, steam-distilled*). It takes over one ton of petals to yield one pound of pure Rose Bulgaria oil. The queen of oils for women, rose is sensual, balancing and uplifting, as well as calming, relaxing and comforting in matters of the heart. In addition, it is good for mature, dry skin. Not for use during pregnancy.

Stock No. 3892-8 (2 ml)

Rosemary Pure Essential Oil
(*Rosemarinus officinalis, steam-distilled*) has a strong aroma that is balancing, invigorating, revitalizing and regenerating. It conditions the scalp and has been used for centuries on oily hair and skin. Not for use during pregnancy or on those with high blood pressure or epilepsy. Can irritate skin.

Stock No. 3914-8 (5 ml)

Sandalwood Pure Essential Oil
(*Santalum album, steam-distilled, wildcrafted*). This sensual oil is calming, balancing and harmonizing. It has a balancing action on the skin. Not for use during pregnancy, with children under the age of 2, or on those with kidney problems.

Stock No. 3915-4 (5 ml)

Thyme Linalol BIO Pure Essential Oil
(*Thymus vulgaris ct. linalol, steam-distilled, organic*), also called sweet thyme, has long been used for its stimulating and

invigorating properties. Thyme Linalol contains fewer irritants than red thyme and can be used on children. Do not use during pregnancy.

Stock No. 3913-2 (5 ml)

Ylang Ylang Complete BIO Pure Essential Oil (*Cananga odorata, steam-distilled, organic*)

is sensual, warming, calming and balancing. Ylang Ylang Complete is good for the skin and for hair. For external use only. Not for use during pregnancy.

Stock No. 3917-7 (5 ml)

Evening Primrose Oil (EPO)

[*Circulatory, Glandular*] contains gamma-linolenic acid (GLA), an essential fatty acid that assists the body in producing prostaglandins (messengers in the body that perform hundreds of important functions). Without an adequate supply of GLA, optimal health is impossible to achieve. Each capsule provides 40 mg of gamma-linolenic acid and 300 mg of linoleic acid, together with 15 IU of vitamin E as a protective antioxidant. Other beneficial oils—linoleic, oleic and palmitic—are contained in each 500 mg capsule.

Take 1 softgel daily with a meal.

Stock No. 1787-7 (90)

EverFlex® with Hyaluronic Acid

[*Structural*] offers the benefits of glucosamine, chondroitin, MSM, hyaluronic acid and devil's claw in one convenient tablet. Glucosamine helps maintain the integrity, lubrication and mobility of joints. Chondroitin promotes cartilage tissue generation and attracts fluid into the cartilage, making it more shock absorbent. Methylsulfonylmethane (MSM) is a form of biologically active sulfur that is found in the human diet. Sulfur is important to joint health for a wide variety of processes. Hyaluronic acid (HA) is an important component of cartilage that plays a crucial role in joint motion and homeostasis. HA promotes the viscosity and elasticity of the fluid surrounding the joints. Devil's claw has long been used to relieve joint pain and has been shown to have anti-inflammatory activity.

Each 2-tablet serving provides a 1,900 mg proprietary blend of glucosamine hydrochloride (from crab shells), MSM, chondroitin sulfate, hyaluronic acid and Devil's Claw root.

Take 2 tablets twice daily with a meal.

Stock No. 948-4 (60)

EverFlex Pain Cream®

[*Structural*] features the cooling relief of menthol plus a unique combination of cetylated fatty acid esters (cetyl myrsitoleate, myristate, palmitoleate, oleate, palmitate and laurate), olive oil and MSM. MSM is a great source of sulfur, an important structural component, while menthol is an approved active ingredient in many pain-relieving topical creams. This cream is easily absorbed through the skin for fast-acting structural support.

NOTE: For external use only. Avoid contact with eyes. If condition worsens, or if symptoms persist for more than seven days or clear up and occur again within a few days, discontinue use of product and consult a physician. Do not apply to wounds or damaged skin. Do not bandage tightly. Keep out of reach of children.

Adults and children 2 years of age and older: Apply to affected area not more than three to four times per day. For children under 2 years of age, consult a physician.

Stock No. 3535-6 (2 oz.)

Everybody's Fiber [*Intestinal*] is a bulk powder product that combines fiber and herbs for cleansing and soothing the digestive system. Fiber is critical to colon health and proper digestive function. And each serving of Everybody's Fiber provides 3 full grams of dietary fiber!

This blend contains apple pectin, a soluble fiber that has adsorbing and bulking properties; slippery elm bark, which forms a gel when mixed with water and helps things slide along smoothly; chamomile flowers; short-chain FOS—a soluble fiber that provides food for friendly microorganisms in the colon; flax meal—provides soluble fiber and supports colon health; marshmallow root, which is soothing and adds fiber. Also contains asparagus stems, peppermint leaves, fennel seeds, uña de gato inner bark, stevia extract, natural peach, apricot and plum flavors, plus malic acid. Everybody's Fiber can be used by...just about everybody!

Mix 1 scoop powder (5 grams) in 4 ounces water or juice and drink daily. Not for use by children under

12 years of age.

Stock No. 1336-6 (4.6 oz.)

Everybody's Formula [*Vital Nutrition*] is a nutritious, high-protein, natural food drink of soy, casein and whey protein. It's enriched with essential vitamins, minerals and enzymes. Everybody's Formula contains nine essential amino acids that must be supplied by the diet. Contains isolated soy protein, calcium, sodium caseinate, fructose, dried whey, natural and artificial flavors, lactalbumin, dl-methionine, magnesium oxide, soybean oil, lecithin, ascorbic acid, ferrous fumarate, niacinamide, vitamin A palmitate, dried honey, licorice extract, thiamine hydrochloride, riboflavin, kelp, bromelain, papain and potassium iodide. This beverage contains less than 1 gram of fat per serving and provides 13 grams of protein.

Add approximately 2 level tablespoons (20 g) of Everybody's Formula to 8 ounces of your favorite juice, water or skim milk.

Stock No. 2939-8 (17 oz., 482 g)

EW [*Nervous*] was designed to support optimal eye health. It contains herbs that support overall health in a variety of ways. Four time-honored herbs make up this formula:
　　Bayberry root bark
　　Golden seal root and rhizome
　　Red raspberry leaves
　　Eyebright aerial parts and extract
Take 2 capsules daily with a meal.

Stock No. 861-3 (100) Ko

Eyebright [*Vital Nutrition*].

Historically used to cleanse and treat eye disorders, eyebright contains tannins, lignans and flavonoids. Each capsule contains 400 mg eyebright.

Take 2 capsules with a meal three times daily.

Stock No. 260-3 (100) Ko

False Unicorn [*Glandular*] is a

long-time favorite of many women who desire nutritional support for the glandular and reproductive systems. Historically, false unicorn was used for female complaints or as a uterine tonic. Each capsule contains 450 mg false unicorn root (*Chamaelirium luteum*).

Take 2 capsules with a meal twice daily.

Stock No. 267-1 (100) Ko

Fat Grabbers[R] [*Weight Loss*]

is an ideal product for anyone wanting to help reduce the level of fat in his or her diet. No stimulants, no questionable ingredients—just wholesome, nutritional substances that won't disrupt normal body processes.

Research conducted in our laboratories has verified many other in vitro experiments performed at independent laboratories showing that lecithin and saponins emulsify fat in aqueous media. The logical extension of this observation to the small intestines is assumed through scientific precedent. The fat-binding properties of fiber from guar gum and psyllium

hulls interfere with the absorption of the emulsified fat from the small intestine. The bound fat molecules are then eliminated.

Using Fat Grabbers in conjunction with a sensible dietary plan will help you create an effective overall weight-management program. Fat Grabbers provides nutrients to help maintain cholesterol levels already within the normal range. The ingredients in Fat Grabbers—guar gum, psyllium hulls, chickweed leaf extract and lecithin—all enjoy a long history of safe use.

NOTE: May cause allergic reaction in persons sensitive to inhaled or ingested psyllium.

Take 4 capsules with 8 oz. pure water with a meal three times daily. Then follow with another glass of water.

Stock No. 2938-5 Trial Size (36) Ko
Stock No. 3035-9 (120) Ko
Stock No. 3030-4 (360) Ko
**Stock No. 2485-4
(20 retail sample packets)** Ko

Fatigue/Exhaustion [*Nervous*]

is a natural homeopathic medicine that assists in alleviating the symptoms of minor fatigue and exhaustion due to sleeplessness, illness, overwork or stress.

Take 10–15 drops under the tongue four–six times daily until symptoms improve, then decrease to twice daily and continue for two–four weeks or as needed until symptoms are relieved. For children under 12, consult your health care professional.

Stock No. 8840-0 (1 fl. oz.)

FCS II [*Urinary, Glandular*]
provides nutritional support for
the female reproductive system. It
contains:
Red raspberry leaves
Blessed thistle aerial parts
Dong quai root
Queen of the meadow leaves
Althea root
Lobelia aerial parts
Ginger rhizome
Black cohosh rhizome and root
Capsicum fruit
Golden seal root
*Take 2 capsules with a meal three
times daily.*
Stock No. 878-7 (100) Ko

Female Comfort [*Glandular*] is
designed to support proper balance
of the female reproductive and
glandular systems. It contains:
Red raspberry leaves
Dong quai root
Ginger rhizome
Licorice root
Black cohosh root
Blessed thistle aerial parts
Marshmallow herb
Queen of the meadow leaves
*Take 2 capsules with a meal three
times daily.*
Stock No. 882-2 (100) Ko

Feminine Tonic [*Glandular*] is a
natural homeopathic medicine for
support of the feminine endocrine
and organ systems.
NOTE: Not recommended for
children under 12.
*Take 10–15 drops under the
tongue three times daily.*
Stock No. 8701-1 (1 fl. oz.)

Fenugreek & Thyme
[*Respiratory*]. Fenugreek herb
contains mucilaginous compounds,
which are gel-like substances known
for their ability to help support
tissues. It is also an herbal source
of selenium, an important trace
mineral that also functions as an
antioxidant. Historically, thyme has
been used to support respiratory
health.
*Take 2 capsules with a meal twice
daily.*
Stock No. 885-1 (100) Ko

Feverfew, High-Parthenolide
[*Nervous*], commonly known
as Bachelor's Buttons, provides
nutrition to the central nervous
system.
This herb offers nutritional
support for migraine headaches.
High-Parthenolide Feverfew
delivers 500 mcg of parthenolide
in a total of 201 mg of feverfew—
from a specially grown "high
parthenolide" feverfew leaf—per
capsule. Parthenolides are sesquiterpene lactones, the major dietary
components of feverfew.
NOTE: Do not take feverfew
during pregnancy.
Take 1 capsule daily with a meal.
Stock No. 288-1 (100) Ko

Fibralgia® [*Structural*] is good
news for millions of Americans
who experience muscle discomfort
and fatigue. When the body needs
energy-producing fuel, it breaks
down muscle protein to create
energy. This product contains malic
acid and magnesium.

Malic acid, found naturally in high concentrations in apples and other fruits and vegetables, plays an important role in cellular energy production. Magnesium is used daily to help with the absorption of several vitamins and minerals, to promote bone strength and to regulate nerve impulses.

Take 1 capsule with a meal three times daily. Consider adding the positive mood-influencing benefits of NSP St. John's Wort to your regimen.

Stock No. 4061-6 (90) Ko

5-HTP Power [*Nervous*] contains hydroxytryptophan, a precursor to serotonin, an important neurotransmitter that helps regulate appetite, mood and sleep. Hydroxytryptophan is converted into serotonin in the body, which may help elevate mood, assist in controlling hunger and promote restful sleep. NSP 5-HTP Power is a blend of three adaptogenic herbs—eleuthero, ashwaganda and suma—along with 5-HTP to help the body adjust to changes. It also contains vitamin B6 and zinc, which support the action of 5-HTP. Each capsule contains 35 mg of 5-HTP.

CAUTION: If taking a prescription medication, consult a health care practitioner before taking this product. Pregnant or nursing women should seek the advice of a health care practitioner before using this supplement. Do not use this product for more than three months without taking a two-week rest.

Take 1 capsule three times daily with a meal. The 35 mg of 5-HTP in this product allows flexibility when adjusting serving size.

Stock No. 2806-4 (60)

5-W [*Glandular*]. This herbal blend supplies nutrients supportive of the female glandular and reproductive systems. The formula contains natural minerals found in plants, which support vitality and healthy tissue growth. This combination includes:

Black cohosh root
Squaw vine whole plant
Dong quai root
Butcher's broom root
Red raspberry leaves

Take 2 capsules three times daily with a meal.

Stock No. 1120-5 (100) Ko

Flash-Ease [*Glandular*] contains black cohosh, a popular herb native to the West. It is widely known for supporting the mature woman's body as she encounters normal glandular challenges and physical changes. In fact, women have used it for decades to help "keep cool" during menopause.

Flash-Ease is a potent, time-release version of this trusted herb. It is standardized to a 2.5 percent concentration of triterpene glycosides (the key active constituent). Flash-Ease also includes dong quai, a noted Chinese herb, to further support the glandular system. Each tablet contains a highly concentrated extract that provides 80 mg of

F

black cohosh.

Take 1 tablet in the morning and 1 at bedtime. Each specially processed tablet slowly releases its contents, providing optimal day and night protection, and delivers 2 mg of triterpene glycocides.

Stock No. 81-4 (60) Ko

Flax Seed Oil with Lignans

[*Circulatory, Immune*]. Several scientific studies show that consumption of omega-3 essential fatty acids (EFAs) can benefit the heart. Flax Seed Oil is a rich source of these EFAs. It also contains lignans—substances known to stimulate immune activity—and linoleic acid, another essential fatty acid. These two fatty acids are termed "essential" because the body cannot manufacture them. EFAs are precursors to prostaglandins.

Until recently, experts believed the best sources of omega-3 were fish oils. While fish oils are a good source, flax seed oil contains twice as much omega-3 essential fatty acids as fish oil products, without the fishy aftertaste. Each softgel capsule contains omega-3, omega-6 and omega-9 essential fatty acids plus lignans.

Take 1–2 softgels with a meal three times daily.

Also available in a liquid for those who desire an easy way to get a greater concentration. One tablespoon equals approximately 14 softgels. Take 1 teaspoonful three times daily.

Stock No. 1583-6 (60) Ko
Stock No. 3162-1 (8 fl. oz.) Ko

Flora Force®, Bifidophilus
(*see Bifidophilus Flora Force*)

Focus Attention [*Nervous, Circulatory*] provides nutrients that help maintain normal brain-stimulation levels while supporting blood circulation and neurotrans-mitter levels in the brain. Focus Attention contains *Ginkgo biloba*, DMAE and *Melissa officinalis* for normal brain function. It encourages restful, balanced mental activity. Available in capsules and a great-tasting powder drink mix.

For optimum utilization, take Focus Attention capsules with NSP Flax Seed Oil softgels or liquid. Focus Attention powder contains flax seed in the blend.

NOTE: Pregnant or lactating women or anyone taking prescription medication should consult a health care professional prior to use.

Over 12 years: Take 2 capsules with a meal twice daily, or take 3/4 teaspoon* powder mixed in 2 oz. water twice daily.

Age 6–12 years: Take 1 capsule with a meal twice daily, or take 1/2 teaspoon* powder in 1.5 oz. water twice daily.

Under 6 years: Consult your health care professional.
*One rounded scoop = 1/4 teaspoon

Stock No. 1833-4 (90)
Stock No. 1843-0 (3.3 oz.) powder

Folic Acid Plus [*Vital Nutrition*]
is essential for human health, especially for the developing fetus. It is important for all women of

childbearing age to get sufficient amounts of folic acid. A healthful diet with adequate folate may reduce a woman's risk of having a child with brain or spinal cord birth defects. Each Folic Acid Plus tablet contains 400 mcg folic acid, plus vitamin C and bee pollen.

Take 1 or 2 tablets daily with a meal.

Stock No. 1585-8 (90) Ko

Food Enzymes [*Digestive, Immune*] is a key product for the digestive system. Foods require processing (digestion), and enzymes are able to break down food compounds for absorption into the bloodstream. A number of different enzymes are needed to deal with differing food compounds. Some of these are produced by the body, some are found in foods. However, many processed foods lack the enzymes needed for proper digestion.

This formulation supplements the body's production of digestive enzymes and those enzymes found in the diet. For example, pepsin is used for the digestion of proteins (betaine hydrochloride or HCl); pancreatin is produced by the pancreas to digest proteins, carbohydrates and fats in the small intestines; mycozyme digests starches; papain and bromelain digest protein; bile salts emulsify fats and prepare them for further digestion by lipase. Taking this product with meals will support the body's digestion of protein, carbohydrates and fats. One capsule will help you digest a minimum of 30 grams of protein, 30 grams of

carbohydrates and 20 grams of fats. Each capsule supplies a proprietary blend of:

Betaine HCl (for proteins)
Bile salt (for fats)
Bromelain (for proteins)
Lipase (contains lactose from milk, for fats)
Alpha-amylase (mycozyme, for starch)
Pancreatin (8xUSP, for all foods)
Papain (for proteins)
Pepsin (1:10,000, for proteins)
Take 1–2 capsules with a meal three times daily.

Stock No. 1836-9 (120)
Stock No. 2494-1
(20 retail sample packets)

Four [*Nervous, Respiratory*] is a nutritional aid for the nervous and respiratory systems. This formula supports the function of breathing. It is so named because there are four herbs in the formula:

Blessed thistle aerial parts
Catnip leaves
Pleurisy root
Yerba santa leaves
Take 2 capsules with a meal twice daily.

Stock No. 892-5 (100) Ko

Frankincense Pure Essential Oil
(*see Essential Oils*)

Free Amino Acids with Magnesium & l-Carnitine
[*Structural*] is primarily for individuals involved in strength and endurance training, especially for times of physical activity, stress and recovery. Amino acids are building blocks of protein that

F

help develop, build and maintain solid muscle tissue. Twenty amino acids are needed by the body to make proteins, 12 of which the body manufactures. The other eight essential amino acids must be supplied in the diet. The eight essential amino acids in this product are formulated to meet the Food and Agricultural Organization/World Health Organization (FAO/WHO) amino acid pattern that helps ensure the most efficient use of amino acids by the human body. Combine this amino acid formula with physical activity and good nutrition to support muscle strength and endurance.

L-Carnitine helps transport fatty acids into the mitochondria, where they are burned for energy. Magnesium acts as a cofactor to help activate enzymes necessary for carbohydrate and amino acid metabolism. Whether you're an athlete or body builder, whether you're physically active or simply need amino acid supplementation, this formula helps support your workout program.

Typical analysis of amino acids per two-tablet serving:

Ingredients	mg
l-Lysine*	90
l-Histidine	16
l-Arginine	22
l-Aspartic acid	88
l-Threonine*	56
l-Serine	41
l-Proline	45
l-Alanine	44
Glycine	16
l-Glutamic Acid	140
l-Cystine	21
l-Valine*	70
l-Methionine*	29
l-Isoleucine*	56
l-Leucine*	100
l-Tyrosine	30
l-Phenylalanine*	56
l-Tryptophan*	14
l-Carnitine	100
Magnesium aspartate	100
Magnesium oxide	150

*Essential amino acids formulated to meet the FAO/WHO amino acid pattern.

This supplement contains no sugars, artificial colors, flavors, preservatives, starch, soy, yeast or wheat products.

Take 2 tablets with a meal three times daily in addition to your daily multiple vitamin and mineral supplement.
Stock No. 3664-6 (60)

FV [*Digestive, Immune*] combination nutritionally supports the digestive, immune and lymph systems. It contains ginger rhizome, capsicum fruit, golden seal root and rhizome, and licorice root.

Take 3 capsules with a meal twice daily.
Stock No. 900-7 (100) Ko

G

GABA Plus [*Nervous*] provides GABA (gamma-aminobutyric acid), an amino acid that plays a role in neurotransmitter and brain activity. This unique formula also includes glutamine and taurine, amino acids that play roles in brain function;

spirulina for its abundance of nutrients; and passionflower, an herb long used to help maintain balance in this system and relieve stress.

NOTE: Consult your health care practitioner before using if you are pregnant, nursing or suffer from any medical condition, or are taking any prescription drug.

Take 1–2 capsules with a meal twice daily.

Stock No. 1823-6 (60) Ko

Gallbladder Formula [*Digestive*]

contains herbs traditionally used to provide nutrients that support the proper function of the digestive system, particularly the liver and gallbladder. Gallbladder Formula provides soothing action. It contains:

Oregon grape root
Ginger root
Cramp bark
Fennel seeds
Peppermint leaves
Wild yam root
Catnip herb

Take 2 capsules with a meal three times daily. For best results, use with Urinary Maintenance and Hydrangea.

Stock No. 1202-0 (100) Ko

Garcinia Combination [*Weight Management*]

boasts *Garcinia cambogia* fruit as its chief ingredient. Garcinia's key component is hydroxycitric acid. NSP combines garcinia with chickweed (offers nutritional support for weight management), l-carnitine (helps in the transport of long-chain fatty acids) and chromium (an essential trace mineral that plays a role in the body's natural regulation of blood sugar; 30 mcg per capsule). The garcinia in this combination has been standardized to 50 percent hydroxy-citric acid.

Take 2 capsules 30 minutes before a meal three times daily.

Stock No. 906-9 (100) Ko

Garlic [*Immune*]

is a member of the family that includes onions, leeks and shallots. An old Welsh saying goes, "Eat leeks in March and wild garlic in May, and all the year after physicians may play." Olympic athletes in ancient Greece chewed a clove at the start of a competition, believing it increased their stamina. Garlic's strong odor is due mostly to a sulfide called allicin. This prized herb exhibits antioxidant, immune-supporting and circulatory-supporting actions. Each capsule contains 550 mg garlic bulb.

Take 1 capsule with a meal twice daily.

Stock No. 290-0 (100) Ko

Garlic, High-Potency, SynerPro® [*Immune*].

The only problem with getting garlic into the diet has always been the distinct odor it leaves on the breath. Now it is possible to manufacture odorless garlic. The question is, does it retain the potency of fresh garlic? Studies have shown that it doesn't.

Nature's Sunshine offers you the finest and most potent garlic on the market with a special coating that helps control the garlic's odor. When broken open, these tablets have a strong garlic odor unlike "odorless" garlic products. Trade-secret processing and careful preparation of each tablet give NSP High-Potency Garlic a special locked-in freshness coating. It contains chlorophyll, which controls odor while assuring a long, effective shelf-life. Because the tablet does not break down for absorption until it reaches the small intestine, you receive the full nutritional value of garlic without the undesirable taste. Moreover, comparing total allicin potential (TAP) with other leading brands shows that Nature's Sunshine leads the pack. NSP High-Potency Garlic is valued above all others for its great potency and superb quality. One 400 mg tablet equals 1,200 mg of fresh garlic, roughly equal to one clove.

Adults: Take 1 tablet with a meal once or twice daily. Children: Take 1/2 tablet with a meal once or twice daily.

Stock No. 292-9 (60) Ko
4 Kids Too!

Garlic Oil [*Immune*] contains the
antioxidant germanium and several sulfur compounds. Each softgel capsule provides 220 mg garlic oil, equivalent to 1,000 mg fresh garlic cloves, in a base of soybean oil to ensure potency. It may be used externally or it can be consumed to support immune function.

Take 1 capsule with a meal three times daily.

Stock No. 1694-6 (60)

Gastro Health [*Digestive*].
NSP spent two years intensively evaluating various herbs in order to create this unique, patented, natural formula designed to support stomach health. Recent scientific studies determined that *H. pylori* bacteria may be a primary cause of ulcers and found that ingredients in this formula may inhibit the activity of *H. pylori*. In clinical studies, deglycyrrhizinated licorice extract (DGLE) helped soothe stomach irritations and relieved associated discomfort. Gastro Health also provides pau d'arco bark extract, clove flower powder extract, *Inula racemosa* root extract and capsicum fruit. Gastro Health provides nutritional support for the stomach during stress, strain and discomfort.

Take 2 capsules with a meal twice daily, plus 2 capsules at bedtime.

Stock No. 917-9 (60) Ko

GC-X [*Circulatory, Intestinal*]
combines herbs traditionally used to support the circulatory, eliminative and immune systems. It contains:
Garlic bulb
Capsicum fruit
Parsley herb
Ginger root
Golden seal root
Eleuthero root
Garlic has been highly touted as one of nature's most all-around nutritive herbs. It has antioxidant, immune-supporting and circulatory-supporting actions. Capsicum is widely known for its ability to stimulate circulatory activity. Parsley is rich in chlorophyll, a natural

deodorizer. Ginger and golden seal are both herbs with time-honored reputations. Eleuthero, an adaptogenic herb, supports energy, stamina and endurance, and may help with concentration.

Take 2 capsules with a meal three times daily.

Stock No. 1212-1 (100) Ko

Geranium Pure Essential Oil
(*see Essential Oils*)

Germanium Combination
[*Immune*] supports the immune system. This product provides an organic form of germanium, a trace mineral. Each tablet contains 30 mg of bis-carboxyethyl germanium sesquioxide in a synergistic base of 100 mg of *Echinacea purpurea* root.

Take 1–3 tablets daily with a meal.

Stock No. 1652-3 (30)

Ginger [*Digestive*] has been
cultivated for thousands of years in China and India. It was written about in many ancient Chinese herbal texts and is an ingredient in as many as half of all Chinese herbal combinations. The Chinese use it to buffer the effects of stronger herbs, and they drink it widely in tea. Ginger nutritionally supports the digestive process and has the ability to help settle occasional stomach upset and prevent motion sickness. The root has a strong, sweet scent. Each capsule contains 500 mg ginger rhizome.

Take 1 capsule with a meal twice daily.

Stock No. 300-6 (100) Ko

Ginkgo Biloba, Time-Release
[*Nervous, Circulatory*]. The growing body of research shows that the extract from the leaves of the oldest tree on earth promotes optimal blood circulation to the brain and supports memory and concentration functions. You know this supplement as *Ginkgo biloba*, one of the five top-selling herbs in the U.S. A powerful free radical scavenger, ginkgo helps protect blood vessels and optimizes the amount of oxygen supplied to brain cells. It may also help support blood flow to the extremities. About 50 pounds of ginkgo leaves are required to produce one pound of extract.

NSP Time-Release Ginkgo Biloba gives you the benefits of ginkgo extract all day long. Each tablet contains 120 mg of concentrated *Ginkgo biloba* extract, standardized to 24 percent ginkgo flavone glycosides and 6 percent terpene lactones. NSP's unique 12-hour, time-release formula provides a constant supply of ginkgo throughout the day.

Take 1 tablet daily, preferably with the morning meal.

Stock No. 898-8 (30) Ko

Ginkgo & Hawthorn Combination [*Circulatory*]
contains Ginkgo leaves concentrate (*Ginkgo biloba*), hawthorn berries and olive leaf extract, used in many cultures to support the circulatory system. This herbal combination supports increased blood circulation and oxygen utilization in the heart

G

muscle. This combination is quite popular in Europe.

Take 1 capsule with a meal three times daily.

Ginkgo/Gotu Kola with Bacopa [*Nervous, Circulatory*].

Ginkgo is famed for boosting circulation to the brain. Gotu kola herb has been called "brain food" by many herbalists. Bacopa is from bacopin, an Ayurvedic compound that stimulates memory through non-specific pathways. Researchers theorize that bacopin allows the body to maintain old neurons and synthesize new neurons more quickly. Bacopin may support memory and may help boost concentration.

This formula combines these two famous herbs with this nutrient to give you complete nutritional benefits in a powerful concentrate. Each tablet provides 40 mg of concentrated ginkgo leaf extract, standardized to 24 percent ginkgo flavone glycosides, 6 percent terpene lactones; 100 mg of gotu kola; and 50 mg *Bacopa monniera* leaves standardized to 20 percent bacosides.

NOTE: Pregnant or lactating women should consult their health care professional prior to taking this supplement.

Adults: Take 1 tablet with a meal three times daily. Children: Take 1/2 tablet with a meal three times daily.

Ginseng, Korean (Panax)

[*Glandular*] is widely used and studied. Ginseng's botanical name, *Panax*, is derived from the Greek word *panakos*, or panacea. As an adaptogen, it is believed to help maintain balance in the body and help the body adapt to stress. Korean ginseng is also famed for its ability to boost energy and support the immune system.

Each Korean ginseng capsule contains 390 mg of the finest Korean ginseng root, with a guaranteed potency of 12 mg ginsenosides per capsule.

Take 1 capsule with a meal twice daily.

Ginseng, Wild American

[*Glandular*] grows in the U.S. and Canada. American ginseng has been harvested as a cash crop for over 200 years. Daniel Boone and Davy Crockett are said to have made large sums of money in ginseng trafficking. At one point, American ginseng was almost wiped out along the eastern seaboard due to overharvesting.

Wild American ginseng's ginsenosides differ from those of Korean ginseng, although the two share similar properties. It is the more expensive of the two ginsengs. American ginseng is considered to have more cooling properties than its Asian counterpart. It is only used after the roots are aged at least four years. Each capsule contains 550 mg of wild American ginseng root.

Take 2 capsules daily with a meal.

Glucosamine [*Structural*] occurs naturally in the body's joints and cartilage and plays a key role in the structural system. As we age, our bodies become less efficient at manufacturing the elements necessary for healthy joint structure. Glucosamine works with nutrients like chondroitin to stimulate rebuilding and maintenance of cartilage. Now you can get glucosamine with the added nutritional benefits of uña de gato (cat's claw), one of the world's foremost tonic herbs. Uña de gato grows in the highland rainforests of Peru, where it has been popular for centuries. Uña de gato provides nutrients to support the body's structural system, plus it's a premier metabolic tonic herb. Each capsule blends 400 mg of glucosamine hydrochloride (from crab shells) with uña de gato. Four capsules daily provide 1,600 mg of glucosamine.

Take 2 capsules with a meal twice daily.
Stock No. 903-4 (60)

Glyco Essentials™ [*Immune, Glandular*].

Sugars are known for the quick boost of energy they give. Many people consume too much sugar. But it is not only the amount of sugar we consume but also the types of sugar that we need to examine. Certain simple sugars serve important structural and functional roles in cell processes and are often lacking in the diet. Glyco Essentials provides the body with a dietary source of eight special sugars known as glyconutrients that aid cellular communication and play a role in building enzymes, hormones and antibodies.

Glyco Essentials contains fucose, glucose, galactose, N-acetylgalactosamine, N-acetylglucosamine, N-acetylneuraminic acid, mannose and xylose in a phytonutrient base of short-chain fructooligosaccharides, aloe vera extract, tragacanth gum, arabinogalactan, beta-glucan, shiitake mushroom extract, cordyceps mushroom extract, maitake mushroom extract, glucosamine sulfate, ghatti gum, guar gum and rice starch.

Take 1 capsule three times daily for maintenance. Take 1 capsule five times a day during periods of immune system stress.
Stock No. 876-5 (90) Ko

Golden Salve [*Skin*]

is a soothing herbal salve containing extracts of comfrey leaf, golden seal root, yarrow flower, white oak bark, black walnut hulls, marshmallow root, lobelia herb, scullcap herb, myrrh gum, mullein herb, wheat germ and chickweed herb in a base of olive oil, beeswax, vitamin E and eucalyptus oil.

Use externally to soothe and moisturize rough, dry or patchy skin and lips. Apply liberally as often as needed.
Stock No. 1698-0 (1 oz.)

Golden Seal [*Immune*]

is native to North America. The plant has been largely overharvested and is periodically in short supply. Its immune-supporting properties are largely due to its hydrastine, berberine and canadine alkaloids. It is said to help support the mucous membranes that line the respiratory, digestive and urinary tracts. Because demand for the herb is high and supplies are low, golden seal is one of the most expensive herbs on the market. For this reason, many herb suppliers are tempted to adulterate supplies of golden seal with other herbs of similar chemical composition, such as Oregon grape. However, only golden seal contains the alkaloid hydrastine. Nature's Sunshine boasts the technology and expertise needed to test golden seal for hydrastine—thus ensuring a pure, unadulterated supply of this valued herb. Each capsule contains 500 mg golden seal root.

NOTE: Pregnant women should not use golden seal since it may influence uterine muscles.

Take 2 capsules with a meal twice daily.

Stock No. 340-7 (100) Ko

Golden Seal/Parthenium Extract

[*Immune*] uses equal amounts of parthenium and golden seal in an extract designed primarily for the nutritional support of the immune system, especially during seasonal changes. Golden seal contains hydrastine and berberine, two major alkaloids. Parthenium contains sesquiterpine esters. The herbs' beneficial nutritional elements are concentrated and rapidly absorbed by the body. Golden Seal/Parthenium extract can be taken in water or straight under the tongue.

Adults: Use 20–25 drops two times daily. Children: Use 10–15 drops in water twice daily. One ml is equal to 1 capsule of golden seal and 1 capsule of parthenium.

Stock No. 1781-5 (2 fl. oz.) Ko

4 Kids Too!

Gotu Kola

[*Nervous*] herb is called "brain food" by many as it may support memory function. Ayurvedic medicine considers gotu kola a nerve tonic that can be used for overall brain and nervous system support. Gotu kola promotes circulation and supports connective tissues. It is thought to support memory and brain function by promoting circulation. Each capsule contains 395 mg gotu kola aerial parts.

Take 1 capsule with a meal three times daily.

Stock No. 360-0 (100) Ko

Grapefruit, Pink BIO Pure Essential Oil (*see Essential Oils*)

Grapine®, High-Potency

[*Immune, Vital Nutrition*] is an optimal blend of the powerful antioxidant proanthocyanidins derived from grape seeds and maritime pine bark. Numerous scientific studies suggest that proanthocyanidins have health benefits, which include capillary-strengthening properties and offsetting cell-damaging free radicals.

Grapine's proanthocyanidins help protect vital nerve tissue from oxidative damage. They are among the most powerful antioxidants found in nature. Antioxidants help to neutralize free radicals—highly active molecules that cause cell damage.

Each tablet supplies 60 mg of proanthocyanidins.

Take 2–4 tablets daily with a meal. 120 lb. person = 120 mg = 2 Grapine tablets.

Stock No. 1699-3 (60)

Grapine® with Protectors, SynerPro® [*Immune, Vital Nutrition*].

Grapine is derived from grape seed and maritime pine bark. Studies have shown that the proanthocyanidins in Grapine are much more powerful as antioxidants than other popular choices. Proanthocyanidins are similar to compounds in bilberry. They appear to provide antioxidant protection to the nervous system. Each tablet provides 20 mg of proanthocyanidins, plus 50 mg of grape skin extract, 20 mg vitamin C and the SynerPro Concentrate base. Grape skin contains anthocyanins that have been linked to maintaining cardiovascular health.

Take 1 tablet with a meal three times daily.

Stock No. 1750-1 (90)

Green Tea Extract [*Immune, Circulatory*]

contains catechins—a type of polyphenol with powerful antioxidants that neutralize free radicals. Green tea also provides antimicrobial immune system support, helps support the vascular blood-clotting function and helps maintain cholesterol levels already within the normal range. It also appears to support healthy kidney function. Each capsule contains 420 mg of standardized green tea extract (80% polyphenols, 60% catechins, 30% EGCG).

Take 1 capsule three times daily with a meal. Three capsules equals 10 cups of liquid green tea. Not recommended for children under 6 or pregnant/nursing women.

Stock No. 1096-6 (60) Ko

GreenZone® (*see pH GreenZone or Ultimate GreenZone*)

Guardian Pure Essential Oil Blend (*see Essential Oils*)

Guggul Lipid [*Circulatory*].

Guggul lipid is a plant extract that has been the subject of several scientific studies that suggest that this extract has the ability to help the body maintain cholesterol and triglyceride levels already within the normal range. It may also help to maintain the blood's already normal viscosity.

Take 1–2 tablets with a meal three times daily.

Stock No. 904-6 (100) Ko

G

H

Hawthorn Berries [*Circulatory*].

Hawthorn is especially popular in Europe, where it is used in a number of herbal tinctures, herbal combinations and teas. The berries' effects on the circulatory system have been well-studied. Key components in the berries appear to enhance heart muscle and circulatory health. Nature's Sunshine offers the nutritional support of hawthorn berries in both capsule and liquid extract form. Extracts are rapidly assimilated by the body and can be mixed in liquid or taken directly under the tongue. Each capsule contains 450 mg hawthorn berries.

Take 2 capsules with a meal twice daily; for liquid, take 15–20 drops with water twice daily. One ml is equal to 2 capsules of Hawthorn Berries.

Stock No. 370-3 (100) Ko
Stock No. 1760-0 (2 fl. oz.)
Liquid Herb Ko

Hay Fever/Pollen (Allergies)
(*see Allergies—Hay Fever/Pollen*)

HCP-X [*Immune, Digestive, Respiratory*].

This famous herbal blend was known traditionally as "herbal composition powder" by American herbalists in the 1800s. HCP-X contains:

Bayberry root bark
Ginger rhizome
Mullein leaves
Capsicum fruit
Clove flowers

Take 2 capsules with a meal three times daily.

Stock No. 1216-5 (100) Ko

Healing AC Cream [*Skin*]

is a homeopathically prepared topical cream that contains the soothing herbal properties of arnica and calendula. It can be used for relief of minor skin symptoms such as scratches, bruises, rashes, sprains, muscle pulls, sunburns and cracked, dry skin.

NOTE: Avoid contact with eyes. Do not use on open wounds or broken skin.

Apply generously and massage the cream gently into the affected area two or three times daily or as needed. May be used by individuals ages 2 through adult.

Stock No. 8723-1 (2 oz.)
4 Kids Too!

Heavy Metal Detox [*Digestive, Intestinal*].

Scientists estimate that over 50 percent of U.S. residents are exposed to heavy metals in their environment. These metals, which include lead, mercury, aluminum, cadmium and arsenic, are found in industrial byproducts as well as in drinking water, pesticides and even things as common as dental fillings and cooking utensils.

Heavy Metal Detox is a potent detoxification support product designed to bind with heavy metals and remove them from the body. This formula also supports the liver it its efforts to cleanse, detoxify and replenish the body with essential minerals. The key ingredient, cilantro, may decrease the level of heavy metals in the body.

Other ingredients include N-Acetyl-Cysteine, apple pectin, sodium alginate, kelp algae, l-methionine, alpha lipoic acid, magnesium and pyridoxal-5-phosphate.

CAUTION: Do not exceed recommended dose. If headache, nausea or diarrhea develop, reduce dosage and see your health care provider.

Take 1 capsule with a meal twice daily.

Stock No. 507-1 (90)

Helichrysum Pure Essential Oil
(*see Essential Oils*)

Herbal Beverage [*Vital Nutrition*] is the perfect coffee substitute, with the taste and aroma of coffee. Made naturally with healthful roasted grains and herbal flavorings, Herbal Beverage contains no caffeine or other ingredients of questionable safety. It contains barley, malt, chicory, rye and flavorings. Herbal Beverage can be enjoyed hot or cold, plain or sweetened with honey and cream.

Hot Drink: Add 1 teaspoonful to a cup of hot water.

Cold Drink: Prepare using 2 teaspoons. Pour over crushed ice and serve.

Stock No. 1600-1 (3.5 oz.) Ko

Herbal CA (*see CA, Herbal*)

Herbal Pumpkin [*Intestinal*]. This herbal combination helps make the intestines hospitable to a balanced microbiological environment. Pumpkin, black walnut and chamomile help create this environment, while the other five herbs help cleanse and lubricate the colon to optimize intestinal function and health. It contains:

   Pumpkin seeds
   Black walnut hulls
   Cascara sagrada bark
   Chamomile flowers
   Mullein leaves
   Marshmallow root
   Slippery elm bark
NOTE: This product contains cascara sagrada. See your health care provider prior to use if: pregnant or nursing, any medical condition exists, or when taking any medication. Read and follow recommendation carefully. Do not use if diarrhea, loose stools, or abdominal pain are present or develop. Use of this product may worsen these conditions and be harmful to your health. Chronic diarrhea can result in serious illness.

Adults: Take 2–3 capsules daily with a meal. Children age 12 and over: Take 1 or 2 capsules daily with a meal. For best results, use with PS II and All Cell Detox.

Stock No. 915-2 (100) Ko

4 Kids Too!

Herbal Punch [*Vital Nutrition*] is a sweet alternative to sugary beverages, with a tropical, fruity flavor that cools you down on hot summer days. Herbal Punch is sweetened with natural honey and also contains water, natural herbal extracts, ascorbic acid, rose hips, and vitamins A, D, C, B1, B2, B6, B12 and niacin.

Add 1 ounce of Herbal Punch concentrate to 7 ounces of water and serve chilled.

Herbal Punch may also be used as a natural dessert topping by pouring it directly over ice cream, puddings, etc.

Stock No. 1610-0 (16 fl. oz.)

4 Kids Too!

Herbal Shampoo [*Hair*] is an

all-natural, pH-balanced formula designed to promote clean, healthy hair. It has a coconut oil base and contains natural conditioners, chamomile extract and chlorophyll. Shampooing often with Herbal Shampoo will help remove dead skin and old hairs. It will also cleanse the area of the sebaceous glands that secrete sebum. Sebum is what the scalp secretes to lubricate hair shafts and the scalp.

Moisten hair thoroughly with water. Apply shampoo and gently massage into scalp and hair. Allow shampoo to remain on hair for a short time to permit conditioning action. Rinse. Repeat if needed.

Stock No. 1697-5 (8 fl. oz.)

Herbal Sleep [*Nervous*] promotes

proper nervous system function by supporting restful sleep and providing soothing and calming properties. The combination consists of:

Valerian root

Passion flower aerial parts

Hops flowers

Take 2 capsules daily with a meal.

Stock No. 940-8 (100) Ko

Herbal Trace Minerals

[*Glandular*] is an herbal supplement that provides nutrients that may be beneficial for the glandular, digestive and eliminative functions. The deep roots of the dandelion and alfalfa plants absorb trace nutrients that are often lacking in common, shallow-rooted vegetables preferred in Western diets. Dandelion root and kelp contain important trace nutrients that are absorbed from the bountiful soils in which they are grown. This formula contains:

Kelp leaves and stems

Dandelion root

Alfalfa aerial parts

Take 1–2 capsules daily with a meal.

Stock No. 980-5 (100) Ko

Herbal Trim® Skin Treatment

[*Skin*]. As the body's most visible organ, the skin performs protective, regulative and eliminative functions. In its protective role, the skin shields the internal organs from microorganisms, weather and injury. The skin also helps regulate body temperature and prevent dehydration. In its eliminative function, the skin excretes unusable substances from the bowel, kidneys, lungs and other organs, a function that has earned it the title, "third kidney."

Nature's Sunshine's Herbal Trim Skin Treatment is a combination of herbs and other substances that complement this vital organ. It contains aloe vera to help provide moisture to smooth and soften dry, patchy skin. It promotes healthy-looking skin tone.

In addition to aloe vera, it contains water, pau d'arco extract, lobelia extract, xanthan gum, citric acid, Tei Fu oil blend (includes menthol, eucalyptus, wintergreen, camphor and clove oils), allantoin, hydrolyzed soy protein, safflower seed oil, lavender oil, carrageenan and soluble collagen.

This easily absorbed, non-greasy, emollient-rich formula offers penetrating improvement for rough, patchy skin.

For external use only.

Stock No. 1669-0 (8 fl. oz.)

Herbasaurs® Bedwetting

[*Urinary*] is a natural homeopathic medicine to assist a child's body in overcoming nighttime bedwetting.

For children 2 or older, take 5–8 drops under the tongue four times daily for at least one month or as needed, reducing upon improvement to once or twice daily for an additional one to three months as maintenance.

Stock No. 8830-1 (1 fl. oz.)

Herbasaurs Chewable Antioxidants with Grapine®

[*Vital Nutrition, Immune*] is designed especially for children. Antioxidants help young, growing bodies fight the damaging effects of free radicals caused by pollutants, sunlight and even exercise. For increased antioxidant protection, this supplement contains beta-carotene, vitamins C and E, Grapine and licorice flavonoid extract (a potent, tasteless antioxidant). Use in conjunction with Herbasaurs

Chewable Multiple Vitamins Plus Iron. Tablets have a pleasant lemon-lime flavor. An Herbasaurs character is stamped on each Dinotab®.

Chew 1–2 tablets daily with a meal. (Note: Grapine is the NSP name for authentic proanthocya-nidins sourced from grape seeds and maritime pine bark.)

Stock No. 3301-5 (120)

Herbasaurs Chewable Elderberry Plus [*Immune, Respiratory*]

nutritionally supports the immune and respiratory systems. Contains elderberry fruit concentrate plus the powerful adaptogens reishi mushroom and astragalus—all known historically for their ability to support the immune system. It's flavored with lemon and lime and sweetened with fructose. Each Dinotab is stamped with a friendly NSP Herbasaurs character.

Chew 1–2 tablets daily with meals.

Stock No. 3300-9 (60) Ko

Herbasaurs® Chewable Vitamins and Minerals [*Vital Nutrition*]

is designed especially for children. Getting your kids to eat their veggies might be a struggle, but you'll never have to beg them to take their Herbasaurs. Not only do these tablets taste good, they contain 12 essential vitamins plus iron that children need to grow strong, healthy bodies. They're sweetened with fructose and contain natural fruit flavor. Contains no sucrose, starch, preservatives, artificial colors or artificial flavors. Each Dinotab® is stamped with an Herbasaurs character.

	Amount per 2 Tablets	% DV Kids 2-3	% DV Kids 4+
Vitamin A (acetate)	5,000 IU	100	100
Vitamin C (calcium ascorbate, ascorbic acid)	60 mg	80	100
Vitamin D	400 IU	50	100
Vitamin E (d-alpha-tocopherol)	30 IU	150	100
Vitamin B1 (thiamine)	1.5 mg	110	100
Vitamin B2 (riboflavin)	1.7 mg	110	100
Niacin (niacinamide)	20 mg	110	100
Vitamin B6 (pyridoxine)	2 mg	150	100
Folic Acid	400 mcg	100	100
Vitamin B12 (cyanocobalamin)	6 mcg	100	100
Biotin	300 mcg	100	100
Pantothenic Acid (d-calcium pantothenate)	10 mg	100	100
Iron (ferrous fumarate)	4.5 mg	20	25
Iodine (potassium iodide)	150 mcg	110	100
Zinc (oxide)	15 mg	90	100
Copper (oxide)	2 mg	100	100
Manganese (amino acid chelate)	2 mg	80	100
Chromium (amino acid chelate)	120 mcg	120	100
Selenium (amino acid chelate)	70 mcg	**	100

**Daily Value not established

- Vitamin A promotes eye health and night vision.
- Vitamin B12 supports myelin sheaths for proper nerve function.
- Vitamin C supports collagen formation and is a powerful water-soluble antioxidant.
- Vitamin B6 can support emotional well-being.

- Important minerals—zinc, copper, manganese, chromium, selenium, iron and iodine—provide a host of valuable health benefits.

This sucrose-free base includes sorbitol, fructose, xylitol, cellulose, guar gum, magnesium stearate and natural flavors.

Children 2–3 years: Chew 1 tablet daily with a meal. Children 4 years and older: Chew 2 tablets daily with a meal.

Stock No. 1593-0 (90)

Herbasaurs Cold [*Respiratory*]

is a natural homeopathic medicine for the relief of symptoms of minor colds, including runny nose, sneezing, headache and minor sore throat pain.

For children and infants over the age of 4 months, take 3–5 drops under the tongue every 15–20 minutes until symptoms improve, then every two–four hours until symptoms are relieved. Administer to children under 4 months only under the advice of a health care professional.

Stock No. 8865-1 (1 fl. oz.)

Herbasaurs Cough Syrup

[*Respiratory*] is a natural homeopathic medicine for the relief of coughs due to common colds or minor throat and bronchial irritation.

For children 1 year and older, take 1 or 2 teaspoonsful as needed for coughing. May be repeated as often as necessary. Not for use in children under 12 months old. This product contains honey.

Stock No. 8855-0 (4 fl. oz.)

Herbasaurs Liquid Multiple Vitamins Plus Iron [*Vital Nutrition*] is for children who would rather take a liquid than a chewable. It contains 12 essential vitamins (including vitamins A, D, E, C, folic acid, thiamine, riboflavin, niacin, B6, B12, biotin and pantothenic acid) plus zinc, iron and antioxidants. It contains no artificial colors, flavors, sucrose or starch, and is sweetened with fructose. For increased antioxidant protection, use with Herbasaurs Chewable Antioxidant with Grapine®.

Children 1–4: Take 1 teaspoonful (5 ml) daily with a meal. Children over 4: Take 2 teaspoonsful (10 ml) daily with a meal.

Stock No. 3330-6 (4 fl. oz.)

Herbasaurs Teething [*Structural*] is a natural homeopathic medicine for the temporary relief of minor gum soreness due to teething in infants and children.

Children and infants over the age of 4 months: Take 3–5 drops under the tongue every 15–20 minutes until symptoms improve, then every two–four hours until symptoms are relieved. Administer to children under 4 months only under the advice of a health care professional.

Stock No. 8885-6 (1 fl. oz.)

Hi Lipase [*Digestive*] is designed for individuals who have difficulty efficiently digesting lipids (fats). Lipases are a class of enzymes that assist in the breakdown of dietary fats. Lipases are produced by the salivary glands, pancreas and stomach. They are also manufactured by certain plants. Hi-Lipase aids digestion of fat-containing foods, including nuts. Contains 240 LU per two-capsule serving.

Take 1 or 2 capsules before consuming high-fat foods. May also be used between meals.

Stock No. 1528-4 (100)

HistaBlock® [*Respiratory*] supports the body in times of respiratory stress. A powerful combination of stinging nettle, quercetin, bromclain and immature orange peel (which contains synephrine), HistaBlock provides nutritional support for the respiratory system. This formula provides antioxidants and supports the body's efforts to maintain mucous membrane health and nasal passage tissues.

Take 2 capsules with a meal twice daily.

Stock No. 776-1 (90)

Ho Shou Wu [*Circulatory, Immune*]. This remarkable herb possesses properties similar to ginseng. It is highly prized in China as an adaptogenic herb. A member of the buckwheat family, ho shou wu contains quercetin that helps protect and maintain blood vessel health.

Take 2 capsules with a meal twice daily.

Stock No. 375-5 (100) Ko

Hops [*Nervous*] grows throughout Europe, Asia and North America. It is perhaps best known for its use in beer brewing. Hops has a calming effect on the nervous system and is a common ingredient in products used to promote restful sleep. It is also valuable as a food as it possesses nervine properties. Each capsule contains 250 mg hops.

Take 2 capsules with a meal twice daily.

Horsetail [*Structural*], also known

as shavegrass, grows throughout most of the world. The ancient Greeks knew of its astringent properties. Horsetail is extremely rich in silica. Silica is found in connective tissues throughout the body and is important in the building and normal repair of healthy connective tissue. The best dietary source of silica is whole grains. Each capsule contains 360 mg horsetail.

Take 2 capsules with a meal three times daily.

HS II® [*Circulatory*] is commonly

used with vitamin C, bioflavonoids and omega-3 fish oil supplements. Hawthorn berry, an herb regarded by the ancient Greeks and Romans as a symbol of hope and happiness, makes up the bulk of this combination. Hawthorn berry is used in Europe in several different formulations. HS II contains:

Hawthorn berries
Capsicum fruit
Garlic bulb

Take 2 capsules with a meal three times daily.

HSN Complex®, Natria [*Skin*]

contains botanicals and herbals to help support healthy hair, skin and nails. The formula includes horsetail, an important source of highly bioavailable silica—an essential building block for structural system health. The additional benefits of hyssop, aloe vera, rosemary, *Ginkgo biloba* concentrate and the potent antioxidant *Rhododendron caucasicum* provide nutrients to support hair, skin and nails.

Take 2 to 3 capsules with a meal twice daily.

HSN-W® (Hair, Skin and Nails Formula) [*Structural, Skin*] contains horsetail stems and

strobilus, dulse fronds, rosemary leaves and sage leaves. These botanicals provide significant amounts of herbal silica (27.9 mg per 100 grams). Researchers have suggested that silica may be important to the human structural system.

Take 3 capsules with a meal twice daily.

HY-A [*Digestive*] is designed to

meet the nutritional needs of the digestive system. Licorice root supports the gastrointestinal tract. Dandelion root was used by many North American Indian tribes for gastrointestinal support. It contains sesquiterpene lactones, which may positively influence digestion. Also contains safflower flowers and horseradish root.

Take 2 capsules with a meal twice daily.

Stock No. 950-0 (100) Ko

HY-C, Chinese [*Glandular*] is

a combination of 16 herbs that nutritionally support the glandular system and associated metabolic processes. According to Traditional Chinese Medicine, this formula is called *bu yin*, which means to "supplement yin." In this case, yin is considered moisture. These herbs work to support the body as it attempts to reduce fire and strengthen water (support associated organs and maintain normal metabolic processes). Its primary herbs include glehnia, rehmannia, ophiopogon and eucommia. HY-C contains:

Glehnia root
Eucommia bark
Rehmannia root
Ophiopogon root
Pueraria root
Trichosanthes root
Achyranthes root
Alisma rhizome
Anemarrhena rhizome
Asparagus root
Hoelen plant
Moutan root bark
Cornus fruit
Licorice root
Phellodendron bark
Schizandra fruit

Take 3 capsules with a meal three times daily.

Stock No. 1886-5 (100)

HY-C TCM Concentrate, Chinese [*Glandular*] contains

the same herbs found in Chinese HY-C but in a highly concentrated blend. This combination of 16 herbs nutritionally supports the glandular system and associated metabolic processes. According to Traditional Chinese Medicine, this formula is called *bu yin*, which means to "supplement yin." In this case, yin is considered moisture. These herbs work to support the body as it attempts to reduce fire and strengthen water (support associated organs and maintain normal metabolic processes). Its primary herbs include rehmannia, ophiopogon and eucommia. HY-C contains:

Glehnia root
Eucommia bark
Rehmannia root tuber
Ophiopogon root tuber
Pueraria root
Trichosanthes root
Achyranthes root
Alisma rhizome
Anemarrhena rhizome
Asparagus root tuber
Hoelen sclerotium
Moutan root bark
Cornus fruit without seeds
Licorice root
Phellodendron stem bark
Schizandra fruit

NOTE: Pregnant or lactating women should consult their health care provider prior to taking this supplement.

Take 1 or 2 capsules with a meal daily. Each capsule is equivalent to 5 capsules of regular Chinese HY-C.

Stock No. 1006-1 (30)

H

Hydrangea [*Urinary*]. Originally used by the Cherokee Indians for kidney support, hydrangea was introduced to early American settlers for similar purposes. A common shrub, hydrangea is a bitter and a solvent. Its solvent properties nutritionally support the urinary system. It contains natural minerals plus silicon, flavonoids, resins and saponins. In this formula, the dried, powdered root is used. Each capsule contains 325 mg hydrangea.

Take 2 capsules with a meal three times daily.

Stock No. 395-6 (100) Ko

Hydrated Bentonite
(*see Bentonite, Hydrated*)

I

I-X [*Circulatory*]. Iron is needed by the body to carry oxygen to the cells where it is combined with glucose for energy production. It also must be present for protein metabolism. By combining herbs that provide natural iron with other elements needed to enhance absorption, a chelated form of iron is created that may be more easily absorbed by the body. This formula is also a source of trace minerals and vitamins. It contains:
   Red beet root
   Yellow dock root
   Red raspberry leaves
   Chickweed herb
   Burdock root
   Nettle herb
   Mullein leaves

Take 2 capsules with a meal three times daily.

Stock No. 1218-4 (100) Ko

IF-C, Chinese [*Immune*] is a combination of 19 herbs designed to support joint health and immunity and calm a stressed fire constitution. Its Chinese name *qing re* can be translated as "clear the heat." These herbs nourish the structural and immune systems by stimulating blood flow and eliminating toxins through a variety of actions. Its primary herbs—schizonepeta, lonicera and forsythia—promote the removal of toxins and may help improve an overall feeling of well-being. IF-C contains:
   Lonicera flowers
   Forsythia fruit
   Chrysanthemum flowers
   Gardenia fruit
   Cnidium rhizome
   Ligusticum rhizome
   Peony root
   Platycodon root
   Schizonepeta herb
   Scute root
   Arctium seed
   Bupleurum root
   Dang gui root
   Phellodendron bark
   Siler root
   Vitex fruit
   Carthamus flowers
   Coptis rhizome
   Licorice root

Take 4 capsules with a meal twice daily.

Stock No. 1875-9 (100)

IF-C TCM Concentrate, Chinese

[*Structural, Immune*] contains the same herbs found in Chinese IF-C but in a highly concentrated blend. This combination of 18 herbs is designed to support joint health and immunity and calm a stressed fire constitution. Its Chinese name *qing re* can be translated as "clear the heat." These herbs nourish the structural and immune systems by stimulating blood flow and eliminating toxins through a variety of actions. Its primary herbs—schizonepeta, lonicera and forsythia—promote the removal of toxins and may help improve an overall feeling of well-being. IF-C TCM contains:

Lonicera flower bud
Forsythia fruit
Cnidium rhizome
Chrysanthemum flowers
Gardenia fruit
Peony root without bark
Platycodon root
Schizonepeta flower
Scute root
Arctium fruit
Bupleurum root
Phellodendron stem bark
Siler root
Dang gui root
Vitex fruit
Carthamus flowers
Coptis rhizome
Licorice root

NOTE: Pregnant or lactating women should consult their health care provider prior to taking this supplement.

Take 1 or 2 capsules with a meal daily. Each capsule is equivalent to

6 capsules of regular Chinese IF-C.
Stock No. 1007-2 (30)

IF Relief [*Structural*] contains a combination of herbal extracts that may support the body's natural process for muscle pain and inflammation relief following exercise and massage. IF Relief contains compounds that may help the body achieve homeostasis. This formula has a very high ORAC value. IF Relief contains turmeric root extract along with mangosteen pericarp extract—a source of potent antioxidants called xanthones. The xanthone gammamangostin appears to partially modulate the production of prostaglandins. IF Relief also contains *Andrographis paniculata* to help modulate certain undesirable responses; boswellia gum extract, which appears to modulate an enzyme that catalyzes leukotriene formation; and white willow bark extract, which contains salicin and appears to modulate the production of prostaglandins.

Take 1 capsule three times daily with meals.

Stock No. 1175-4 (90) Ko

IGF-1 [*Structural*] (insulin-like growth factor 1) is a metabolite of human growth hormone. Scientists have discovered that an extract of the velvet on the antlers of a particular species of deer (*Cervi parvum cornu*) provides IGF-1 and all of its benefits.

Researchers have found that deer antler velvet contains eight known growth factors, prostaglandins,

I

nerve-protective fatty acids, prohormones, amino acids and components of cartilage (including glucosamine, chondroitin sulfate, collagen type I and II and minerals).

NSP IGF-1 is concentrated and cold-processed to assure optimum bioactivity. Its liposome delivery system ensures optimum absorption. NSP takes great care to harvest the deer antler velvet in the most humane and careful ways.

Each bottle contains at least 2,500 nanograms of IGF-1 and other insulin-like growth factors.

Spray twice under your tongue three times daily. Hold for 20 seconds before swallowing for best results.

Stock No. 966-1 (1 fl. oz. spray)

Immune Stimulator [*Immune*]

is a blend of natural ingredients known to support and boost the immune system. Its antioxidant activity protects the integrity of DNA. This formula promotes macrophage activity, which strengthens the body's natural defense system.

Immune Stimulator is a combination of:

• Beta-glucans—long-chain polysaccharides that stimulate the immune system into action. Beta-glucans increase the production of macrophages, T-cells, natural killer cells and cytokines.

• Arabinogalactan stimulates natural killer cells and macrophage activity. It also helps increase the flora of Bifidobacteria and Lactobacillus, two beneficial types of intestinal flora.

• Colostrum is the first milk produced by mammals before the onset of lactation. Rich in immune-enhancing transfer factors, colostrum supports the immune system of the newborn. It helps protect beneficial microorganisms in the intestinal tract to bolster their defenses.

• Reishi mushroom and maitake mushroom are from the same family (polyporaceae), and their similar polysaccharide content is thought to boost immune activity, increase the activation of natural killer cells and activate macrophages.

• Cordyceps protects genes by promoting the integrity of DNA. Cordyceps increases T-cell and B-cell activity, important to immune response.

For maintenance, take 1 capsule between meals two or three times daily. For periods of immune system stress, take 6–10 capsules daily. Complementary products include Protease Plus, Olive Leaf Extract and VS-C®.

Stock No. 1839-3 (90)

Indole-3-Carbinol [*Glandular*]

is a powerful antioxidant found in the cell walls of cruciferous vegetables. The compounds in these vegetables that may protect cells from oxidative damage are called indoles, among them Indole-3-Carbinol and its metabolites. These compounds may work by binding to or activating certain receptors in the body to protect cells. Indole-3-Carbinol also acts as an antioxdant. This compound may be helpful in the metabolism of estrogens, protecting breast tissue and reproductive organs from cell damage. Indole-3-Carbinol is formulated in a base of broccoli sprout and broccoli powder, a known source of indoles, bringing the total dietary indole content to 200 mg per serving.

Take 2 capsules daily with a meal.

Stock No. 1506-4 (60)

Inflammation [*Immune*] is a
natural homeopathic medicine for relief of general and localized inflammation with its accompanying heat, swelling, redness and pain due to arthritis, rheumatism, minor injuries or infections. Do not give this product for pain for more than five days. If pain persists or gets worse, or if new symptoms occur, consult your health care provider.

Take 10–15 drops under the tongue every hour until symptoms improve, then four times daily until symptoms are relieved. For children under 12, consult your health care provider.

Stock No. 8810-3 (1 fl. oz.)

Influenza [*Immune*] homeopathic
remedy relieves minor influenza symptoms, including stomach and abdominal pain, body aches, chills, fever, bronchitis, cough and thirst.

NOTE: Do not give this product for pain for more than five days. If pain persists or gets worse, or if new symptoms occur, consult your health care professional. As with

any drug, if you are pregnant or nursing a baby, seek the advice of a health care professional before using this product.

Take 10–15 drops under the tongue every 10–15 minutes, or as needed, until symptoms improve, then decrease to hourly, then to four times daily until symptoms are relieved. For children under 12, consult your health care professional.

Stock No. 8770-9 (1 fl. oz.)

Intestinal Soothe & Build
[*Intestinal*] is designed to provide nutrients that support the lower bowel. Ingredients in the formula help relieve occasional bloating pressure and soothe the intestinal tract. The lower bowel contains millions of microorganisms to help the body process nutrients. Improperly digested or slow-moving food may affect the balance of intestinal flora. This formula contains botanicals historically used to aid in the digestive process:

Slippery elm bark
Chamomile flowers
Plantain leaves
Rose hips fruit
Bugleweed aerial parts
Marshmallow root concentrate

Take 3 capsules with a meal three times daily.

Stock No. 1106-2 (100) Ko

IN-X [*Immune, Intestinal*] supports
the immune system and the body's eliminative channels. Contains:

Echinacea aerial parts
Black walnut hulls

Althea root
Golden seal root and rhizome
Plantain leaves
Bugleweed aerial parts
Parthenium root

Golden seal supports the immune system and helps maintain an environment more hospitable to microbiological balance. Black walnut hulls are prized for their fame in folk herbology due to their cleansing properties. Althea root (better known as marshmallow) contains mucilage, which supports mucous membrane health. Historically, parthenium has been used in a manner similar to echinacea for immune system support. Plantain helps maintain internal tissues. Bugleweed herb was used historically for respiratory support.

Take 2 capsules with a meal twice daily.

Stock No. 1220-1 (100) Ko

Iron, Chelated [*Circulatory*]

provides a form of iron (ferrous gluconate) that's usually well-absorbed by the body. In this formulation, the iron is enhanced with vitamin C, calcium and a unique base of rose hips, chickweed herb, mullein leaves, thyme herb and yellow dock root. Each tablet contains:

	Amount	% DV
Iron	25 mg	140
(ferrous gluconate, amino acid chelate)		
Vitamin C		
(ascorbic acid)	50 mg	80
Calcium	64 mg	6
(di-calcium phosphate, amino acid chelate)		
Phosphorus	35 mg	4
(di-calcium phosphate)		

Iron is used by the body in making myoglobin (supplying oxygen for muscle contractions) and hemoglobin, the central molecule of red blood cells, which travel to the lungs to pick up oxygen and deliver it to the tissues. Iron is also involved in energy metabolism.

Take 1 tablet daily with a meal.

Stock No. 1784-8 (180) Ko

J

Joint Support [*Structural, Nervous*]

provides a host of nutrients beneficial to the structural system. Individual ingredients in this formula are traditionally used for the following: maintaining joint tissues, supporting the body during physical stress to joints, helping the body clear uric acid, promoting normal muscle health, supporting a balanced nervous system, promoting protein digestion, nourishing the nervous system and more. It contains:

Alfalfa aerial parts
Horsetail stems and strobilus
Bromelain fruit
Catnip leaves
Celery seed
Black cohosh root
Yarrow aerial parts
Capsicum fruit
Slippery elm bark
Valerian root
Hydrangea root extract
Yucca root extract
White willow bark
Burdock root
Sarsaparilla root

NOTE: Pregnant or lactating women should consult their health care provider prior to taking this supplement.

Take 2 capsules with a meal three times daily. For best results, use with MSM, Calcium–Magnesium and MSM/Glucosamine Cream.

Stock No. 810-8 (100) Ko

Jojoba [*Skin, Hair*]. The pressed seeds of this plant produce an oil that is used extensively in the cosmetic business, especially in products for the hair and skin. The yellow oil is somewhat like vegetable oil. A few drops lightly massaged into the hair and scalp after shampooing helps cleanse and moisturize the scalp. Jojoba also lightly coats the hair, giving it extra shine, body and protection. Jojoba oil makes an excellent conditioning treatment.

After shampooing, apply a few drops to the scalp and rub vigorously over entire scalp area.

Stock No. 1695-1 (0.5 fl. oz.)

JP-X [*Glandular, Urinary*] contains juniper and parsley plus five other herbs to nutritionally support the reproductive and digestive functions of the body. It also helps to support the kidneys and bladder. JP-X contains:

Dong quai root
Juniper berries cones
Parsley leaves
Uva ursi leaves
Ginger rhizome
Marshmallow root
Golden seal root extract

Take 2 capsules with a meal three times daily.

Stock No. 1222-7 (100) Ko

Juniper Berries [*Urinary*] are found on the evergreen juniper shrub, which grows widely throughout the Northern Hemisphere. Because the berries take between two and three years to fully ripen, the same plant can have unripe green and ripe blue berries at the same time. The berries' nutritional profile includes quercetin, proanthocyanidins and volatile oil. Juniper berries are particularly supportive of the urinary system as they help the body maintain proper fluid balance. Each capsule contains 400 mg juniper berry cones.

Take 2 capsules with a meal twice daily.

Stock No. 400-4 (100) Ko

K

Kava Kava [*Nervous*] comes from the rhizome of the *Piper methysticum* plant (of the pepper family), indigenous to Polynesia and Indonesia. Historically it was prepared as a ceremonial drink to welcome visiting dignitaries. According to legend, the kava kava drinker often felt utter contentment and a greater sense of well-being.

Today kava kava is used to help reduce normal anxiety without impairing mental function. It may help promote more restful sleep in those struggling with occasional restlessness. Plus, it may help relax muscles. Each capsule contains 200 mg kava kava root concentrate.

CAUTION: Do not use while driving a motor vehicle or operating machinery. Not intended for use by pregnant or lactating women. Not for use by persons under age 18. Consult a health-care professional prior to use if you have liver problems, frequently use alcohol or take any medication. Stop use if you develop symptoms that may signal liver problems. Do not exceed recommended dose. Keep out of reach of children.

Take 1 capsule with a meal twice daily. Take 1–2 capsules 30 minutes before bedtime.

Stock No. 405-9 (60) Ko

KB-C, Chinese [*Structural, Urinary*]

is a combination of herbs used for kidney and bone support. Its Chinese name *jian gu* can be translated to mean "strengthen the bones." It is designed to strengthen the water element. In Traditional Chinese Medicine, it is used to nourish the kidneys and nutritionally support the urinary and structural systems, eliminating water and providing extra joint support. Its primary herbs include achyranthes and eucommia. This supplement contains 18 herbs:

Eucommia bark
Cistanche herb
Achyranthes root
Dipsacus root
Drynaria rhizome
Hoelen plant
Morinda root

Rehmannia root
Astragalus root
Cornus fruit
Dang gui root
Dioscorea root
Epimedium herb
Ligustrum fruit
Liquidambar fruit
Lycium fruit
Panax ginseng root
Atractylodes rhizome

NOTE: Pregnant or lactating women should consult their health care provider prior to taking this supplement.

Take 3 capsules with a meal three times daily.

Stock No. 1883-3 (100)

KB-C TCM Concentrate, Chinese

[*Structural, Urinary*] contains the same herbs found in KB-C but in a highly concentrated blend. This combination of herbs is used for kidney and bone support. Its Chinese name *jian gu* can be translated to mean "strengthen the bones." It is designed to strengthen the water element. In Traditional Chinese Medicine, it is used to nourish the kidneys and nutritionally support the urinary and structural systems, eliminating water and providing extra joint support. Its primary herbs include achyranthes and eucommia. This supplement contains 18 herbs:

Eucommia bark
Cistanche stem
Achyranthes root
Dipsacus root
Drynaria rhizome
Hoelen sclerotium

Morinda root
Rehmannia root tuber
Astragalus root
Cornus fruit without seeds
Dang gui root
Dioscorea rhizome
Epimedium leaf
Ligustrum fruit
Liquidamber fruit
Lycium fruit
Panax ginseng root
Atractylodes rhizome
NOTE: Pregnant or lactating women should consult their health care provider prior to taking this supplement.

Take 2 capsules with a meal daily. Each capsule is equivalent to 5 capsules of regular Chinese KB-C.

Stock No. 1016-0 (30)

Kelp [*Glandular*], commonly referred to as seaweed, grows along coastlines around the world. Kelp contains naturally varying amounts of trace minerals, which may be useful in maintaining proper glandular function and metabolism. Because the plant's nutrients come in a natural form, they are easily assimilated by the body. Each capsule contains 525 mg kelp.

Take 2 capsules with a meal twice daily.

Stock No. 410-3 (100) Ko

Kidney Activator [*Urinary*] nutritionally supports the urinary system, specifically bladder and kidney health. Parsley and uva ursi support urinary health. Juniper berries support the urinary system (especially the kidneys), helping the body's efforts to maintain proper fluid balance. It contains:
Juniper berries
Parsley leaves
Uva ursi leaves
Dandelion root
Chamomile flowers
NOTE: Pregnant or lactating women should consult their health care professional prior to taking this supplement.

Take 2 capsules daily with a meal; ATC concentrated, take 1–2 capsules daily with a meal.

Stock No. 970-2 (100) Ko
Stock No. 973-9 (50) Ko
ATC Concentrated

Kidney Activator, Chinese

[*Urinary*] is a Chinese combination of 16 herbs designed to support the urinary and lymphatic systems. Kidney Activator is called *qu shi*, which can be translated as "to get rid of dampness." In Traditional Chinese Medicine, it is said to promote kidney function and to help clear retained water from the body, which may positively affect joints. Its primary herbs include morus, areca, hoelen, alisma and astragalus. The formula contains:
Hoelen sclerotium
Siler root
Chaenomeles fruit
Morus root bark
Astragalus root
Psyllium seed
Alisma rhizome
Peony root without bark
Atractylodes rhizome
Magnolia bark
Polyporus sclerotium

Cinnamon twig
Citrus peel
Ginger rhizome
Typhonium rhizome
Licorice root
NOTE: May cause allergic reaction in persons sensitive to inhaled or ingested psyllium. Pregnant or lactating women should consult their health care provider prior to taking this supplement.

Take 3 capsules with a meal three times daily.

Stock No. 1872-5 (100)

Kidney Activator TCM Concentrate, Chinese [*Urinary*]

contains the same herbs found in Chinese Kidney Activator but in a highly concentrated blend. This Chinese combination of 16 herbs is designed to support the urinary and lymphatic systems. Kidney Activator is called *qu shi*, which can be translated as "to get rid of dampness." In Traditional Chinese Medicine, it is said to promote kidney function and to help clear retained water from the body, which may positively affect joints. Its primary herbs include morus, hoelen, alisma and astragalus. The formula contains:

Hoelen sclerotium
Siler root
Chaenomeles fruit
Morus root bark
Astragalus root
Psyllium seed
Alisma rhizome
Peony root without bark
Atractylodes rhizome
Magnolia bark
Polyporus sclerotium
Cinnamon twig
Citrus peel
Ginger rhizome
Typhonium rhizome
Licorice root
NOTE: May cause allergic reaction in persons sensitive to inhaled or ingested psyllium. Pregnant or lactating women should consult their health care provider prior to taking this supplement.

Take 1 or 2 capsules with a meal daily. For best results, use with Combination Potassium. Each capsule is equivalent to 7 capsules of regular Chinese Kidney Activator.

Stock No. 1040-0 (30)

Kidney Drainage [*Urinary*]

provides herbs to support the kidneys. Every day the kidneys filter nearly 200 liters of fluid from the bloodstream. They excrete toxins, metabolic wastes and excess ions and reabsorb necessary metabolic byproducts. These two bean-shaped structures also regulate the volume and chemical composition of the blood. Good nutrition and fluid intake support kidney function and promote proper waste removal and healthy tissue.

Kidney Drainage contains *Asparagus officinalis* and plantain leaf, which may help support fluid removal in the kidneys. Juniper berries support the urinary system as it works to maintain proper fluid balance. Goldenrod increases the production of urine without reducing levels of important electrolytes.

Take 1 ml (approximately 15–20 drops or 1/4 teaspoon) in water twice daily.

Stock No. 3168-4 (2 fl. oz.) Ko

Kudzu/St. John's Wort Combination [*Nervous*].

Evidence now associates daidzin, a constituent of kudzu root, with potential reduction in alcohol consumption.

Hypericin, an active constituent in St. John's wort, supports the nervous system. There is evidence that links hypericin to the alleviation of stress. Each capsule of Kudzu/St. John's Wort Combination contains 1 mg of daidzin and 1 mg hypericin.

NOTE: While taking this product, avoid exposure to strong sunshine and tanning rays (tanning salons). Consult your health care provider before using this product if you are taking prescription anti-depressive drugs, including selective serotonin uptake inhibitors, as well as any MAO inhibitors.

Take 1 capsule with a meal three times daily.

Stock No. 975-6 (100) Ko

L

l-Carnitine [*Vital Nutrition*] is

an amino acid from which certain proteins are made. It is synthesized in the liver and kidneys. The body requires l-carnitine for the transport of long-chain fatty acids into the cells. L-carnitine also supports the overall health of the heart. It is not found in vegetable foods but is mostly found in animal muscle tissue. Each capsule contains 295 mg of natural l-carnitine.

Take 1–3 capsules daily with a meal.

Stock No. 1632-6 (30) Ko

l-Glutamine [*Nervous*] is an amino

acid (a protein building block) that is important in supplying the brain with energy. Its main function is to support cellular growth, energy and repair. L-glutamine also plays a role in the health of the immune system, the digestive tract and the muscles. Each capsule contains 500 mg of l-glutamine.

Take 1–2 capsules daily with a meal.

Stock No. 1776-0 (30) Ko

L

l-Lysine [*Structural, Circulatory, Immune*] is an essential amino

acid (cannot be produced by the body) required by the body for the manufacture of proteins. It helps ensure adequate absorption of calcium and the formation of collagen for bone, cartilage and connective tissue. L-lysine strengthens circulation and helps the immune system manufacture antibodies. It also has been used for cold sores. Each capsule contains 474 mg of l-lysine monohydrochloride.

Take 1 capsule with a meal three times daily.

Stock No. 1631-4 (100) Ko

L. Reuteri [*Intestinal*].

Lactobacillus reuteri occurs naturally in the intestinal flora of humans and other animals. Reuteri helps to strengthen the body's natural defenses and maintain equilibrium in the gastrointestinal tract as it repopulates friendly flora in the gut. This strain secretes reuterin, a substance with powerful properties that helps maintain microorganic balance in the gut.

L. Reuteri may be taken with Probiotic Eleven to accelerate the growth of other beneficial strains. It helps soothe occasional intestinal discomfort and is recommended for use after cleansing. L. Reuteri is suitable for young children and adults—anyone who may need extra friendly flora. This product does not require refrigeration, so it's also great for travel.

Adults and children: Chew 1 tablet daily to maintain balance in the intestinal tract or as needed for gastrointestinal distress.

Stock No. 1559-0 (60)

4 Kids Too!

Lactase Plus [*Digestive*]. The lactase and protease enzymes in Lactase Plus help many people who have difficulty digesting dairy products by aiding the breakdown of milk sugar and milk protein.

Take 1–2 capsules up to 3 times daily before consuming foods and beverages containing lactose.

Stock No. 1655-2 (100)

Lavender Fine Pure Essential Oil (*see Essential Oils*)

LB Extract® [*Intestinal*] is formulated to meet the nutritional needs of the intestinal system.

Historically, many Native American tribes used cascara sagrada bark for its laxative effect. Senna and buckthorn have similar properties and encourage bowel movement. Psyllium adds bulk to the stool and encourages proper elimination. Licorice helps support the respiratory tract and digestive function. Other herbs add important nutritional elements.

LB Extract contains:
Cascara sagrada bark
Senna leaves
Buckthorn bark
Alfalfa aerial parts
Psyllium seed hulls
Licorice root
Rhubarb root
Barberry bark
Ginger rhizome
Slippery elm bark

LB Extract is similar to LB-X capsules and LBS II Vegitabs, but it's easier to take. Liquid extracts are rapidly absorbed and highly concentrated.

NOTE: This product contains cascara sagrada, buckthorn and senna. See your health care provider prior to use if: pregnant or nursing, any medical condition exists, or when taking any medication. Read and follow recommendation carefully. Do not use if diarrhea, loose stools or abdominal pain are present or develop. May cause allergic reaction in persons sensitive to inhaled or ingested psyllium.

Adults: Add 1 teaspoon to a glass of water or juice. Children 6–12: Take 1/2 teaspoon. Children 1–6: Take 1/4 teaspoon. Do not use this product for longer than 10 days at a time.

LBS II® [*Intestinal*].

This herbal laxative supports proper waste elimination and encourages colon cleansing. It contains:

Cascara sagrada bark
Buckthorn bark
Licorice root
Ginger rhizome
Oregon grape root and rhizome
Capsicum fruit
Turkey rhubarb root
Couch grass rhizome
Red clover flowers

NOTE: This product contains cascara sagrada, buckthorn and Turkey rhubarb. See your health care provider prior to use if pregnant or nursing, any medical condition exists, or when taking any medication. Read and follow recommendation carefully. Not intended for prolonged use. Do not use if diarrhea, loose stools, or abdominal pain are present or develop. Use of this product may worsen these conditions and be harmful to your health. Chronic diarrhea can result in serious illness.

Take 2–4 capsules/tablets daily with a meal. Complementary product: Psyllium Hulls.

LB-X [*Intestinal*]

formula is designed to assist the body's normal bowel functions. This combination contains crude fiber to provide bulk for natural bowel function. LB-X encourages the elimination of waste and supports colon cleansing. It contains:

Cascara sagrada bark
Dong quai root
Turkey rhubarb root
Capsicum fruit
Golden seal root
Ginger root
Oregon grape
Fennel seed
Red raspberry leaves
Lobelia herb

NOTE: This product contains cascara sagrada and Turkey rhubarb. See your health care provider prior to use if pregnant or nursing, any medical condition exists, or when taking any medication. Read and follow recommendation carefully. Do not use if diarrhea, loose stools, or abdominal pain are present or develop. Use of this product may worsen these conditions and be harmful to your health. Chronic diarrhea can result in serious illness.

Take 2–4 capsules daily with a meal.

Lecithin [*Nervous, Circulatory*]

is a fat-like substance called a phospholipid. It is produced daily by the liver if the diet is adequate. Lecithin is needed by every cell in the body and is a key building block of cell membranes; it maintains cell membrane flexibility. Lecithin

L

protects cells from oxidation and largely comprises the protective sheaths surrounding the nerves in the brain and nervous system. It is composed mostly of B vitamins, phosphoric acid, choline, linoleic acid and inositol. Although it is a fatty substance, it is also a fat emulsifier. Emulsifiers in the body play an important role in fat digestion and circulatory health. Choline is useful for making acetylcholine, an important neurotransmitter.

NSP Lecithin is derived from soybeans and is hermetically sealed in softgels. No carrier has been added, and freshness is guaranteed. Each softgel contains 480 mg lecithin.

Take 2 softgels with meals three times daily.

Stock No. 1660-5 (270)

Lemon BIO Pure Essential Oil
(*see Essential Oils*)

Licorice Root [*Glandular, Respiratory*].
We know this herb for its wide use as a candy flavoring, but its value goes far beyond that. The dietary use of licorice goes back several thousand years. Licorice root has been used by traditional herbalists as a general tonic and for respiratory support. It also supports the liver. Licorice is included in many Chinese herb combinations to balance the other herbs. It has a reputation for helping the entire body to maintain balance and for promoting well-being. Licorice contains the triterpenoid saponin glycyrrhizin. Each capsule contains 396 mg licorice root (ATC concentrated 410 mg).

Take 2 capsules with a meal three times daily. ATC concentrate. Take 1 capsule with a meal twice daily. Liquid: Take 20–25 drops (1 ml) with water three times daily. One ml is equal to 2 capsules of licorice root.

Stock No. 420-6 (100) Ko
Stock No. 424-5 (50)
ATC Concentrated Ko
Stock No.1780-9 (2 fl. oz.)
Liquid Herb Ko

Liquid B12 Complete [*Vital Nutrition, Glandular, Nervous*].
The B vitamins offer many health benefits. They help promote energy, maintain the nervous system, improve immune functions and buffer the effects of stress. Notably, the B vitamins influence the health of most of the internal organs of the body.

Vitamins can be obtained from the diet, but some of the vitamins, especially B and C vitamins, are easily lost or destroyed during cooking and processing. Liquid B vitamins may be essential for vegetarians since dietary sources of vitamin B12 are mostly foods of animal origin. Supplementing with Liquid B12 Complete helps replenish the body's supply of these vitamins.

Each 1 ml serving (17–18 drops) contains:

	Amount	% DV
B12	1,000 mcg	16,666
(as cyanocobalamin)		
Niacin	10 mg	50
(as niacinamide)		

B6	1.0 mg	50
(as pyridoxine HCl)		
Vitamin B2	0.85 mg	50
(as riboflavin)		
Vitamin B1	0.50 mg	35
(as thiamine)		

Take 1 ml (17–18 drops) once daily. Hold under the tongue for 30 seconds before swallowing. May take an additional dose as needed for energy.

Stock No. 1588-7 (2 fl. oz.) Ko

Liquid Calcium [*Vital Nutrition*].

An adequate supply of basic minerals like calcium and magnesium is vital to overall health. Women are especially sensitive to the supply of minerals in their diets—often due to hormonal fluctuation and pregnancy—which may be a consistent reason why these minerals are so important among mature women.

Help replenish the minerals your body needs by adding Liquid Calcium to your diet. It's a balanced nutritional supplement made with calcium, magnesium, vitamin D and zinc to support bone health. Liquid Calcium maintains the level of natural bone mineralization with aging. It supports the structural integrity of bone tissues, especially among elderly people. And it may support optimal bone mineral-ization and integrity. It may also be used to help maintain balanced pH levels, due to the fact that it provides calcium that can replace calcium borrowed from the bones and other organs.

Adults: Take 1 tablespoon with a meal twice daily. Children: Take 1 tablespoon with one meal daily.

Stock No. 3191-6 (16 fl. oz.)

Liquid Cleanse [*Intestinal*].

This effective herbal cleanse is easy to swallow—no tablets or capsules—and has a pleasant raspberry flavor. Key ingredients include:
• Aloe vera leaf, which soothes the digestive tract
• Red raspberry concentrate, which provides a pleasing flavor and antioxidant benefits
• Senna leaves, known for their laxative properties. Senna is used in the medical field to cleanse the bowels in preparation for a colonoscopy.
• Barberry root bark, which soothes the intestinal wall
• Ginger rhizome, known to support digestion
• Dandelion root, which helps the liver and gallbladder in removing waste
• And capsicum fruit, a digestive aid
Because it's a liquid, more people can take it and feel its benefits.

NOTE: This product contains senna. See your health care provider prior to use if: pregnant or nursing, any medical condition exists or when taking any medication. Read and follow recommendation carefully. Do not use if diarrhea, loose stools or abdominal pain are present or develop. Not intended for prolonged use. Use of this product may worsen these conditions and be harmful to your health. Chronic

L

diarrhea can result in serious illness.

Take 1 ounce (30 ml) daily as part of your personal cleansing program.

Stock No. 3193-1 (16 fl. oz.)

Liver Balance, Chinese

[*Digestive, Nervous*] is a Chinese combination of 12 herbs designed to support the needs of a stressed wood constitution. The Chinese call this formula *tiao he*, which can be translated to mean "harmonizing." In Traditional Chinese Medicine, it is used to support both the digestive and nervous systems, optimizing liver health and reducing stress. Its primary herbs—scute, peony, bupleurum and atractylodes—have been used traditionally to maintain normal nervous system function during mental stress and to support the upper digestive system during tension and distress. It contains:

Bupleurum root
Peony root
Typhonium rhizome
Cinnamon twig
Dang gui root
Fushen plant
Scute root
Zhishi fruit
Atractylodes rhizome
Panax ginseng root
Ginger rhizome
Licorice root

Take 4 capsules with a meal twice daily.

Stock No. 1860-1 (100)

Liver Balance TCM Concentrate, Chinese [*Digestive, Nervous*]

contains the same herbs found in Chinese Liver Balance but in a highly concentrated blend. This combination of 12 Chinese herbs is designed to support the needs of a stressed wood constitution. The Chinese call this formula *tiao he*, which can be translated to mean "harmonizing." In Traditional Chinese Medicine, it is used to support both the digestive and nervous systems, optimizing liver health and reducing stress. Its primary herbs—scute, peony, bupleurum and atractylodes—have been used traditionally to maintain normal nervous system function during mental stress and to support the upper digestive system during tension and distress. It contains:

Bupleurum root
Peony root without bark
Typhonium rhizome
Cinnamon twig
Dang gui root
Fushen sclerotium with root
Scute root
Zhishi fruit
Atractylodes rhizome
Panax ginseng root
Ginger rhizome
Licorice root

NOTE: Pregnant or lactating women should consult their health care provider prior to taking this supplement.

Take 1 or 2 capsules with a meal daily. Each capsule is equivalent to 5 capsules of regular Chinese Liver Balance.

Stock No. 1008-8 (30)

Liver Cleanse Formula

[*Digestive*]. The liver performs many important functions in the body. It supports digestive functions by secreting bile for emulsification of fat, controlling the metabolism of nutrients (including alcohols) and serving as a reservoir for many nutrients and metabolites. The liver's involvement in metabolic functions make it susceptible to stressors.

Liver Cleanse Formula is a blend of herbs and nutrients specially formulated to nourish the liver and to support natural cleansing functions. Together, the ingredients of Liver Cleanse have been formulated to provide nutritional support to the liver and gallbladder, promote cleansing and detoxification, and support digestive function. This formula consists of herbs historically used to cleanse, detoxify and nourish, and provide support to the gastrointestinal tract. Contains:

Red beet root
Dandelion root
Parsley herb
Horsetail herb
Yellow dock root
Black cohosh root
Birch leaves
Blessed thistle herb
Angelica root
Chamomile flowers
Gentian root
Goldenrod herb

Take 1 capsule with a meal three times daily.

Stock No. 1010-3 (100) Ko

LIV-J [*Digestive*] is an herbal blend that has been used traditionally to support digestion, support and cleanse the digestive system and nourish the liver and spleen. These herbs naturally contain trace vitamins and minerals. LIV-J contains:

Dandelion root
Rose hips fruit
Barberry root bark
Fennel seeds
Parsley leaves
Red beet root
Horscradish root extract

Take 2 capsules with a meal three times daily and before bedtime.

Stock No. 1011-4 (100) Ko

Lobelia [*Respiratory*] herb possesses many properties that make it valuable to the respiratory system. One of its key constituents, lobeline, is thought to act in a way similar to nicotine. Each capsule of NSP Lobelia herb contains 375 mg lobelia. Lobelia Essence contains 44–47 percent alcohol, water and apple cider vinegar. It can be added to baths or used in external cosmetic preparations.

Take 1 capsule daily with a meal. Add essence to a bath, relaxing poultices or other external applications.

Stock No. 430-1 (100) Ko
Stock No. 1765-8 (2 fl. oz.) Ko

LOCLO® [*Vital Nutrition*]. LOCLO makes it easy to get essential fiber into the diet. This exciting product contains fiber from several different sources, including psyllium hulls, apple fiber, cinnamon bark, acacia gum, flax seed, guar gum and oat bran. Each serving provides

3.8 grams total dietary fiber (3.2 grams soluble fiber and 0.6 grams insoluble fiber) and it tastes great. In addition, LOCLO contains the nutritious SynerPro concentrate base, which includes powders of broccoli flowers, turmeric root, rosemary leaf, red beet root, tomato fruit, carrot root, cabbage leaf, hesperidin, grapefruit bioflavonoid and orange bioflavonoid. It also contains stevia leaf extract. LOCLO is naturally sodium-free.

Take this product as recommended. Drinking enough water is essential. Avoid use if you have ever had esophageal narrowing or swallowing difficulties. May cause allergic reaction in persons sensitive to inhaled or ingested psyllium.

Add 1 tablespoon to 8 oz. liquid and stir. Drink immediately.

Stock No. 1348-4 (12 oz.) Ko

Lung Support, Chinese

[*Respiratory*] is a Chinese combination of 16 herbs specially formulated to supplement the needs of a weakened metal constitution. The Chinese call this formula *fu lei*, which can be translated to mean "strengthen the weak and thin." Lung Support is considered a lung tonic formula. Its primary herbs-anemarrhena, aster, bupleurum and astragalus—have been used in Traditional Chinese Medicine to boost the immune system, build energy and support the respiratory system. The formula includes:

Astragalus root
Aster root
Qinjiao root
Platycodon root
Anemarrhena rhizome
Bupleurum root
Dang gui root
Lycium bark
Ophiopogon root
Panax ginseng root
Atractylodes rhizome
Blue citrus peel
Citrus peel
Typhonium rhizome
Schizandra fruit
Licorice root

Take 3 capsules with a meal three times daily.

Stock No. 1887-6 (100)

Lung Support TCM Concentrate, Chinese

[*Respiratory*] contains the same herbs found in Chinese Lung Support but in a highly concentrated blend. This Chinese combination of 16 herbs is specially formulated to supplement the needs of a weakened metal constitution. The Chinese call this formula *fu lei*, which can be translated to mean "strengthen the weak and thin." Lung Support TCM is considered a lung tonic formula. Its primary herbs—anemarrhena, aster, bupleurum and astragalus—have been used in Traditional Chinese Medicine to boost the immune system, build energy and support the respiratory system. The formula includes:

Astragalus root
Aster root
Qinjiao root
Platycodon root
Anemarrhena rhizome

Bupleurum root
Dang gui root
Lycium fruit
Ophiopogon root tuber
Panax ginseng root
Atractylodes rhizome
Blue citrus peel
Citrus peel
Typhonium rhizome
Schizandra fruit
Licorice root
NOTE: Pregnant or lactating women should consult their health care provider prior to taking this supplement.
Take 2 capsules with a meal daily. Each capsule is equivalent to 5 capsules of regular Chinese Lung Support.
Stock No. 1004-3 (30)

Lutein [*Vital Nutrition*].
Years ago, researchers established a link between a diet rich in dark, leafy, green vegetables and overall macular health. Recently, researchers have found that adding vegetables high in the phytonutrient lutein to your diet helps support macular health.

The macula lutea is a yellow spot at the center of the retina (the back of the eye). The density of the pigment in the macula decreases with age. Lutein (a carotenoid) helps protect the macula lutea because of its capacity to filter short-wave visible light. It intensifies the yellow color of the macula and promotes lasting eye health.

Due to their antioxidant properties, lutein and zeaxanthin (another carotenoid) may also help protect the lipid membranes of the macula lutea against oxidation. They support eye health and visual function. Lutein may also support breast health and may be of particular importance to women. Getting more lutein in the diet or through supplementation is especially important for women.

NSP Lutein provides 10 mg lutein per capsule. Also available in Perfect Eyes, which provides 3 mg lutein per capsule.
Take 1 capsule once or twice daily with a meal.
Stock No. 1855-6 (60) Ko

Lymph Gland Cleanse [*Immune, Glandular*]
provides nutrients that help support glandular function and promote optimal immunity. Parthenium has often been confused with echinacea because of reported immune-boosting properties. Lymph Gland Cleanse provides an herbal source of many trace minerals and vitamins. Lymph Gland Cleanse contains:
Parthenium root
Golden seal root and rhizome
Yarrow aerial parts
Capsicum fruit
Take 2 capsules with a meal three times daily.
Stock No. 960-4 (100) Ko

Lymph Gland Cleanse–HY
[*Immune, Circulatory*] helps meet the nutritional needs of a stressed immune system and is particularly helpful to the circulatory system, which benefits the lymphatic system. The herbal components provide a natural source of several

minerals. It consists of:
Parthenium root
Yarrow aerial parts
Myrrh gum
Capsicum fruit
Take 2 capsules with a meal three times daily.

Stock No. 920-3 (100) Ko

Lymphatic Drainage

[*Circulatory*]. The lymphatic system consists of a myriad of delicate vessels found in almost every tissue of the body that contains blood vessels. These vessels perform essential functions, including the transportation of nutrients from the small intestine into the interstitial space and the removal of waste products from cellular metabolism. A vast array of materials must be transported by this system through small movements such as the pressure changes that occur during breathing and pulsations from arterial circulation. Consequently, efficient lymphatic system drainage is helpful to promoting overall health.

Lymphatic Drainage is designed to aid the drainage of the lymphatic system. It may help disperse lymphatic fluid and improve nutrient absorption, thus enhancing immune function. The ingredients in Lymphatic Drainage work together to support the lymphatic system. This formula contains cleavers, red clover, stillingia root and prickly ash bark.

Take 1 ml (approximately 15–20 drops or 1/4 teaspoon) in water twice daily.

Stock No. 3171-7 (2 fl. oz.) Ko

Lymphomax® [*Immune*] is an all-herbal formula designed to meet the nutritional needs of the body's lymphatic system. Mullein helps promote natural respiratory function. Lobelia contains lobeline, an active ingredient that helps stimulate the respiratory system, which supports breathing. Plantain may help protect the liver against cellular damage due to its antioxidant effects, and it helps maintain the lymphatic system. Cleavers (also known as clivers) has reported diuretic, astringent and tonic effects. This herb is used historically to cleanse the lymphatic and other glandular systems. Red root is traditionally used for supporting the lymph system. It contains components that help make the body environment more acceptable to microorganic balance. Lymphomax also contains bayberry root bark, alfalfa herb, chamomile flowers, echinacea root, yarrow flowers and garlic bulb. Lymphomax is a blend of reported blood-purifying, cleansing and supporting herbs for the circulatory and lymphatic systems.

Take 2 capsules with breakfast and lunch.

Stock No. 4077-6 (100) Ko

Lymphostim [*Immune*]

homeopathic remedy helps boost the immune system, relieve infection and treat both mental and physical fatigue.

Take 10–15 drops under the tongue three to four times daily. For children under 12, consult your health care professional.

Stock No. 8710-4 (1 fl. oz.)

Maca [*Glandular*]. Maca (*Lepidium meyenii*) is a tuber that is a member of the radish family. It grows in the Andean mountains. It may provide a natural means for improving sexual desire and performance. Also known as Peruvian ginseng, maca may help enhance physical energy and endurance. As an adaptogen, it helps promote stamina and buffer the effects of stress. Animal studies show improvement in male subjects.

NSP Maca contains standardized pure root extract, with a guaranteed potency of macaenes and macamides in the ratio of 4:1.

Take 1 capsule with a meal three times daily.

Stock No. 1117-2 (90) Ko

Magnesium [*Nervous*] is the central atom in the chlorophyll molecule, and in physiology it activates the ATP energy system. More than 300 enzymes require the presence of this mineral. Sixty percent of the body's magnesium is found in the bones, and the rest is found mainly in the soft tissues and blood. Magnesium is necessary for the metabolism of vitamin C, phosphorus, potassium and sodium. It should be taken when using calcium supplements. It is important to the nervous system and for the synthesis of certain proteins.

Each tablet contains 250 mg of magnesium oxide and magnesium amino acid chelate, which provide 62.5 percent of the Daily Value for this nutrient. NSP Magnesium comes in a base of licorice root, kelp plant, peppermint leaves and white willow bark.

Take 1 tablet daily with a meal.

Stock No. 1786-6 (180)

Magnesium Complex [*Vital Nutrition, Structural*]. Magnesium is an essential mineral. It is present in more than 300 enzymatic systems where it is crucial for energy production and other metabolic functions. The heart, brain and kidneys cannot function without adequate levels of this nutrient.

Magnesium Complex combines two excellent forms of magnesium—citrate and malate. Studies show that magnesium citrate and malate are soluble and among the best forms of magnesium. Each capsule provides 100 mg magnesium.

Take 2 capsules twice daily with meals.

Stock No. 1859-8 (100) Ko

Marshmallow [*Respiratory*]. Marshmallow has a high mucilage content. It has been used historically for respiratory support and to soothe inflamed mucous membranes. Each capsule contains 450 mg marshmallow root.

Take 1 capsule with a meal twice daily.

Stock No. 440-0 (100) Ko

Marshmallow & Fenugreek [*Respiratory*] is a combination that nutritionally supports the respiratory system. Marshmallow has demulcent properties, while fenugreek possesses mucilaginous compounds. Also contains slippery elm bark, which is mucilaginous and supportive of delicate body tissues. *Take 2 capsules with a meal twice daily.*

Stock No. 843-1 (100) Ko

Massage Oil [*Skin*] is a light,
non-greasy massage and body oil featuring a blend of unscented apricot kernel oil, sweet almond oil, hazelnut oil, borage oil and vitamin E. NSP Massage Oil is high in essential fatty acids and is nourishing to the skin. Use it alone or as a carrier oil for NSP's 100 percent pure essential oils.

Dilute 7–15 drops of essential oil per tablespoon of massage oil. Use liberally on desired areas.

Stock No. 3928-7 (4 fl. oz.)

Master Gland® [*Glandular*]
is a key product that provides nutritional supplementation for the glandular system. Hormones that are produced by these glands influence the health of the entire body. Vitamins and minerals are needed for proper function of these glands. Two capsules contain:

	Amount	% DV
Vitamin A	900 IU	20
(as beta-carotene)		
Vitamin C	60 mg	100
Vitamin E	14 IU	50
Pantothenic acid	24 mg	240
Zinc (gluconate)	6 mg	40
Manganese	1 mg	50
(amino acid chelate)		
Potassium (citrate)	20 mg	*
Lecithin	27 mg	*

All of this is contained in a base of nutrient-rich herbs: licorice root, alfalfa aerial parts, asparagus stem extract, black walnut hulls, parsley leaves, parthenium root, thyme leaves, dandelion root, dong quai root, eleuthero root, kelp leaves and stem, lemon bioflavonoids, schizandra fruit, marshmallow root extract and uva ursi leaf.

Take 2 capsules with breakfast and 2 capsules with lunch daily.

Stock No. 3040-3 (120) Ko

Mega-Chel® [*Circulatory*] is a key
product for the circulatory system. It contains a large array of nutrients to support the entire circulatory system. Four tablets provide the following:

	Amount	% DV
Vitamin A	13,333 IU	266
(beta-carotene, palmitate)		
Vitamin C	1,333 mg	2,200
(ascorbic acid)		
Vitamin D	216 IU	53
Vitamin E	133 IU	446
(d-alpha tocopherol)		
Vitamin B1	66 mg	4,446
(thiamine)		
Vitamin B2	16 mg	980
(riboflavin)		
Niacin	33 mg	166
Vitamin B6	50 mg	2,500
(pyridoxine HCl)		
Folic acid	133 mcg	33
Vitamin B12	83 mcg	1,386
(cyanocobalamin)		
Biotin	33 mcg	10
Pantothenic acid	166 mg	1,666
(d-calcium pantothenate)		
Calcium	133 mg	13
(amino acid chelate, dicalcium phosphate, d-calcium pantothenate)		
Iron	3.3 mg	20
(ferrous fumarate)		
Phosphorus	96 mg	10
(di-calcium phosphate)		
Iodine	42 mcg	26

(potassium iodide)		
Magnesium (amino acid chelate, magnesium oxide)	133 mg	33
Zinc (gluconate, oxide)	10 mg	66
Selenium (amino acid chelate)	83 mcg	120
Copper (copper gluconate)	83 mcg	4
Manganese (amino acid chelate)	1.6 mg	83
Chromium (amino acid chelate)	66 mcg	53
Potassium (gluconate)	133 mg	*
p-Aminobenzoic acid (PABA)	83 mg	*
Inositol	13 mg	*
Coenzyme Q10	3.3 mg	*
l-Cysteine HCl	250 mg	*
l-Methionine	58 mg	*

*Daily Value not established

The formula also contains citrus bioflavonoids, rutin, adrenal substance, spleen substance, thymus substance, cod liver oil, ginkgo leaf (*Ginkgo biloba*) and hawthorn berries. Each tablet is yeast-free and contains natural forms of the above ingredients for increased assimilation.

CAUTION: If pregnant or planning pregnancy, daily vitamin A intake should not exceed 5,000 IU. Quantities in excess of 10,000 IU may result in reproductive hazards or birth defects. Beta-carotene as a natural source of vitamin A poses no such risk. Close lid tightly and keep out of reach of children.

Begin by taking 1 tablet twice daily for a week. Then take 2 tablets twice daily for the second week. Gradually increase to 4 tablets with a meal twice daily.

Maintain this level for three to four months. Then gradually taper off in a similar manner.

Stock No. 1611-1 (180)

Stock No. 4050-6 (90)

Melatonin Extra® — 3 mg

[*Glandular*] is an exclusive NSP formula containing melatonin, a natural compound produced by the pineal gland (located in the center of the brain). Melatonin is vitally important to health when you consider three factors: aging, energy and sleep. As people age, they produce less melatonin.

Melatonin can help restore the body's natural sleep rhythm. Used as directed, it may help you feel more alert and satisfied after a full night of rest. In addition, mounting evidence shows that melatonin acts as a powerful antioxidant, meaning it may benefit the body's immune system.

Each capsule of Melatonin Extra contains 3 mg of melatonin (derived from non-bovine sources), combined with *Ginkgo biloba* concentrate (standardized to 24 percent glycosides), *Ginkgo biloba* leaves (may aid circulation to the brain), eleuthero (a famous adaptogen known to have a calming effect on the nervous system) and 30 IU (100 percent Daily Value) of vitamin E (d-alpha tocopherol from soy).

CAUTION: Melatonin should not be taken during the day; it may cause drowsiness. It is not recommended for use by children, teenagers or pregnant or lactating women. Do not take this product when driving a motor vehicle or

M

operating machinery.

Take 1 capsule 30 minutes prior to bedtime.

Stock No. 2830-4 (60)

Men's Formula [*Glandular*] is specifically formulated for men 40 and older who seek a nutritional boost for a healthy prostate gland. Each capsule contains saw palmetto extract (*Serenoa repens*) standardized to 20 percent essential fatty acids; pumpkin seeds (*Cucurbita pepo*); pygeum bark extract (*Prunus africana*) standardized to 2.5 total sterols, calculated as beta-sitosterol; gotu kola aerial parts; standardized lycopene concentrate, a powerful antioxidant; stinging nettle extract (*Urtica dioica*) standardized to 2 percent plant silica; and zinc. Saw palmetto supports the prostate gland and the urinary system. It protects the prostate gland from active forms of testosterone. Lycopene has been shown to have a protective effect on the prostate gland. Gotu kola herb supports the nervous system and promotes endurance.

For intensive use: Take 3 capsules twice daily with morning and evening meals. For maintenance: Take 2 capsules daily with a meal.

Stock No. 3112-7 (60)

Men's X-Action® *(see X-Action, Men's)*

Menopause [*Glandular*] is a natural homeopathic medicine for the relief of symptoms associated with menopause, including nervous irritability, bloating, cravings, discomfort and hot flashes.

Adult women take 10–15 drops under the tongue every two hours until symptoms improve. Then decrease to every four hours or as needed. Do not take this product for more than five days. If symptoms do not improve after 10 days, consult your health care professional. Not recommended for girls under 12 years of age.

Stock No. 8728-2 (1 fl. oz.)

Menstrual [*Glandular*] is a natural homeopathic remedy for the relief of the minor pain and discomfort of premenstrual syndrome and menstrual periods.

Take 10–15 drops under the tongue every 10–15 minutes or as needed until symptoms improve. Then decrease to every one or two hours, then to four times daily until symptoms are relieved. If symptoms persist or change, consult your health care provider.

Stock No. 8702-9 (1 fl. oz.)

Menstrual Reg [*Glandular*]. Menstruation may be uncomfortable, especially when it is accompanied by cramping, bloating and mild mood changes. Menstrual Reg is designed to help reduce these symptoms by balancing hormone levels. Menstrual Reg contains herbs traditionally used to provide all-over support to the female body. This formula contains lady's mantle aerial parts, shepherd's purse aerial parts, yarrow (leaf, flower and aerial

parts), black haw root, nettle leaves, sarsaparilla root, chaste tree fruit concentrate and false unicorn root.

Take 2–3 capsules with a meal three times daily. For a more immediate effect, it can be taken in larger amounts for short periods of time, i.e., every two hours for a period of several days. For best results, this formula should be taken over several months.

Stock No. 1125-3 (100) Ko

MetaboMax EF® [*Weight Management*]

is a nourishing, caffeine- and ephedra-free formula that may help to reduce appetite and support energy levels. As part of an overall program that involves increased activity and calorie restriction, this safe formula supports weight-management goals. Cordyceps, eleuthero root and chromium boost energy and help buffer the effects of stress. Ingredients include:

Lotus leaf extract
Green tea extract
Fructus aurantia (synephrine)
Garcinia fruit
l-Carnitine
Cordyceps powder
Eleuthero root
Chromium
Bee pollen
Spirulina
Vitamin E
Kelp leaves and stems

Take 1–2 tablets before meals three times daily.

Stock No. 3008-5 (90)

MetaboStart EF® [*Weight Management*]

is a caffeine- and ephedra-free program that combines the following products to support weight management from several angles:

MetaboMax EF
Fat Grabbers®
Carbo Grabbers®
7-Keto™
Conjugated Linoleic Acid (CLA)

The convenient, pre-packaged program helps you stick to your weight-management goals wherever you go.

NOTE: May cause allergic reaction in persons sensitive to inhaled or ingested psyllium.

Take the contents of 1 AM packet (1 MetaboMax EF, 1 7-Keto, 3 Fat Grabbers, 1 Carbo Grabbers) before breakfast, 1 NOON packet (2 MetaboMax EF, 3 Fat Grabbers, 1 Carbo Grabbers) before lunch, and 1 PM packet (3 Carbo Grabbers, 2 CLA) before your evening meal. Be sure to drink a lot of water throughout the day.

Stock No. 3018-6 (14-day supply)

Migraquel® [*Nervous*]

is a natural homeopathic remedy for the relief of pain and other symptoms associated with throbbing, debilitating cluster headaches.

NOTE: Do not take this product for more than five days. If symptoms do not improve after 10 days, consult your health care professional. If you are pregnant or nursing, consult your health care provider.

Take 10–15 drops under the

M

tongue every 10–15 minutes or as needed until symptoms improve. Then decrease to hourly, then to four times daily until symptoms are relieved. For children under 12, consult your health care professional.

Milk Thistle Combination

[*Digestive*]. Milk Thistle Combination provides nutrients that must be present for the liver to perform its 500 or more functions. This long-time favorite boasts the same liver-protecting and free-radical fighting ingredients as in the previous formula, plus N-Acetyl-Cysteine (NAC). NAC optimizes the production of glutathione in the liver. Glutathione is used in the breakdown and elimination of toxins in the body. NAC is also a powerful antioxidant that helps support the liver and may support the eyes and respiratory system.

Milk thistle helps protect the liver from the toxins it collects and breaks down. It contains a constituent called silymarin, which has been the subject of numerous studies. Silymarin may help stabilize cellular membranes, preventing the intake of some toxins and subsequent tissue damage.

	Amount per 2 Tablets	% DV	Amount per 4 Tablets	% DV
Vitamin A	14,000 IU	280	28,000 IU	560
(beta-carotene, contains soy)				
Vitamin C	480 mg	800	960 mg	1600

These are mixed in a base of milk thistle extract (80 percent silymarin, 140 mg), N-Acetyl-Cysteine (50 mg), dandelion root (150 mg), choline bitartrate (60 mg) and inositol (60 mg).

Take 2 tablets with a meal twice daily.

Milk Thistle Time-Release

[*Digestive*] provides a consistent supply of silymarin (a constituent of milk thistle) to the liver, which may help protect the liver against ingested toxins. The liver performs 500-plus functions, including filtering and destroying toxins in the body. Providing it with proper nutrients allows this essential organ to function at top capacity.

Silymarin may help stabilize cellular membranes, preventing the intake of some toxins and subsequent tissue damage. It also stimulates protein synthesis in liver cells and has antioxidant properties.

One tablet of NSP Time-Release Milk Thistle contains 350 mg milk thistle herb extract, providing 80 percent (280 mg) silymarin.

Take 1 tablet with a meal twice daily.

Mineral-Chi Tonic, Chinese

[*Vital Nutrition, Glandular*] is a special blend of tonic herbs and a full spectrum of naturally chelated trace minerals extracted from the plant vegetation of an ancient seabed. Mineral-Chi contains the following renowned Chinese tonic herbs used in Traditional Chinese Medicine to boost and maintain balance in the body's energy system:

Gynostemma herb

Lycii berry
Schizandra berry
Eleuthero root and rhizome
Astragalus root
Deglycyrrhizinated licorice root
Reishi mushroom (ganoderma)
Ginger rhizome
Ginkgo biloba leaf

Each serving also provides 180 mg of potassium, an electrolyte that plays a role in many important functions throughout the body. It also contains purified water, white grape juice, glycerin, sodium benzoate, citric acid and natural apple and cherry flavors.

Take 1 tablespoon in the morning and 1 tablespoon in the evening daily. Mix with water or juice if desired.

Stock No. 1818-3 (32 fl. oz.)

Mold, Yeast & Dust (Allergies)
(*see Allergies—Mold, Yeast & Dust*)

Monthly Maintenance®
[*Glandular*] provides nutrients that may be beneficial during a woman's monthly cycle. Four capsules provide the following:

	Amount	% DV
Vitamin A	3,333 IU	66
(beta-carotene, contains soy)		
Vitamin C	222 mg	373
(ascorbic acid)		
Vitamin D	89 IU	23
(cholecalciferol)		
Vitamin E	133 IU	446
(d-alpha tocopherol)		
Thiamine	11 mg	753
(vitamin B1)		
Riboflavin	11 mg	666
(vitamin B2)		
Niacin	11 mg	56
(niacinamide)		
Vitamin B6	66 mg	3,333
(pyridoxine)		
Folic acid	44 mcg	13
Vitamin B12	11 mcg	186
(cyanocobalamin)		
Biotin	13 mcg	5
Pantothenic Acid	11 mg	113
(d-calcium pantothenate)		
Calcium	33 mg	3
(di-calcium phosphate)		
Iron	3 mg	20
(ferrous gluconate)		
Phosphorus	34 mg	3
(di-calcium phosphate)		
Iodine	33 mcg	20
(potassium iodide)		
Magnesium	66 mg	16
(oxide, stearate)		
Zinc (oxide)	5 mg	33
Selenium	5 mcg	6
(amino acid chelate)		
Copper	0.11 mg	6
(gluconate)		
Manganese	2 mg	100
(amino acid chelate)		
Chromium	20 mcg	20
(amino acid chelate)		
Potassium	22 mg	*
(citrate)		
Choline	111 mg	*
Inositol	111 mg	*
PABA	11 mg	*
(para-aminobenzoic acid)		
Bioflavonoids	11 mg	*

*Daily Value not established

All of the above come in a base of herbs: peony root, dong quai root, bupleurum root, hoelen plant, atractylodes rhizome, codonopsis root, alisma bark, licorice root, magnolia bark, ginger root, peppermint leaves, moutan root, gardenia fruit and cyperus rhizome.

Take 4 capsules with a meal three times daily during the last 10 days of the menstrual cycle (10 days before the onset of menstruation).

Stock No. 1812-0 (180)

M

Mood Elevator, Chinese

[*Nervous*] is composed of 17 herbs used in Traditional Chinese Medicine as a "fire enhancing" combination to regulate and untrap the chi (vitality). Its two key ingredients, bupleurum root and cyperus rhizome, may support the liver, the organ (according to Chinese philosophy) that plays an integral role in mood. According to Traditional Chinese Medicine, when the liver is functioning at its peak, positive mood may be maintained. Its Chinese name *jie yu* can be translated to mean "relieve depression."

This combination includes:
Perilla leaves
Cyperus rhizome
Chih-shih fruit
Typhonium rhizome
Aurantium peel
Bamboo sap
Bupleurum root
Cnidium rhizome
Gambir stem
Hoelen sclerotium
Ophiopogon root tuber
Ginger rhizome
Panax ginseng root
Platycodon root
Tang-kuei root
Coptis rhizome
Licorice root
Take 4 capsules with a meal twice daily.

Stock No. 1878-8 (100)

Mood Elevator TCM Concentrate, Chinese

[*Nervous*] contains the same herbs found in Chinese Mood Elevator but in a highly concentrated blend. Traditional Chinese Medicine would consider this a "fire enhancing" combination to regulate and untrap the chi (vitality). Its two key ingredients, bupleurum root and cyperus rhizome, may support the liver, the organ (according to Chinese philosophy) that plays an integral role in mood. According to Traditional Chinese Medicine, when the liver is functioning at its peak, positive mood may be maintained. Its Chinese name *jie yu* can be translated to mean "relieve depression."

This combination includes:
Perilla leaves
Cyperus rhizome
Chih-shih fruit
Typhonium rhizome
Aurantium peel
Bamboo sap
Bupleurum root
Cnidium rhizome
Gambir stem
Hoelen sclerotium
Ophiopogon root tuber
Ginger rhizome
Panax ginseng root
Platycodon root
Tang-kuei root
Coptis rhizome
Licorice root
NOTE: Pregnant or lactating women should consult their health care provider prior to taking this supplement.
Take 1 or 2 capsules with a meal daily. Each capsule is equivalent to 5 capsules of regular Chinese Mood Elevator.

Stock No. 1035-7 (30)

MSM [*Structural, Circulatory*], or methylsulfonylmethane, is a naturally occurring organic form of dietary sulfur used by our bodies every day. Sulfur is a major component in many of the body's proteins, hormones, enzymes and tissues.

Take 2 tablets with a meal three times daily.

Stock No. 4059-4 (90)

MSM/Glucosamine Cream

[*Structural*] provides the body with MSM, a source of organic sulfur (an important constituent of the body's tissues), and glucosamine, a building block of cartilage. These nutrients are micro-encapsulated into a patented liposome delivery system for concentrated, long-lasting delivery to the desired area. MSM/Glucosamine Cream supports joints, cartilage and connective tissue and promotes skin health and appearance. Fragrance-free. Contains 4 percent glucosamine sulfate and 2 percent MSM in a naturally derived cream base.

Apply liberally as needed to the skin and joint areas.

Stock No. 3522-4 (2 oz.)

Mullein [*Respiratory*] is known by many names, including Donkey's Ears, Bunny's Ears and Velvet Plant. Its high mucilage content and mild saponins make it a support for the respiratory system. Mucilage absorbs water in the windpipe and becomes slippery. Each capsule contains 290 mg mullein.

Take 2 capsules with a meal twice daily.

Stock No. 460-7 (100) Ko

Multiple Vitamins and Minerals, SynerPro®

[*Vital Nutrition*] contains 100 percent of the Daily Value for 16 essential vitamins and minerals in the SynerPro concentrate base. This important combination also contains varying amounts of seven other vitamins and minerals.

	Amount per Tablet	% DV	Amount per 2 Tablets	% DV
Vitamin A (as beta-carotene)	2,500 IU	50	5,000 IU	100
Vitamin C	30 mg	50	60 mg	100
Vitamin D	200 IU	50	400 IU	100
Vitamin E (as d-alpha tocopherols)	15 IU	50	30 IU	100
Thiamine (Vitamin B1)	0.75 mg	50	1.5 mg	100
Riboflavin (Vitamin B2)	0.85 mg	50	1.7 mg	100
Niacin (as nicotinic acid)	10 mg	50	20 mg	100
Vitamin B6	1 mg	50	2 mg	100
Folic Acid	200 mcg	50	400 mcg	100
Vitamin B12	3 mcg	50	6 mcg	100
Biotin	150 mcg	50	300 mcg	100
Pantothenic Acid	5 mg	50	10 mg	100
Calcium	125 mg	15	250 mg	30
Iron	9 mg	50	18 mg	100
Phosphorus	90 mg	10	180 mg	20
Iodine	75 mcg	50	150 mcg	100
Magnesium	50 mg	15	100 mg	30
Zinc	7.5 mg	50	15 mg	100
Selenium	25 mcg	35	50 mcg	70
Copper	1 mg	50	2 mg	100
Manganese	0.5 mg	25	1 mg	50
Chromium	50 mcg	40	100 mcg	80
Molybdenum	38 mcg	50	76 mcg	100

Take 1 tablet with a meal twice daily.

Stock No. 1644-1 (60)

M

Multiple Vitamins & Minerals, Time-Release [*Vital Nutrition*]

provides 100 percent or more of the Daily Value of 16 essential vitamins and minerals in a time-release formula. In addition, the proportions of vitamins and minerals complement each other and are combined in a unique base of nutrients. It contains no sugar, starch, artificial colorings or flavorings. Each tablet provides:

	Amount	% DV
Vitamin A	10,000 IU	200
Vitamin C	250 mg	420
Vitamin D	1,000 IU	250
Vitamin E	30 IU	100
Vitamin B1	25 mg	1,660
Vitamin B2	25 mg	1,470
Niacin	50 mg	250
Vitamin B6	25 mg	1,250
Folic Acid	0.4 mg	100
Vitamin B12	50 mcg	830
Biotin	0.3 mg	100
Pantothenic Acid	50 mg	500
Calcium	50 mg	5
Iron	20 mg	110
Phosphorus	31 mg	4
Iodine	0.15 mg	100
Magnesium	3 mg	1
Zinc	30 mg	200
Selenium	50 mcg	70
Copper	2 mg	100
Manganese	3 mg	150

These nutrients are in a complementary base of yucca root, PABA, choline bitartrate, inositol, lemon bioflavonoids, rutin, hesperidin, alfalfa herb, kelp plant, chamomile flowers, dandelion root, rose hips fruit and extract, myrrh gum, golden seal root and wheat germ.

CAUTION: If you are pregnant or planning pregnancy, your daily vitamin A intake should not exceed 5,000 IU. Quantities in excess of 10,000 IU may result in reproductive hazards or birth defects.

Take 1 tablet daily with a meal.

Myrrh Pure Essential Oil
(*see Essential Oils*)

N

N-Acetyl Cysteine [*Circulatory, Glandular, Immune*] is essential

for the body to mount a defense against free radicals, and it supports the natural elimination of harmful toxins. This nutrient is a precursor to glutathione, one of the body's most powerful antioxidants. Consequently, N-acetyl cysteine can step up the body's own efforts to combat oxidative stress and damage. N-acetyl cysteine protects healthy cells against damage from oxidative stressors. Its principal benefits include protecting the liver, cardiovascular system, skin and eyes. NSP N-Acetyl Cysteine contains turmeric for added liver support. Provides 250 mg N-acetyl cysteine per tablet.

NOTE: Consult a medical professional before taking this product if you are currently undergoing any treatment for cancer.

Take 1 tablet twice daily with a meal. Do not exceed recommended dose. If symptoms of headache, nausea or diarrhea develop, reduce dosage and see your health care practitioner.

Natria®—Nature's Skin Nutrition™ [*Skin, Hair*] is an innovative hair- and skin-care line formulated with naturally derived, nourishing ingredients that condition, strengthen and protect your hair and skin. Natria products feature herbal and botanical extracts, powerful vitamins and antioxidants, and a collection of ingredient complexes that hydrate, protect and help improve the look of visibly damaged hair and skin to help renew a more youthful appearance.

Natria products address two skin needs: nourishing and balancing. The Nourishing regimen provides rich rewards for normal to dry skin. The Balancing regimen offers pure results for combination to oily skin.

Each new product is formulated with one or more of the following ingredient complexes that are exclusive to Nature's Sunshine and provide essential elements for complete hair and skin nutrition.

NatriMins™—Important vitamins deposit antioxidants and vital nutrients directly to the skin.
NatriXtracts™—Essential herbal and botanical extracts provide natural, skin-nourishing benefits.
NatriPlex™—A unique moisture-replenishing complex protects against harmful external elements and ensures optimal hydration.
NatriNew™—This powerful skin renewal complex reduces the visible signs of aging, restoring skin's youthful appearance.
NatriZymes™—Specialized DNA defense enzymes protect against and help correct the visible signs of aging caused by sun exposure.

NatriSomes™—Targeted liposomes release active ingredients into the areas of the skin where they are needed most.
NatriSpheres™—Hair repair spheres bind naturally to the hair shaft to help repair, restore and restructure the hair. Natria products are dermatologist tested, safety tested and allergy tested and contain all-natural fragrance and color.

Natria® Acne Treatment Gel

[*Skin*] is a powerful combination of natural ingredients that treat the most common concerns associated with acne, helping to clear current blemishes while preventing future breakouts. Salicylic acid encourages proper exfoliation to slough off dead skin cells and unclog pores. Licorice extract helps maintain a balanced moisture level while alpha-glucan oligosaccharides help create a beneficial skin environment. Algae extract and *Artemisia princeps* leaf extract provide skin-soothing properties.

Apply a thin layer evenly over face until completely absorbed. Follow with moisturizer as needed. Use morning and evening. For best results, use in conjunction with the Natria Balancing Regimen.

Stock No. 6017-8 (30 ml/1 fl. oz.)

Natria Advanced Recovery Cream

[*Skin*] drenches your skin with instant hydration to rapidly boost and sustain moisture levels and replenish what your skin loses throughout the day. This rich cream combines the finest ingredients to

N

let you wake up to younger-looking skin. Advanced Recovery Cream replenishes skin throughout the night. As your skin rests, microcaccus lysate, a specialized enzyme, improves appearance. Botanical extracts like aloe, green tea and grape seed naturally replenish the skin's barrier with essential moisture and help prevent water loss. Vitamins A, B, C and E support the skin with potent, free radical-fighting antioxidants. This rich cream hydrates with luxurious emollients and humectants like squalene and sodium PCA that add luster and restore a vital look.

With fingertips, smooth gently and evenly over face and neck. Apply after using Natria Nourishing Cleansing Lotion, Nourishing Toner and Skin Refining Serum.

Stock No. 6007-9 (50 ml/1.7 fl. oz.)

Natria Advanced Recovery Lotion [*Skin*] is designed for

Combination/Oily skin. As you sleep, your skin's absorption is most efficient. Advanced Recovery Lotion quenches the skin's thirst for moisture and helps maintain an ideal level of hydration. Each morning your skin looks and feels better than the night before. This skin-healthy formula includes microcaccus lysate, a unique enzyme that helps improve skin appearance and luster. Natural skin components like farnesol and farnesyl acetate are incorporated for their oil-balancing properties. An emollient blend of natural plant extracts feeds skin's lipid layer, reinforces its barrier and supplies vital hydration. Antioxidant-rich plant extracts and powerful vitamins A, B, C

and E support and protect skin from the drying environment.

Dispense a small amount onto fingertips. Smooth gently and evenly over face and neck. Apply after using Natria Balancing Cleansing Gel, Balancing Toner and Skin Refining Serum.

Stock No. 6008-1 (50 ml/1.7 fl. oz.)

Natria Balancing Cleansing Gel [*Skin*] contains a natural blend

of non-soap cleansing agents to rid skin of makeup, surface debris and excess oils that can clog pores. Antioxidants from essential vitamins A, B, C and E supply reinforcement against environmental aggressors. Botanical extracts like aloe, green tea, chamomile, *Ginkgo biloba*, ginseng, sea lettuce and grape seed soften, soothe, protect, stimulate and rejuvenate your skin's look. A soft, fresh foam will leave your skin feeling ultra-clean and looking bright, smooth and revived.

With fingertips, gently massage into a light lather over face and neck. Rinse thoroughly with warm water. Use morning and evening. Follow with Natria Balancing Toner and Skin Refining Serum.

Stock No. 6001-7 (125 ml/4.2 fl. oz.)

Natria Balancing Daily Defense Lotion SPF 15 [*Skin*]

hydrates with a light, quick-absorbing formula. More than just a moisturizer, Balancing Daily Defense Lotion contains sunscreen, providing SPF 15, which shields from destructive UVA and UVB rays. Microscopic plankton extracts help renew the skin against the look of visible damage and telltale lines. This balancing lotion also contains farnesol and farnesyl acetate, which are naturally occurring components found in the skin that help supplement the skin's natural oil production. A specialized, moisture-replenishing complex ensures that optimal hydration and balance are achieved. Natural antioxidants from skin-nutritious vitamins and botanical extracts reinforce the skin against the drying environment.

With fingertips, smooth gently and evenly over face and neck. Use after Natria Balancing Cleansing Gel, Balancing Toner and Skin Refining Serum.

Stock No. 6006-8 (75 ml/2.5 fl. oz.)

Natria Balancing Toner [*Skin*]

balances your skin's natural pH and oil levels and prepares the skin for optimal moisturizing. Essential vitamins A, B, C and E slough away any remaining impurities and create balanced skin texture. Balancing Toner also purifies beneath the skin's surface, minimizing and tightening pores for a clean, refined appearance. Witch hazel promotes even skin tone. Extracts of cinnamon, ginger and burnet absorb extra oil. This alcohol-free formula bathes the skin in extracts of algae and rejuvenates its youthful look while replenishing the skin's natural barrier.

Moisten a cotton pad and sweep gently over face and neck after cleansing with Natria Balancing Cleansing Gel. Follow with Skin-refining Serum.

Stock No. 6003-0 (180 ml/6 fl. oz.)

Natria Deep Detoxifying Mask [*Skin*]

draws out excess oils, impurities and toxins from within the epidermis. Provides a mild cooling sensation as kaolin and bentonite clays gently exfoliate skin surface for an even tone and texture. These concentrated clays promote a healthy complexion. Ginger extract purifies and absorbs extra oil. Organic and mineral components offer powerful antioxidant protection and impart freshness, firmness and uniformity to the skin. As skin is deep-cleansed, it is left feeling soft, smooth and free from impurities as surface toxins are effectively neutralized.

After cleansing, apply an even amount over face and neck, avoiding eye and mouth areas. Leave on for 10 minutes or until dry. Rinse thoroughly with warm water. Use once or twice a week.

Stock No. 6011-6 (100 ml/3.4 fl. oz.)

Natria Five-Phase Eye Refine

[*Skin*] defends and hydrates fragile skin around the eyes as it fights the most visible signs of aging and stress around the eyes. It provides proper hydration and replenishes skin. It improves firmness and helps complement skin's collagen and elastin. Its NatriNew complex helps visibly smooth lines and wrinkles. Five-Phase Eye Refine reduces the appearance of puffiness and the look of dark circles. Additionally, the formula provides antioxidant protection and age-defying benefits.

Stock No. 6012-4 (.5 fl. oz.)

Natria Irish Moss Hand & Body Lotion

Natria Irish Moss Hand & Body Lotion [*Skin*] is designed for overall skin care needs and promotes skin health, suppleness and elasticity. This improved formula contains a unique moisture-replenishing complex that protects against harmful, external drying elements and ensures optimal hydration. It also provides important vitamins (A, B, C and E) that deposit vital nutrients directly to the skin. Herbal and botanical extracts, including Irish Moss extract, aloe vera gel, (green tea), comfrey root extract, Icelandic moss and *Morinda citrifolia* juice provide natural, skin-nourishing benefits. This formula comes in a tube for easier dispensing and has a pleasant, natural fragrance and color.

Apply generously as needed to hands and body to promote soft, smooth skin. For best results, use with Natria Moisture Full Body Wash.

Stock No. 6021-0 (250 ml/8.4 oz. tube)

Natria Lip Balm SPF 15

Natria Lip Balm SPF 15 [*Skin*] defends delicate lips with UVA and UVB protection. SPF 15 provides 15 times your skin's natural sun defense. Pure plant extracts and vitamins A, B, C and E soothe and condition the delicate lip area, supply skin-essential antioxidants and provide long-lasting moisture.

Apply liberally to lips as often as needed.

Stock No. 6019-0 (0.15 oz.)

Natria Moisture Full Body Wash

Natria Moisture Full Body Wash [*Skin*] is a nutrient-rich formula that provides an energized and revitalized look to the skin with a soft, lathering gel. It protects against dryness with conditioning cleansers and penetrating hydrators. Cleansing agents derived from natural sources gently and effectively clean the skin. Aloe, green tea leaf extract, stinging nettle and other herbal and botanical extracts indulge skin with nourishing properties. Vitamins A, B, C and E soak into the skin where they deposit free-radical fighting antioxidants. Moisture Full Body Wash leaves your skin thoroughly clean, moisturized and refreshed.

In shower or bath, squeeze a generous amount into hands or onto a washcloth or shower sponge. Lather over entire body. Rinse thoroughly.

Stock No. 6020-4 (250 ml/8.4 fl. oz.)

Natria Nourishing Cleansing Lotion

Natria Nourishing Cleansing Lotion [*Skin*] gently and effectively cleanses without stripping the skin's natural barrier or disrupting its delicate moisture balance. Natural soap-free cleansers lift away all traces of makeup and eliminate impurities that accumulate on the skin. A smooth, creamy lather leaves skin feeling soft, healthy and thoroughly clean. It hydrates and conditions while restoring vital moisture and nutrients.

With fingertips, gently massage into a light lather over face and neck. Rinse thoroughly with warm water or tissue off. Use both morning and evening. Follow with Natria Nourishing Toner and Skin Refining Serum.

Stock No. 6000-6 (125 ml/4.2 fl. oz.)

Natria Nourishing Daily Defense SPF 15

[*Skin*] fills your skin with moisture and essential nutrients, providing immediate hydration in a lightweight formula. During the daytime, SPF 15 shields against harmful UVA and UVB rays, and plankton extract aids in rejuvenating the skin by minimizing the visible signs of sun exposure. A blend of skin's natural barrier components preserves optimal moisture content. Squalene and cocoa butter restore vital moisture as sweet almond and apricot kernel oils impart skin-softening properties. Pure plant extracts condition, while essential vitamins A, B, C and E provide age-defying benefits and antioxidant protection against scavenging free radicals. Leaves your skin moisturized, strengthened and protected.

With fingertips, smooth gently and evenly over face and neck. Apply after using Natria Nourishing Cleansing Lotion, Nourishing Toner and Skin Refining Serum.

Stock No. 6005-2 (75 ml/2.5 fl. oz.)

Natria Nourishing Toner

[*Skin*] sweeps away any impurities left after cleansing and helps balance the skin's pH level as it prepares skin for moisturizing. It contains natural, conditioning humectants to moisturize skin and strengthen its resistance to the environment. Essential vitamins A, B, C and E slough away any remaining impurities and create balanced skin texture for an enhanced look and feel.

After cleansing with Natria Nourishing Cleansing Lotion, moisten a cotton pad and sweep gently over face and neck. Follow with Skin Refining Serum.

Stock No. 6002-3 (150 ml/6 fl. oz.)

Natria Restoring Shampoo

[*Hair*] is a gentle, thorough cleansing shampoo that is ideal for daily use. Plant-derived cleansers combine with pure botanical extracts, including aloe, nettle and chamomile to improve hair's appearance and manageability. A wholesome blend of vitamins, including A, B, C and E, strengthens hair and provides reinforcement against drying environmental elements. Jojoba, peppermint and tea tree oils invigorate and revitalize the scalp and hair. Microscopic spheres filled with an active hair-repair complex bind to hair keratin where they remain attached for hours. This unique hair repair complex lets your hair shine with restored health and beauty.

Apply shampoo to wet hair. Lather and rinse thoroughly. Repeat as desired.

Stock No. 6030-8 (240 ml/8 fl. oz.)

Natria Restructuring Conditioner

[*Hair*] protects and strengthens hair while restoring natural luster and shine. Herbal and botanical extracts provide needed moisture to stressed or overworked hair, helping to repair and prevent damage to hair shafts.

After shampooing, apply

N

*conditioner to wet hair. Leave
on for 2–3 minutes for light
conditioning, longer for deeper
conditioning. Rinse thoroughly.*

Stock No. 6031-9 (240 ml/8 fl. oz.)

Natria Skin Refining Serum

[*Skin*] is a special treatment to refine
your skin and restore its youthful look.
It works within the skin to reduce the
visible signs of aging and restore your
natural radiance. This remarkable,
acid-free skin refiner is infused with
a special renewal complex comprised
of glucosamine HCl, algae extract and
a skin-beneficial yeast extract that
allows cells to regenerate naturally
by removing surface level cells that
are already dead. Skin Refining
Serum improves skin's appearance
immediately and keeps working
over time to help reduce the visible
signs of aging. As new, youthful skin
is revealed, skin takes on a vibrant
appearance.

*Dispense a small amount onto
fingertips. Apply gently and evenly
over face and neck. Allow serum to
absorb completely before applying
moisturizer. Use morning and
evening following your Natria
cleanser and toner.*

Stock No. 6004-5 (30 ml/1 fl. oz.)

Natria Sun Screen SPF 30

[*Skin*] supplies broad-spectrum UVA
and UVB protection. It contains
titanium dioxide, considered one
of the best forms of sun protection
because it works immediately and
acts as a physical barrier. Natria Sun
Screen is fortified with DNA defense
enzymes to protect skin and help
improve the look of visible signs of
sun-aged skin. Plant extracts soothe
and condition, while vitamins A, B,
C and E provide antioxidants to
counteract the free-radicals caused by
sun exposure.

*Adults and children 6 months
of age or older, apply evenly over
face and body before sun or water
exposure. Reapply after swimming,
excessive perspiration or after towel
drying.*

Stock No. 6018-2 (3.4 fl. oz.)

Natria Triple Effect Age Relief Cream [*Skin*]. The skin is constantly
subjected to the intrinsic and external
aging process and eventually begins
to show signs of aging. Triple Effect
Age Relief Cream goes on rapidly
for immediate and long-lasting
results in helping to support youthful-
looking skin. Its powerful triple
action visibly reduces the signs of
aging. Acetyl hexapeptide-3 and
hydrolyzed *Hibiscus esculentus*
decrease the visible depth and
appearance of wrinkles caused by
repeated facial muscle contraction.
Palmitoyl oligopeptide and palmitoyl
tetrapeptide-3 improve firmness and
tone. Saccharomyces/xylinum black
tea helps to maintain skin thickness
and suppleness.

*Apply a moderate amount over
the entire face and neck, including
the area around the eyes and
mouth. Massage gently into the
skin until completely absorbed. For
maximum results, use both morning
and night.*

Stock No. 6013-1 (3) ml/1 fl. oz.)

Nattozimes Plus [*Circulatory*]

is an alternate to nattokinase, a protease compound formed during the soybean fermentation process that offers circulatory benefits. While natto has been consumed in Japan for thousands of years, only recently have scientists realized the health benefits of nattokinase. Because nattokinase is often expensive, unavailable or unstable, NSP designed Nattozimes Plus, which blends protease enzymes with supporting herbs to nourish the circulatory system.

Nattozimes Plus may help improve blood flow as it helps dissolve fibrin. It also supports platelet aggregation levels already within the normal range and helps maintain already-normal blood flow. Nattozimes Plus is a mixture of fungal enzymes (nattozimes), hawthorn berries, capsicum fruit, dandelion leaf and resveratrol. All of these offer health benefits to the circulatory system.

NOTE: Do not use or handle this product if you are taking blood thinning medications, have a bleeding disorder or if you are allergic to Aspergillus.

Take 1 capsule between meals twice daily on an empty stomach. Each capsule contains 165 mg of nattozimes material, providing 2,500 fibrin units (FU).

Stock No. 520-7 (60)

Natural Changes® [*Glandular*].

Around the age of 50, many women experience menopause and its symptoms due to a natural decrease in hormone levels. Natural Changes combines our most popular nutritional supplements for mature women into easy-to-use packets. The finest herbs, essential fatty acids and antioxidant nutrients nourish the body naturally to help cope with these changes. Each packet contains two capsules of C-X (black cohosh root, squaw vine herb, licorice root, blessed thistle herb, eleuthero root, false unicorn root, sarsaparilla root), one Skeletal Strength® (for structural support), one Wild Yam with Chaste Tree, one Flax Seed Oil (provides essential fatty acids) and one Nutri-Calm® (an excellent source of vitamins B and C).

Take the contents of 1 packet in the morning and another packet in the evening.

Stock No. 4055-2 (42 packets)

NatureSeal® Cookware.

NatureSeal five-ply cookware with tight-fitting, self-sealing lids decreases nutrient and flavor loss by cooking foods in their own juices. Too often the nutrients and flavor are boiled right out of food. This five-ply, aluminum core and stainless steel cookware can be used at lower temperatures, which prevents food shrinkage and makes cooking more energy-efficient. Features durable, stainless-steel construction. Available in 12-piece set and open stock pieces. Good health begins with healthy food preparation.

Stock No. 7112-1 12-pc. set
Stock No. 7012-2 12-quart pan with cover
Stock No. 7032-4 Square griddle
Stock No. 7004-7 4-quart pan with cover

Nature's Cleanse (*see Dieter's Cleanse*)

Nature's Chi® TCM Concentrate

[*Glandular, Immune, Circulatory*] is an ephedra-free blend of 15 herbs designed to invigorate, to reduce the body's desire to eat and to boost immunity and blood circulation by improving the flow of internal energy, or chi. Nature's Chi can also support cellular energy levels and energize the body during physical activity without causing nervousness or insomnia.

This combination is a Chinese TCM concentrate blend of:

Astragalus root
Tang-kuei root
Fo-ti root
Eleuthero root
Cinnamon twig
Peony root without bark
Forsythia fruit
Gardenia fruit
Panax ginseng root
Hoelen sclerotium
Mint leaves
Schizonepeta flower
Scute root
Siler root
Licorice root

Take 1–2 capsules twice daily between meals.

Stock No. 836-8 (30)

Nature's Cortisol Formula®

[*Weight Management, Glandular*]. Researchers have begun to notice a connection between cortisol levels and weight-management indicators, such as calorie consumption and weight gain. Cortisol is a hormone produced in the adrenal glands in response to stress. It promotes the formation of glucose, which is used as fuel during stressful situations.

Nature's Cortisol Formula contains Relora® to help the body manage stress and maintain cortisol levels already within the normal range. Other key ingredients—banaba, holy basil, chromium and vanadium—help maintain blood glucose levels already within the normal range. This product also features DHEA, a hormone precursor that interacts with the adrenal glands, and which subsequently may help to lower cortisol production. Nature's Cortisol Formula also features decaffeinated green tea extract (60% EGCG), l-theanine (supports the body during times of stress) and calcium ascorbate.

NOTE: Not for use by individuals under the age of 18 years.

Take 1 capsule with a meal three times daily.

Stock No. 3209-4 (90)

Nature's Fresh (Deodorizer & Stain Remover).

This widely tested deodorizer utilizes a special formulation of enzymes gleaned from plant sources. These enzymes work as deodorizers to break down the molecular structure of stains without harming fabric. Nature's Fresh Enzyme Spray is hypoallergenic, unscented, non-irritating and environmentally safe. It comes in a 16 oz. bottle with spray attachment.

Stock No. 9834-7 (16 fl. oz)

Nature's Hoodia Formula®

[*Weight Management*]. Used for centuries by the San tribesmen of the Kalahari Desert to reduce hunger, *Hoodia gordonii* was first studied by the South African national laboratory in a study of indigenous foods. When researchers fed this succulent plant to animals, the animals began to lose weight. After years of study, scientists now theorize that hoodia appears to affect the brains of laboratory animals by making the stomach feel full and reducing the desire to eat.

Nature's Sunshine has combined *Hoodia gordonii* with other natural ingredients that may help in your weight-management efforts. Nature's Hoodia Formula contains a blend of *Hoodia gordonii*, *Caralluma fimbriata*, dry apple cider vinegar, *Garcinia cambogia*, l-carnitine, gymnema leaves, chromium, marshmallow root and psyllium hulls.

Take 1–2 capsules between meals three times daily.

Stock No. 3009-8 (90)
Stock No. 3019-9
(20 retail sample packets)

Nature's Noni®, capsules

[*Nervous, Structural, Digestive, Intestinal, Respiratory, Immune*]. Ancient manuscripts cite morinda plants as an ingredient in many health preparations. Historically, *Morinda citrifolia* targets the digestive, intestinal, respiratory and immune systems. It is particularly useful in supporting the nervous and structural systems (especially supports healthy joints) and for skin health. This tonic formula offers the benefits of two species of Morinda (*citrifolia* and *officinalis*), dehydrated and encapsulated for your convenience. Nature's Sunshine combines a careful blend of plant parts (citrifolia fruit, root and leaves plus officinalis root) to ensure maximum health benefits.

NOTE: Pregnant or lactating women should consult their health care provider prior to taking this supplement

Take 1–2 capsules with a meal three times daily.

Stock No. 457-6 (100)

Nature's Noni®, Juice

[*Immune, Structural, Nervous, Digestive, Intestinal, Respiratory*] is *Morinda citrifolia* fruit juice. The juice contains unique phytonutrients and antioxidants. Phytonutrients nourish the body's cells, organs and tissues. They also fight free radical damage caused by harmful chemicals, pollution and a host of other free radical-generating processes. Nature's Noni juice is particularly useful for promoting healthy skin, healthy joints and a general feeling of well-being. Years of native use suggest that the many benefits of the morinda fruit come from these phytonutrients, antioxidants and its other physiologically unique ingredients. Nature's Noni contains reconstituted *Morinda citrifolia* fruit juice, natural flavors and no preservatives. The natural blend of flavors gives Nature's Noni juice a pleasant tropical taste.

As a dietary supplement, adults take 2 tablespoons (1 oz.) daily, preferably before meals. Children take 1 tablespoon daily.

Stock No. 4042-7
(two 1-quart bottles)
Stock No. 4066-7 (16 fl. oz.)

N

Nature's Phenyltol® with NEM

[*Structural*] is formulated to support articular health. This reformulation features DL-phenylalanine and natural eggshell membrane (NEM). DL-phenylalanine contains D-phenylalanine and L-phenylalanine. D-phenylalanine is thought to modulate the activity of an enzyme that degrades endorphins. L-phenylalanine is an essential amino acid that is metabolized into l-tyrosine, which in turn is converted to the important mood-supporting neurotransmitters norepinephrine, epinephrine and l-dopamine.

NEM is the soft membrane that separates the eggshell from the fluid egg inside the shell. This membrane contains glucosamine, chondroitin sulfate, hyaluronic acid and collagen. Glucosamine is a building block of cartilage and helps replenish synovial fluid to lubricate the joint and to absorb shock. Chondroitin may also provide building blocks to the cartilage and help replenish hyaluronic acid. Hyaluronic acid supports body tissue, while collagen is important to the cartilage, tendons and skin. Nature's Phenyltol with NEM also contains white willow bark, *Morinda citrifolia* and wood betony.

Take 2 capsules daily with a meal.

Stock No. 1180-3 (60)

Nature's Prenatal®
Multivitamins and Minerals

[*Vital Nutrition*]. Formulated for pregnant and lactating women with 800 mcg of folic acid, Nature's Prenatal provides a balanced combination of vitamins and minerals to support the nutritional needs of both mother and baby. It also contains ginger root to help support the stomach. It's free of artificial colors, flavors, preservatives, sweeteners, sugar, yeast, gluten, lactose, milk and wheat.

Each tablet contains:

	Amount	% DV
Vitamin A (beta-carotene)	5,000 IU	60
Vitamin C (ascorbic acid)	70 mg	120
Vitamin D (fish oil)	400 IU	100
Vitamin E (d-alpha tocopherol from soy)	30 IU	100
Vitamin B1 (thiamine mononitrate)	3 mg	180
Vitamin B2 (riboflavin)	3 mg	150
Niacin (niacinamide)	17 mg	85
Vitamin B6 (pyridoxine hydrochloride)	3 mg	120
Folic acid (folacin)	800 mcg	100
Vitamin B12 (cyanocobalamin)	5 mcg	60
Biotin	30 mcg	10
Pantothenic acid (d-calcium pantothenate)	5 mg	50
Iron (ferrous fumarate)	27 mg	150
Iodine (potassium iodide)	75 mcg	50
Magnesium (oxide)	75 mg	20
Zinc (gluconate)	7 mg	50
Copper (gluconate)	1 mg	50

Other ingredients: di-calcium phosphate, ginger rhizome, cellulose and magnesium stearate.

Take 1 tablet daily with a meal.

Stock No. 4917-8 (180)

Nature's Sea Calcium

[*Structural*] is derived from *Lithothamnium*, a hard, brittle red algae that grows off the southwestern coast of Ireland. In these pure, mineral-rich waters, *Lithothamnium* congregates to form large beds of stone-like algae. The seaweed's mineralized matrices contain high concentrations of naturally occurring, plant-sourced calcium along with up to 70 other minerals, including magnesium, boron, copper and zinc. *Lithothamnium* provides a renewable source as the plant is left undisturbed.

Nature's Sea Calcium naturally promotes bone health and density. And its high buffering capacity makes it ideal for supporting and maintaining normal range pH levels.

Nature's Sea Calcium has a large surface area and a porous structure, which may increase its bioavailability. This formula contains a proprietary blend of short-chain fructo-oligosac-charides, which, when converted to short-chain fatty acids by beneficial flora in the body, have been shown to improve calcium absorption. Available in both powder and capsules.

Take 1 capsule with a meal three to four times daily. Provides 100 mg calcium per capsule. Powder: Mix two level scoops in 8 oz. water or juice, stir and drink. Provides 325 mg calcium per serving.

Stock No.1577-5 (120 capsules) Ko
Stock No. 1576-9 (75 g) Ko

Nature's Spring® Water Treatment

The human body is about 70 percent water, and experts say we should each drink at least 64 fluid ounces of water daily. Our need for an untainted water supply is clear.

Chlorine is added to public water supplies to kill bacteria, and people assume that it is removed, but often it is not. And microorganisms aren't the only potential health hazard in water. Heavy metals such as lead and cadmium can and do get into some public drinking water. In addition, various herbicides, pesticides and farming chemicals have seeped into deep well water over the years. Just a few toxic parts per million can be enough to build up toxic levels in the body over time.

With increasing awareness of problems in many municipal water systems, more people are reaching for alternatives to questionable tap water and expensive bottled water. Nature's Sunshine has the finest option for household or portable use in the Nature's Spring Water Treatment system.

Nature's Spring Reverse Osmosis (RO)

With years of expertise in the production of countertop reverse osmosis water treatment systems, Nature's Sunshine has developed an improved Nature's Spring RO device to meet the growing challenges facing our drinking water. This unit is still designed around a semi-permeable membrane that allows only pure water, oxygen and a small amount of minerals to pass through, while sending everything else down the drain. This technology has been used for decades to purify seawater into drinking water.

When combined with the purifying abilities of activated carbon, reverse osmosis is a proven method for making great-tasting, high-quality drinking water for your family.

The new and improved Nature's Spring is a four-stage system that offers one unit for all city water systems and solid-block activated carbon in the pre- and post-filters. It also has a special timer with indicator lights so you know when to change the filters.

The four stages of the improved Nature's Spring RO unit:

Stage One

Water first enters a 5-micron pre-filter that is 12 inches long. It removes any large sediment or debris that may damage the membrane.

Stage Two

A solid-block, activated carbon filter (inside the sediment pre-filter) removes excess chlorine to protect the PA membrane and assists in removing chloramines.

Stage Three

An efficient Polyamide (PA) reverse osmosis membrane produces purified, highly oxygenated drinking water. Reverse osmosis effectively reduces total dissolved solids, including fluoride, lead and cadmium.

Stage Four

A 12-inch, solid-block, activated carbon filter removes traces of any pollutants while improving the taste.

This improved Nature's Spring RO unit features snap-on use, with a yield of 35 gallons of pure drinking water per day. One unit works on all potable water supplies. It's also easier to service.

Stock No. 1935-3

Treated water must be stored for use. Remember, since chlorine is no longer in the water, it is susceptible to harboring germs from the air. Keep it covered and cool in a glass or polycarbonate container.

RO Accessories

Polycarbonate Water Bottles

Collect and store your reverse osmosis water in one-gallon jug-style bottles with screw-top lids. Fill with RO water then put in the refrigerator for easy cold-water dispensing.

Stock No. 1746-9 (2) one gallon

Rectangular two-gallon containers fit nicely on the top shelf of your refrigerator. Built-in spigot means easy pouring of delicious, cold water. Screw-top lid.

Stock No. 1939-0 (1) two gallon w/spigot

Five-gallon bottle with cap fits any standard water service unit.

Stock No. 1904-7 (1) five gallon

Nature's Sweet Life™ Dark Chocolate Bar [*Vital Nutrition*].

Indulge in delicious chocolate without the calories and oral detriment of sugar. Unlike typical candy bars, these chocolate bars provide nutrients that benefit the body. Each dark chocolate bar is packed with antioxidants and sweetened with all-natural xylitol. Xylitol's unique molecular structure translates to a very limited effect on blood sugar levels, making it the perfect sweetener for those concerned with blood sugar balance, weight loss or carb counting. Xylitol provides just 40% of the calories that sucrose does. It has a great dark chocolate taste with no artificial aftertaste. Xylitol is safe for diabetics, hypoglycemics, children and pregnant women.

The **Cardio** bar benefits the circulatory system and is flavored with natural raspberry for a deliciously tempting treat. It contains dark chocolate, freeze-dried raspberry, omega-3 fatty acids, coenzyme Q10, ascorbic acid (vitamin C), pyridoxine acid (vitamin B6), folic acid, cyanocobalamin (vitamin B12), xylitol and flax seeds.

The **Calcium Crunch** bar provides 35% of the recommended daily value for calcium, and it's fortified with magnesium and phosphorus to help support the needs of the structural system. It contains dark chocolate, crisp rice, tri-calcium phosphate, magnesium oxide, vitamin D3, vitamin C (sodium ascorbate), omega-3 fatty acids, xylitol and flax seeds.

Eat as desired. It may take a few days for the body to become accustomed to digesting xylitol. We recommend that you gradually introduce xylitol into the diet over a period of a few weeks.

Cardio Bar
Stock No. 5450-4 Ko
(28 bars, 1.27 oz. each)
Calcium Crunch Bar
Stock No. 5451-0 Ko
(28 bars, 1.27 oz. each)

Nature's Sweet Life Mouthwash

[*Structural*]. Over 20 years of clinical studies confirm that regular use of xylitol helps improve dental health. When used in the mouth, xylitol helps prevent plaque-forming micro-organisms from adhering to your teeth. Rinsing with xylitol-containing mouthwash regularly helps freshen breath and clean the mouth, neutralizing odors and unpleasant taste. Dentists recommend sugar-free mouthwashes as they do not promote the development of tooth decay.

Nature's Sweet Life Mouthwash contains water, xylitol, vegetable glycerin, peppermint oil, citric acid, PEG-40 hydrogenated castor oil, calcium glycerophosphate, *Aloe barbadensis* leaf juice, sodium benzoate, potassium sorbate and grapefruit seed extract.

Rinse while swishing around in the mouth for at least one minute and then expel. Use after meals, before bedtime or whenever desired.

Stock No. 5425-6 (16 fl. oz.)

N

Nature's Sweet Life™ Xylitol

Bulk [*Structural*] looks and tastes like table sugar, but it's a natural low-calorie, low-carb substitute. Xylitol was discovered over 100 years ago, and has been widely used for many decades. It can be used to sweeten foods and beverages or in cooking and baking (although it is not recommended for use in pastries or hard candy). Xylitol does not promote tooth decay as it helps prevent bacteria from adhering to teeth. It is safe for use by diabetics, children and pregnant women.

CAUTION: This product and other products containing xylitol must not be given to pets.

Use as desired to sweeten foods and beverages.

Stock No. 5435-3 (1 lb. bag) Ko

Nature's Sweet Life Xylitol Gum [*Structural*] freshens breath, cleans teeth and promotes dental health with all of the flavor and none of the harmful effects of sugar-laden gum. Chewing gum after a meal stimulates the production of saliva, which washes the teeth and neutralizes harmful acid produced by bacteria. Regular use of xylitol has been shown to help reduce dental plaque—the first stage of cavity development, tartar formation and tooth staining—and promote better oral health.

Nature's Sweet Life Xylitol Gum contains xylitol, gum base, natural flavor from either spearmint oil, peppermint oil or cinnamon oil, vegetable glycerin, gum arabic, soy lecithin and beeswax.

Chew after or between meals to freshen breath and promote oral health.

Cinnamon Stock No. 5400-8 (100)
Peppermint Stock No. 5408-4 (100)
Spearmint Stock No. 5405-0 (100)

Nature's Sweet Life Xylitol Mints [*Structural*]. We all have bad breath at one time or another, but no one wants it. Xylitol Mints help freshen the mouth and actually help promote oral health. Lactic acid, the most damaging acid for your teeth, is produced by the fermen- tation of sugar by bacteria. However, bacteria can't ferment xylitol, which results in less tooth-destroying acid and promotes an inhospitable environment for unwanted micro- organisms.

Nature's Sweet Life Xylitol Mints contain xylitol, calcium lactate, magnesium stearate, gum arabic, natural berry, lemon or peppermint flavor, glazing agent and beeswax.

Use after or between meals to freshen breath and promote dental health.

Berry Stock No. 5412-2 (240)
Lemon Stock No. 5415-1 (240)
Peppermint Stock No. 5410-7 (240)

Nature's Three [*Intestinal*] includes psyllium, oat fiber and apple fiber to support the normal functions of the bowel. Each 10-calorie serving provides 2 g of dietary fiber—1 g of soluble and 1 g of insoluble fiber. Both are naturally present in food and are important to colon health, but are not present in many foods in today's typical diet. May cause allergic reaction in persons sensitive to inhaled or ingested psyllium.

Mix 1-1/2 teaspoons with 8 oz. water or juice.

Stock No. 1345-0 (12 oz.)

Nebulizing Diffuser (from France) features silent operation and an output control that easily diffuses over a 300–600 square-foot area. Our diffuser ionizes undiluted essential oils into an ultra-fine vapor that remains suspended in the air for maximum availability and minimum waste. In addition, it features a convenient on/off switch, is easy to

clean, and is designed with a glass injector so that oils do not come into contact with any metal parts.

Stock No. 3932-2

Nebulizing Diffuser Maintenance Kit contains two
replacement corks, extra air tube, pipe cleaner, 2 oz. bottle of cleaner, extra clip and screw and instructions.

Stock No. 3930-7
Stock No. 3933-4
(Glass Nebulizer Replacement)

Neroli Pure Essential Oil (see Essential Oils)

Nerve Control [Nervous] is a
blend of valerian, passion flower, catnip, hops and wood betony herbs that have a calming effect on the nervous system and have been used for centuries to nutritionally support people with occasional restlessness, anxiety and stress.

Nerve Control contains:
Black cohosh root
Valerian root
Capsicum fruit
Passion flower herb
Catnip herb
Hops flower
Wood betony herb
Take 2 capsules with a meal twice daily.

Stock No. 1242-4 (100) Ko

Nerve Eight® [Nervous] supports
proper nervous system function. Four of its ingredients help calm nerves and support restful sleep. White willow and Devil's claw may help reduce cellular stress associated with pain. Capsicum and ginger have an overall soothing effect on the digestive system. Hops, valerian and wood betony are calming to the nervous system. Nerve Eight contains:
Capsicum fruit
White willow bark
Hops flowers
Valerian root
Wood betony aerial parts
Ginger rhizome
Devil's claw root
Black cohosh root extract
NOTE: Pregnant or lactating women should consult their health care provider prior to taking this supplement.
Take 2 capsules with a meal three times daily.

Stock No. 873-6 (100) Ko

Nervous Fatigue Formula, Chinese [Circulatory] is an
herbal combination that Traditional Chinese Medicine would consider a fire-enhancing formula. Its Chinese name *yang xin* translates to "nurture the heart." "Weakness" in the fire element usually manifests itself in the digestive, cardiovascular or reproductive system. Nervous Fatigue helps relieve stress and helps support digestion and promote sleep. Its key herbs include zizyphus, biota and schizandra. The formula contains 18 herbs:
Schizandra fruit
Biota seed
Cistanche stem
Cuscuta seed
Dang gui root
Lycium fruit
Ophiopogon root tuber

Succinum amber
Acorus rhizome
Astragalus root
Dioscorea rhizome
Hoelen sclerotium
Lotus seed
Panax ginseng root
Polygala root
Polygonatum rhizome
Ziziphus seed
Rehmannia root tuber
Take 3 capsules with a meal three times daily.

Stock No. 1884-7 (100)

Nervous Fatigue TCM Concentrate, Chinese

[*Circulatory*] contains the same herbs found in Nervous Fatigue formula but in a highly concentrated blend. Traditional Chinese Medicine would consider this a fire-enhancing formula. Its Chinese name *yang xin* translates to "nurture the heart." "Weakness" in the fire element usually manifests itself in the digestive, cardiovascular or reproductive systems. Nervous Fatigue TCM helps relieve stress and helps support digestion and promote sleep. Its key herbs include jujuba, biota and schizandra. The formula contains:

Schizandra fruit
Biota seed
Cistanche stem
Cuscuta seed
Dang gui root
Lycium fruit
Ophiopogon root tuber
Succinum amber
Acorus rhizome
Astragalus root

Dioscorea rhizome
Hoelen sclerotium
Lotus seed
Panax ginseng root
Polygala root
Polygonatum rhizome
Ziziphus seed
Rehmannia root tuber
NOTE: Pregnant or lactating women should consult their health care provider prior to taking this supplement.

Take 2 capsules daily with a meal. Each capsule is equivalent to 4 capsules of regular Chinese Nervous Fatigue.

Stock No. 1017-1 (30)

Nervousness [*Nervous*] is a natural homeopathic medicine for relief of occasional nervousness and irritability caused by simple nervous tension and stress.

Take 10–15 drops under the tongue every 10–15 minutes or as needed until symptoms improve. Then decrease to every one or two hours, then to four times daily until symptoms are relieved. For children under 12, consult your health care professional.

Stock No. 8711-0 (1 fl. oz.)

NF-X [*Glandular*]. This traditional formula supports female reproductive health. NF-X contains the following herbs in a proprietary blend:

Golden seal root
Capsicum fruit
Ginger root
Uva ursi leaves
Cramp bark

Squaw vine herb
Blessed thistle herb
Red raspberry leaves
False unicorn root
Take 2 capsules with a meal three times daily.

Stock No. 1232-3 (100) Ko

Niacin [*Circulatory, Nervous*].

Niacin (vitamin B3) is important to the nervous system. The body's energy system also requires niacin for proper function. Each tablet contains 250 mg of non-flushing niacin (as niacinamide), which is 1,250% of the Daily Value. It is combined in a base of hops flowers and feverfew herb. For best results, take niacin in conjunction with other B vitamins.

Take 1 tablet daily with a meal.

Stock No. 1797-0 (90) Ko

Nopal [*Digestive, Glandular*] is

a cactus plant commonly known as the prickly pear. It contains pectins and mucilage that are beneficial to the digestive system. Nopal is a low-glycemic-index food that is commonly consumed for its nutrient content. Several human studies show possible hypoglycemic effects. Nopal supports digestion and helps maintain blood-sugar levels that are already within the normal range. NSP Nopal combines the benefits of two different plant species into one powerful formula. Each capsule contains 400 mg nopal.

Take 2 capsules with a meal three times daily.

Stock No. 475-3 (100) Ko

Nutri-Burn® [*Weight Management, Vital Nutrition*] is a caffeine-

free, ephedra-free, high-protein, weight-loss meal replacement drink mix. Each serving of this delicious drink mix provides 30 g whey protein fiber (6 g choc., 3 g vanilla), 210 calories, 14 g carbs (8 g of countable carbs), 4 g fat and at least 60% of the Daily Value of 14 vitamins and minerals with 100% of calcium. The ingredients in Nutri-Burn were selected to support the muscles during weight loss and to energize and build the body. Nutri-Burn contains whey protein (neutral pH), *Garcinia cambogia*, L-carnitine, chromium, CLA, lecithin, vegetable fiber, decaffeinated green tea extract (with 60% EGCG), vanadium and essential vitamins and minerals.

Mix 2 rounded scoops of Nutri-Burn powder in 8 ounces of cold water in the NSP Power Shaker.

**Chocolate Fudge Stock No. 3204-5
(1,240 g/20 servings)
Vanilla Stock No. 3208-1
(1,251 g/20 servings)**

Nutri-Calm® [*Nervous*] is a key

product designed to support the nervous system, especially when under stress. During times of stress, the body rapidly loses B vitamins. Nutri-Calm provides generous amounts of these nutrients in a base of herbs known to support optimal nervous system health.

	Amount per Tablet	% DV	Amount per 3 Tablets	% DV
Vitamin C	400 mg	667	1,200 mg	2,000
Vitamin B1 (thiamine)	20 mg	1,333	60 mg	4,000

Vitamin B2 (riboflavin)	20 mg	1,180	60 mg	3,540
Niacinamide	40 mg	200	120 mg	600
Vitamin B6 (pyridoxine)	20 mg	1,000	60 mg	3,000
Folic acid	125 mg	30	375 mcg	90
Vitamin B12 (cyanocobalamin)	33 mcg	570	100 mcg	1,710
Biotin	100 mcg	30	300 mcg	90
Pantothenic Acid	80 mg	800	240 mg	2,400

Other ingredients include schizandra fruit, choline (bitartrate), inositol, bee pollen, Para-amino benzoic acid (PABA), lemon bioflavonoids, valerian root concentrate, passion flowers concentrate and hops flowers concentrate.

Take 1 tablet with a meal three times daily.

Stock No. 1617-3 (100)
Stock No. 4803-3 (60)
Stock No. 2493-9
(20 retail sample packets)

O

Olive Leaf Extract [*Immune, Circulatory*] supports several circulatory needs, including maintaining blood pressure levels already within the normal range and maintaining arteries by providing free radical protection against LDL (bad cholesterol). In addition, olive leaf may possess antimicrobial properties. NSP Olive Leaf Extract is standardized to 12% oleuropein, the key active ingredient.

Take 1–3 capsules daily with meals.
Stock No. 204-7 (60) Ko

Oregano, Wild, Pure Essential Oil (*see Essential Oils*)

Oregon Grape [*Digestive, Circulatory*] has been used historically to support skin health and to address chronic skin conditions. It contains a powerful antimicrobial alkaloid called berberine, which is also found in golden seal root. The liquid herb is suspended in an all-natural glycerin base. Liquid herbs are highly concentrated and easily assimilated.

Take 1/4 to 1/2 teaspoon in water three times daily with a meal.

Stock No. 3395-9
(2 fl. oz.) Liquid Herb Ko

P

Pain [*Structural*] is a natural homeopathic medicine for the relief of minor pain associated with neuralgia, backache and sciatica.

NOTE: Do not take this product for more than five days. If symptoms do not improve after 10 days, consult your health care professional.

Take 10–15 drops under the tongue every 10–15 minutes or as needed until symptoms improve. Then decrease to every one or two hours, then to four times daily until symptoms are relieved. For children under 12, consult your health care professional.

Stock No. 8709-5 (1 fl. oz.)

Pantothenic Acid [*Nervous*], also known as vitamin B5, is manufactured in part by intestinal microorganisms. This water-soluble vitamin is necessary for proper adrenal function, the conversion of fat and sugar into energy, the maintenance of normal growth and tissue replacement, and the development of the central nervous system. It works in tandem with the other B-complex vitamins. Pantothenic acid is needed to make steroid hormones and the neurotransmitter acetylcholine. The body may need increased amounts of this vitamin when under physical stress. For best results, take Pantothenic Acid in conjunction with other B vitamins. Each capsule provides 250 mg of d-calcium pantothenate or 2,500% of the Daily Value.

Take 1 capsule daily with a meal.

Stock No. 1640-2 (100) Ko

Papaya Mint Chewable Tablets

[*Digestive*] nutritionally support the digestive system, but they can also be used as tasty breath mints. Papaya fruit contains an enzyme called papain that can break down protein, while peppermint leaves contain aromatic compounds that trigger the production of digestive fluids. Tablets contain papaya fruit, peppermint leaf, fructose and sorbitol.

Chew 2 tablets with a meal three times daily, or use between meals as a breath freshener.

Stock No. 485-6 (70)

Para-Cleanse [*Intestinal*] is a

10-day program designed to support the efforts of the intestinal system in cleansing. This carefully formulated herbal combination supports a healthy intestinal environment. Each packet contains 6 capsules total, consisting of the following: 1 capsule of Paw Paw Cell-Reg™, 1 capsule of Herbal Pumpkin combination (a blend of pumpkin seeds, black walnut hulls, cascara sagrada bark, chamomile flowers, mullein leaves, marshmallow root and slippery elm bark), 2 capsules of Yeast/Fungal Detox (Echinacea root, caprylic acid, sodium propionate, sorbic acid, pau d'arco, garlic bulb, oregano, selenium and zinc) and 2 capsules of Artemisia Combination (two species of artemisia, wormwood and mugwort, along with elecampane root, clove flower buds, garlic bulb, ginger root, spearmint herb, olive leaf and turmeric root).

NOTE: See your health care provider prior to use if: pregnant or nursing, any medical condition exists or when taking any medication. Read and follow recommendation carefully. Not intended for prolonged use. Do not use if diarrhea, loose stools, or abdominal pain are present or develop. Use of this product may worsen these conditions and be harmful to your health. Chronic diarrhea can result in serious illness.

Take 2 packets each day, one 15 minutes before breakfast and one 15 minutes before dinner. Drink at least 8 oz. of pure water with the capsules. Continue the program for 10 days. Eat lots of fresh fruits and vegetables (especially leafy greens) and whole grains. Avoid red meats, coffee, alcohol, sugar and fried foods. You may wait 10 days and repeat the program as needed.

Stock No. 4081-0 (20 packets)

O
P

Parasites [*Intestinal*] is a natural homeopathic medicine for the relief of minor intestinal symptoms such as bloating, abdominal pain, flatulence and diarrhea.

Take 10–15 drops under the tongue four times daily for at least one month. Then take half the dosage for an additional three months as maintenance. For children under 12, consult your health care professional before using this product. If symptoms persist or change, consult your health care provider.

Stock No. 8735-6 (1 fl. oz.)

Parsley [*Urinary*] is the well-known sprig of green that typically garnishes your dinner plate. Its high chlorophyll content makes it a natural breath freshener, even in buffering the odor of garlic. Herbalists use the leaves to nutritionally support the kidneys and urinary system, but the whole plant can be used for general nutritional needs. Each capsule contains 335 mg parsley leaves.

Take 2 capsules with a meal twice daily.

Stock No. 490-9 (100)

Parthenium [*Immune, Urinary*], also known as Missouri Snake Root, is a perennial herb indigenous to North and South America and the West Indies. In years past, parthenium was often mislabeled as echinacea by herbal suppliers, but the plant's properties are different from those of echinacea. Parthenium has been used traditionally to support the immune system.

Take 2 capsules with a meal twice daily.

Stock No. 265-5 (100) Ko

Passion Flower [*Nervous*] leaves have been used traditionally as a mild calmative. In fact, Algonquin Indians used passion flower tea to help soothe their nerves. Passion flower supports the nervous system in a variety of ways. Many have found that it helps with relaxation of tense muscles. It is widely used to promote a restful night's sleep. Each capsule contains 360 mg passion flower.

Take 1 capsule with a meal twice daily.

Stock No. 500-3 (100) Ko

Patchouli Pure Essential Oil
(*see Essential Oils*)

Pau D'Arco [*Immune*] bark comes from a tree that grows primarily in Argentina and Brazil. The tree is known as taheebo. Unlike other trees in its midst, pau d'arco does not develop fungus growth. It contains a chemical called lapachol, which may account for the herb's traditional use in strengthening and supporting the immune system. Pau d'arco also has been used traditionally to maintain a healthy circulatory system.

Nature's Sunshine's pau d'arco comes from Brazil. It is available in a variety of forms, including capsules, bulk for tea, liquid extract and soothing lotion. Each capsule contains 500 mg pau d'arco.

Take 2 capsules with a meal three times daily. Five capsules are equivalent to two cups of Taheebo tea. Liquid: Take 1/2 teaspoon with water three times daily. Bulk: Add 1 heaping tablespoon to 2 pints boiling water and remove from heat. Steep for 20 minutes and strain. Makes 4 cups. Lotion is for external use only.

Stock No. 504-2 (100) Ko
Stock No. 505-5 (270) Ko
Stock No. 1372-7 (7 oz.) Tea Ko
Stock No. 1774-2 (2 fl. oz.) Liquid Herb Ko
Stock No. 1614-4 (4 fl. oz.) Lotion

Paw Paw Cell-Reg® [*Immune*].

Because health begins in the body's cells, it is important to support the health of all cells. Paw Paw Cell-Reg is a unique product that selectively targets specific cells to enhance the overall health of the body. Over 50 active compounds exist in Paw Paw Cell-Reg, and these complex chemicals are called acetogenins. Acetogenins affect the production of ATP in the mitochondria (the powerhouse) of the cell. ATP is the major source of cellular energy. By selectively modulating the production of ATP in specific cells, the acetogenins affect the viability of specific cells and the growth of blood vessels that nourish them.

A clinical study with over 100 participants showed that the paw paw extract, containing a mixture of acetogenins, supports the body's normal cells during times of cellular stress.

Paw Paw Cell-Reg is the only standardized acetogenin product available. Nature's Sunshine uses an extract of the twigs from the North American paw paw tree, which contains the most concentrated amount of acetogenins. Each capsule contains 12.5 mg of standardized paw paw twig extract.

Co-Q10, Thyroid Support and 7-Keto™ may decrease the effectiveness of this product. Only those with cellular abnormalities should take this product on a regular/daily basis. Do not take this product if you are pregnant, think you may become pregnant, or if you are breastfeeding.

Take 1 capsule with food four times daily. Do not exceed recommended serving size or nausea may occur.

Stock No. 511-3 (120)

PBS [*Digestive, Glandular*] is

designed to nourish the pancreas and help maintain blood sugar levels that are already within the normal range. PBS contains burdock root, nopal leaves, eleuthero root, horseradish root and golden seal root. Golden seal has traditionally been employed to support the liver. Nopal and burdock root support blood sugar levels already within the normal range. Eleuthero acts as a tonic for the body. And horseradish aids digestion.

Take 3 capsules with a meal three times daily.

Stock No. 1054-7 (100) Ko

PDA [*Digestive*] supplements the

body's digestive secretions with hydrochloric acid (HCl). The stomach manufactures hydrochloric acid to break down proteins. But, as people age, they may produce less HCl, which can affect the amount of

P

protein they can break down and ultimately absorb. Inefficient protein digestion can affect the viability of the intestinal flora that feast on these compounds.

Each capsule of PDA provides 325 mg of betaine HCl, supplying diluted hydrochloric acid and 20 mg of pepsin, a natural protein-digesting enzyme.

Take 1–4 capsules with a meal three times daily.

Stock No. 1837-5 (200)

Peppermint Pure Essential Oil
(*see Essential Oils*)

Peppermint Oil [*Digestive*].
This popular flavoring has a variety of uses in herbology. A couple of drops can be added to a glass of water or a cup of hot water for a soothing, refreshing after-meal drink. Peppermint (*Mentha piperita*) has been used to help promote digestion and has cooling and stimulating properties. Many people put a touch of Peppermint Oil on the temples.

While other manufacturers may be tempted to sell oil of cornmint or menthol as peppermint oil, Nature's Sunshine sells only pure, unadulterated peppermint oil. A little goes a long way.

Add 1–2 drops to 8 oz. hot (tea) or cold water for a refreshing after-meal drink.

Stock No. 1706-8 (.17 fl. oz.)

Perfect Eyes® [*Circulatory, Vital Nutrition*].
Our eyes are constantly exposed to sunlight and artificial lighting, which can generate free radicals that have harmful effects on ocular cells. After middle age, our natural antioxidant production decreases, and the pigments in our eyes change.

Perfect Eyes gives your eyes the nutritional support they need to protect against free radical damage. This formula contains lutein, an important antioxidant that may protect against the advancement of age-related macular degeneration. It also contains N-Acetyl-Cysteine (NAC). Aging bodies can easily convert NAC into the eye-protecting antioxidant glutathione, defending the eye from harmful free radicals. These two key ingredients reduce oxidative damage to retinal cells and thus help protect the eye. Perfect Eyes also contains bilberry fruit, curcuminoids powder extract, eyebright herb, alpha and beta carotene, lycopene, zeaxanthin, cryptoxanthin, zinc gluconate, selenium, taurine, quercetin and hesperidin. Two capsules provide 6 mg lutein.

Take 2 capsules daily with a meal.

Stock No. 4075-0 (60) Ko

pH GreenZone® [*Vital Nutrition, Immune*]
contains healthful ingredients to provide the body with balanced nutrition and energy-rich nutrients. It includes asparagus powder, broccoli powder and kale powder for their alkalizing properties. This unique formula helps maintain balanced pH and provides a powerhouse of nutrition. It facilitates energy-yielding metabolism while promoting waste elimination and immune health.

Contains spirulina algae, amaranth seed, natural lemon juice, lecithin, chlorella, sprouted kamut whole leaf 5:1 extract, alfalfa juice concentrate, sprouted barley grass aerial parts, apple pectin, acerola cherry fruit extract, bee pollen, lemongrass aerial parts, brown rice, spinach leaves and stems, astragalus root, *Echinacea purpurea* root, milk thistle fruit, asparagus stem, broccoli flowers, kale whole leaf, ginger rhizome, flaxseed, beet extract, orange bioflavonoid, royal jelly, bladderwrack whole plant, elderberry 5:1 extract, hawthorn berries, red grape skin extract, eleuthero root, *Ginkgo biloba* leaf concentrate 24%, licorice root, polyphenol catechins (from green tea extract), rhodenol root and sodium copper chlorophyllin.

Mix 1–3 teaspoons of pH GreenZone powder into 16–32 oz. of pure water or juice two to three times daily.

Stock No. 1091-5 (131.3 g/15 servings)

Phyto-Soy® [*Glandular, Circulatory*]. Soy is in great demand because of its healthful benefits for the immune, glandular and circulatory systems. Soy is a source of isoflavonoids, including genistein, which helps protect the body.

Phyto-Soy contains 48 times more isoflavonoids than comparable amounts of tofu, 25 times more than tempeh, and 10 times more than roasted soybeans. NSP Phyto-Soy is certified as non-genetically modified (non-GMO). Three capsules supply 36 mg isoflavones, 28 mg of which are genistein glycosides.

Take 1 capsule with a meal

three times daily.

Stock No. 4981-5 (90) Ko

Pink Grapefruit BIO Essential Oil (*see Essential Oils*)

PLS II [*Intestinal*] provides nutrients to support proper intestinal function. It contains slippery elm bark, marshmallow root, golden seal root and rhizome and fenugreek seed. Slippery elm, marshmallow and fenugreek have soothing properties. Golden seal helps soothe the mucous membranes that line the digestive tract. It also has immune-supporting properties.

Take 2 capsules with a meal three times daily.

Stock No. 1029-4 (100) Ko

PMS [*Glandular*] is a natural homeopathic medicine for the relief of symptoms associated with PMS, including nervous irritability, bloating, cravings, discomfort and hot flashes.

NOTE: Do not take this product for more than five days. If symptoms do not improve after 10 days, consult your health care professional. Not recommended for girls under the age of 12.

Take 10–15 drops under the tongue every two hours until symptoms improve or as needed. Then decrease to every four hours until symptoms are relieved.

Stock No. 8738-5 (1 fl. oz.)

Potassium Combination
[*Digestive*]. Adequate potassium levels are essential for the body's active transport pump, which moves

P

nutrients into cells. This herbal formula nutritionally supports the body's enzyme system and is a source of trace minerals compatible with potassium utilization. Each capsule contains 40 mg of elemental potassium from dipotassium phosphate in a base of:

Kelp stems and leaves
Dulse fronds
Alfalfa aerial parts
Horseradish root
White cabbage leaf
Horsetail stems and strobilus

Take 2 capsules with a meal three times daily.

Stock No. 1673-3 (100) Ko

Pregnenolone [*Glandular, Nervous*] is a hormone that can be converted into other hormones produced by the glands. Nature's Sunshine's pregnenolone is derived from the highest quality wild yam root. This natural form has an impressive record for safety and effectiveness.

CAUTION: Not for use by persons under the age of 40, persons with severe benign hypertrophy hormone-responsive cancer, or anyone with a medical condition or taking prescription medication. Pregnant or nursing women should consult a health care professional before using this product.

Take 1–2 capsules daily with a meal.

Stock No. 1824-4 (60)

Prevention [*Immune*]. This natural homeopathic medicine relieves and prevents symptoms associated with minor infections, including inflammation, secondary infections, colds and influenza.

NOTE: If symptoms persist or change, contact your health care professional. As with any drug, if you are pregnant or nursing, seek the advice of a health care professional before using this product. Keep this and all medicines out of the reach of children.

Take 10–15 drops under the tongue 1–3 times daily as a preventive health measure, or with other remedies for colds, influenza and minor infections and illness.
For children under 12, consult your health care professional.

Stock No. 8827-9 (1 fl. oz.)

Proactazyme® Plus [*Digestive*]. Digestive enzymes may be in short supply in some people, and supplementing with them allows the body to get maximum nutrition from the diet and supports efficient digestion. Proactazyme Plus contains amylase, glucoamylase, lipase, cellulase, invertase, malt diastase, alpha galactosidase and peptidase to digest all types of food. It also contains a blend of protease formulated to digest proteins at various pH levels ranging from 3.0 to 6.0. This formula helps break down sugars, vegetable fibers, long-chain starches and proteins and contains only plant-sourced enzymes.

Take 1–2 capsules with or between meals daily.

Stock No. 1525-0 (100)

Probiotic Eleven® [*Intestinal, Digestive, Immune*] represents a unique combination of healthful probiotics to help maintain and replenish intestinal supply. These microorganisms perform essential functions in the body and are affected by aging, adverse intestinal pH, microbial interactions, environmental and dietary temperatures, stress, physiological factors, peristalsis, bile acids, host secretions and immune responses.

Probiotic Eleven provides 11 species of live microorganisms that exert many beneficial health effects. Among other things, they support digestion, promote immunity and aid in the elimination of toxins. Probiotics also help regulate intestinal functions and can greatly support colon function. This specially formulated blend contains strains of important gut-beneficial organisms and prebiotics (non-digestible foodstuffs, including fiber) that serve as food for the probiotics in the colon. Clinical studies have shown that short- and long-chain fructo-oligosaccharides (FOS) may improve growth of friendly microorganisms, enhance mineral absorption, support bowel health and function, and promote immune function.

Ingredients include deleted strains of *Bifidobacterium bifidum*, *B. infantis*, *B. longum*, *Lactobacillus bulgaricus*, *L. brevis*, *L. plantarum*, *L. rhamnosus*, *L. salivarius*, *Streptococcus thermophilus*, *L. acidophilus*, *L. casei* and inulin. This product is recommended for individuals who regularly experience occasional constipation or other minor concerns or discomforts of the gastrointestinal tract. It is also recommended after colon cleansing.

Take 1–2 capsules daily with a meal.

Stock No. 1510-1 (90)

Pro-G-Yam® Cream [*Glandular*]

is a fragrance-free body cream containing natural progesterone. Each ounce contains 5 mg progesterone in a unique herbal base designed for maximum skin absorption and efficacy—wild yam, chamomile, ginkgo, horsetail and yucca. Also available in concentrated 500 mg/oz. formula.

To use, simply apply 1/4 teaspoon of cream gently into soft skin regions, such as the inside upper arm, inner thigh or abdomen once or twice daily. Rotate application to a different area of the body each day. Use no more than one tube per month. For external use only.

Stock No. 4927-2 (2 oz.)

Pro-G-Yam® Cream 500 with 500 mg progesterone per ounce.

Stock No. 4936-5 (2 oz.)

Pro-Pancreas Formula

[*Glandular*] contains 13 herbs that provide nutrients that support healthy function of the pancreas. It contains:

Juniper berries cones
Slippery elm bark
Licorice root
Garlic bulb
Yarrow aerial parts
Capsicum fruit
Golden seal root extract
Uva ursi leaf extract
Dandelion root
Marshmallow root
Nettle leaves
Mullein leaf extract

P

White oak stem inner bark
Take 2 capsules with a meal three times daily.
Stock No. 1027-9 (100) Ko

Protease Plus [*Digestive, Immune*]

provides supplemental protease enzymes that break down proteins into smaller proteins and amino acids, maximizing digestion.

As we grow older, our bodies produce fewer enzymes. When a suboptimal level of protease enzyme exists, undigested proteins can pass through the intestinal tract and remain undigested. These have been linked to effects on overall health and vitality.

Protease Plus may support immunity by possibly activating macrophages and natural killer cells. NSP's formula provides a full spectrum of plant-derived trace minerals, which help activate enzymes. Each capsule of NSP Protease Plus contains 60,000 HUT protease in a base of beet root fiber and plant-sourced trace mineral concentrate.

Take 1–3 capsules between meals.
Stock No. 1841-7 (90)

Protease, High-Potency

[*Immune*] delivers 180,000 HUT's protease with a full spectrum of plant-derived trace minerals. Enjoy the same benefits of three Protease Plus capsules in one capsule of High-Potency Protease.

Take 1 to 3 capsules between meals up to three times daily.
Stock No. 1876-1 (60)

PS II® [*Glandular*] provides nutrition for the male glandular system. Complementary products include vitamin A, C, zinc, bee pollen and saw palmetto. This formula provides herbs that supply varying amounts of macro and trace minerals. It contains:

Pumpkin seed
Saw palmetto
Licorice root
Black cohosh root
Gotu kola aerial parts
Capsicum fruit
Golden seal root and rhizome
Ginger rhizome
Dong quai root
Lobelia aerial parts
Kelp leaves and stem
Take 1 capsule with a meal three times daily.
Stock No. 1050-8 (100) Ko

Psyllium Hulls [*Intestinal*].

Psyllium is also referred to as plantago. It has one of the highest levels of soluble fiber known—much more than that of oat bran. Encapsulated psyllium hulls are a convenient way to add essential fiber to the daily diet. Psyllium hulls can play an important part in helping the body maintain cholesterol levels that are already within the normal range and may help to support cardiovascular health. Each capsule contains 465 mg psyllium hulls.

NOTE: May cause allergic reaction in persons sensitive to inhaled or ingested psyllium.

Take 2 capsules with at least 8 oz. water with a meal twice daily.
Stock No. 545-9 (100) Ko

Psyllium Hulls Combination

[*Intestinal*] provides bulk to the diet. The hulls absorb several times their weight in liquid. Psyllium has high amounts of soluble fiber that has a mucilaginous quality. NSP Psyllium Hulls Combination contains psyllium hulls, hibiscus flower and licorice root in bulk rather than encapsulated form. Psyllium hulls can play an important part in helping the body maintain cholesterol levels that are already within the normal range and may help to support cardiovascular health.

NOTE: May cause allergic reaction in persons sensitive to inhaled or ingested psyllium.

For adults: Mix 2 teaspoons in a glass of water or juice.

For children 6 years and over: Mix 1/4 teaspoon in 1/2 glass of water or juice at bedtime.

Stock No. 1375-6 (13 oz.) Ko

Psyllium Seeds

[*Intestinal*] are small and dull-colored, covered with a thin, white hull. They contain 10–30% mucilage. When placed in water, their outer walls swell to form a layer of mucilage around the seed. This mucilage may serve as a lubricant and help to cleanse the areas through which it passes. The seeds have been used in Europe for intestinal health since the 16th century, but they weren't accepted in the U.S. until the early 1900s. As an all-natural vegetable substance, psyllium's purely mechanical action to promote colon health and provide pure bulk fiber in the diet is exceptional. Nature's Sunshine offers the seeds in encapsulated form. Each capsule contains 600 mg psyllium seeds.

NOTE: May cause allergic reaction in persons sensitive to inhaled or ingested psyllium.

Take 2 capsules with a meal twice daily.

Stock No. 540-4 (100) Ko

P-X®

[*Urinary, Glandular*]. This traditional formula was designed to nutritionally support the urinary system. It contains:

Juniper berries
Golden seal root
Capsicum fruit
Parsley herb
Ginger root
Eleuthero root
Uva ursi leaves
Queen of the meadow leaves
Marshmallow root

Take 2 capsules with a meal three times daily with at least 8 oz. water.

Stock No. 1234-5 (100) Ko

R

Recovery

[*Structural*] helps keep the body hydrated and replaces certain nutrients that are used or perspired away during higher levels of activity. This drink nourishes the body both during and after activity. It helps replenish liquids and lost electrolytes, and helps to balance acid levels in the muscles during exercise. Recovery also helps replenish electrolytes lost due to other conditions and is recommended for young children, adults and seniors.

Recovery contains fructose, citric acid, potassium citrate, natural orange flavor, tricalcium phosphate, maltodextrin, rice syrup solids, xanthan gum, magnesium oxide, potassium chloride, sodium chloride, inositol, vitamin A, vitamin C, niacin, glycine, l-taurine, vitamin B6, riboflavin, thiamine hydrochloride, folic acid, biotin and cyanocobalamin. Each 15 g serving also contains chromium (50 mcg), chloride (50 mg), l-carnitine (2.5 mg) and inositol (50 mg).

Add 1 level scoop (15 g) of drink mix powder to 8 oz. cold water and stir. Drink during or after activity or increased physical exertion.

Stock No. 3662-2 (14 oz.)

Red Beet Root Formula [*Vital Nutrition*] is designed to replenish

nutrients the body might need while fasting or during periods of weakness. The glands may require additional nutrients as the body uses energy stores. This combination contains:

Licorice root
Red beet root
Fennel seeds
Hawthorn berries
Take 2 capsules five times daily.

Stock No. 870-0 (100) Ko

Red Clover [*Circulatory*] is a

purple-flowered plant that dots fields across America. It contains isoflavones, including genistein (also found in soy). Isoflavones are phytoestrogens that may help support cardiovascular health. Red clover may also promote skin health. The blossoms and leaves provide trace amounts of some minerals and vitamins. Each capsule contains 320 mg red clover flower tops.

Adults: Take 2 capsules with a meal three times daily. Children: Take 1 capsule with a meal three times daily.

Stock No. 550-9 (100) Ko
4 Kids Too!

Red Clover Blend [*Circulatory*]

contains estrogen-like compounds known as isoflavones that may help support the cardiovascular system and may be beneficial for the female glandular system. The formula contains red clover blossoms, burdock root, pau d'arco bark and sage leaves. Place several drops in hot water for a pleasant-tasting tea. Or, take it directly under the tongue or in juice.

Take 1 teaspoonful with a meal three times daily.

Stock No. 3420-9 (2 fl. oz.) Ko
Liquid Herb, 4 Kids Too!

Red Raspberry [*Glandular*]. The

leaves of this popular fruit plant are widely used in herbology for their vitamin and tannin content. Red raspberry possesses astringent qualities, and the leaves have been used by women for centuries as a support to the reproductive system. Many find that the astringent compounds in red raspberry leaves also help support the digestive system. Each capsule contains 360 mg red raspberry leaves.

Take 2 capsules with a meal three times daily.

Liquid: Adults: Take 1/2 to 3/4 teaspoon in water with a meal three times daily. For tea, use 1/2 teaspoon in hot water. Children: Take 1/4 to 1/2 teaspoon in water three times daily with a meal.

Stock No. 560-8 (100) Ko

Stock No. 3425-4 (2 fl. oz.)

Red Yeast Rice [*Circulatory*] supports the body's ability to maintain cholesterol levels already within the normal range, and it offers nutritional support to the circulatory system. Those using red rice products should supplement with coenzyme Q10 (Co-Q10), because red yeast rice can interfere with the normal production of this important liver metabolite. Each capsule contains 600 mg of Red Yeast Rice (*Monoascus purpureus*).

WARNING: Do not use this product if you are pregnant, may become pregnant, or are breast feeding because using this product may cause birth defects. Consult your health care provider before using if you are currently taking any cholesterol-lowering agents. Cholesterol levels should be checked regularly. For adults 20 years of age or older. People with or at risk for liver disease should not use this product. Keep out of the reach of children.

Take 2 capsules with a meal two to three times daily.

Stock No. 558-3 (120) Ko

RG-Max™ [*Circulatory*] amino acid drink mix is designed to help support heart function and blood vessel flexibility. RG-Max contains 10 different amino acids, which are used by the body to help repair and build muscles, including the heart muscle. Improved circulation can help support increased energy and stamina levels and may help support male sexual function.

Red grape extract in RG-Max also provides powerful antioxidant benefits, which also protects the circulatory system. All-natural xylitol makes RG-Max taste great without the harmful effects of sugar on the teeth and circulatory system.

RG Max contains xylitol, l-arginine, citric acid, natural strawberry flavor, natural lemon juice, malic acid, silicon dioxide, red grape skin extract, taurine, l-isoleucine, l-leucine, l-methionine, l-tyrosine, l-threonine, N-acetyl-l-cysteine, l-glutamine and acetyl-l-carnitine.

Adults: Mix one level scoop in 8 oz. water, shake well and drink. One serving provides 5 g l-arginine.

Stock No. 586-3 (573.3 g)

Roman Chamomile Essential Oil (*see Essential Oils*)

Rose Bulgaria Essential Oil (*see Essential Oils*)

Rose Hips [*Vital Nutrition*] come from the rose plant—they are what remains after the petals fall off. Historically they have been used as a source of vitamin C and contain other vitamins. Each capsule contains 560 mg rose hips.

Take 2 capsules with a meal three times daily.

Stock No. 580-1 (100) Ko

Rosemary Pure Essential Oil (*see Essential Oils*)

R

Safflowers [*Intestinal*]. Safflowers have been used traditionally to help support liver and gallbladder function and may help in the normal removal of toxins from the body. They also provide nutritional aid for the intestinal system. Each capsule contains 420 mg safflowers.

Take 1 capsule with a meal twice daily.

Stock No. 600-2 (100) Ko

Sage [*Immune*]—the garden variety, not the desert variety—is grown extensively in its native Mediterranean region. Sage is highly astringent and aromatic. Extracts of sage have antioxidant properties; they act as a preservative, which probably explains sage's wide use as a meat seasoning for centuries. Its aromatic properties help sage create an environment that is friendly to microbial balance. Each capsule contains 330 mg sage.

Take 1 capsule with a meal twice daily.

Stock No. 610-1 (100) Ko

St. John's Wort [*Nervous*] is an important herb for the nervous system. Wort comes from an Old English word meaning "plant" or "root." This plant is named for St. John, the Baptist. It has long been popular for supporting the nervous system. St. John's wort contains hypericin, a natural compound that has been shown to help support the nervous system by helping to promote positive mental attitude and mood. NSP combines St. John's wort with passion flower, an herb with a long history of nervous system support. Each capsule contains 300 mg St. John's wort standardized to 0.3% hypericin.

CAUTION: While taking this product, avoid exposure to strong sunshine and tanning rays or tanning salons. It is advisable to wear sunglasses when being exposed to strong sunlight conditions. Consult your health care provider before using this product if you are taking prescription antide-pressive drugs, including selective serotonin uptake inhibitors, as well as any MAO inhibitors.

Take 1 capsule with a meal three times daily.

Stock No. 655-3 (100) Ko

St. John's Wort, Time-Release

[*Nervous*] is known for its benefits to the nervous system. It supports emotional balance and a feeling of well-being. St. John's wort helps maintain a positive outlook and healthy motivation.

Time-Release St. John's Wort contains the finest raw St. John's wort herb, standardized to contain 0.3% hypericin in a base of 450 mg St. John's wort extract powder. St. John's wort contains many physiologically active constituents. Hypericin appears to support positive mood. Another constituent, hyperforin, may have powerful mood-enhancing properties.

CAUTION: While taking this product, avoid exposure to strong sunshine and tanning rays or tanning salons. It is advisable to wear sunglasses when being exposed to strong sunlight conditions. Consult your health care provider before using this product if you are taking prescription antidepressive drugs, including selective serotonin uptake inhibitors, as well as any MAO inhibitors.

Take 1 tablet in the morning and 1 in the evening for all-day, all-night support.

Stock No. 653-1 (60)

SAM-e [*Nervous*] (S-Adenosyl-methionine tosylate) helps the body with mood, emotional well-being, energy, liver health, joint health and mobility. It is a natural compound found in every living cell, and it is involved in important biochemical reactions throughout the body, especially in the manufacture of neurotransmitters in the brain and maintenance of cartilage. SAM-e has been popular in Europe for 20 years. Each tablet contains 200 mg SAM-e (from S-adenosyl-methionine).

CAUTION: If you are taking prescription antidepressants or have bipolar (manic) depression, consult your physician before or during the use of this product. Pregnant or lactating women should consult their health care provider prior to taking this supplement.

Take 1 tablet once or twice daily on an empty stomach with 8 oz. water. For best results, take SAM-e with folic acid and Vitamin B12.

Stock No. 1845-2 (30)

Sandalwood Pure Essential Oil
(*see Essential Oils*)

Sarsaparilla [*Glandular*]. The deep roots of this plant are brewed as a tasty spring tonic, resembling the flavor of root beer. Sarsaparilla is traditionally used to support the circulatory system and the liver. It also has tonic properties and has been used traditionally for skin support. It may also promote normal digestion and appetite. Each capsule contains 375 mg sarsaparilla root.

Take 2 capsules with a meal twice daily.

Stock No. 620-8 (100) Ko

Saw Palmetto [*Glandular*] is used primarily to support glandular tissues (especially the prostate gland) and to maintain optimal balance in hormone levels. Scientific research validates its use for supporting prostate health. Each capsule contains 550 mg saw palmetto fruit.

Take 2 capsules with a meal three times daily.

Stock No. 630-4 (100) Ko

Saw Palmetto Concentrate
[*Glandular*], known scientifically as *Serenoa repens*, is well-known for the support its berries offer to the prostate gland. Two softgel capsules daily provide 320 mg of this standardized concentrate, the amount suggested in recent clinical studies to maintain men's hormonal balance. Each softgel capsule provides a minimum of 85 percent fatty acids and phytosterols, including beta-sitosterol. These fatty acids are the most sought-after components in saw palmetto.

Take 1 capsule with a meal twice daily.

Stock No. 635-9 (60)

S

SC Formula (shark cartilage) [*Immune*]. Shark cartilage is a pure source of an important family of carbohydrates called mucopolysaccharides. Typical assays report that more than 20 percent of its weight is mucopolysaccharides, over 20 percent is protein, more than 4 percent is chondroitin sulfate and less than 1 percent is fat. Shark cartilage also contains vital amino acids plus other important nutrients.

SC Formula is composed of 100 percent freeze-dried shark cartilage combined with reishi mushroom (also known as ganoderma). Reishi mushroom has a long history of use in China and is found in nearly 30 percent of Chinese herbal formulas. No chemical agents, solvents or bleaches are used in processing this product. Various sharks are used, none of which is an endangered species. The cartilage used by NSP is a byproduct of sharks caught for human consumption.

Take 3 capsules with a meal three times daily.

Stock No. 1602-8 (100)

Sciatica [*Structural*] is a natural homeopathic medicine for the relief of lower back pain due to sciatica or overexertion.

Take 10–15 drops under the tongue every 10–15 minutes, or as needed. As symptoms improve, decrease to every one or two hours, then to four times daily until symptoms are relieved. Not recommended for children under 12. If symptoms persist or change, contact your health care provider.

Stock No. 8820-6 (1 fl. oz.)

Sea Salt Shaker. This all-natural salt is void of fillers and other additives that are commonly used in everyday white table salt. Sea salt is mined from pure salt deposits of an ancient sea that covered most of North America thousands and thousands of years ago. Try this salt and you'll taste the difference!

Sprinkle on foods as desired for taste.

Stock No. 150-6 (2–7.5 oz.)

Seasonal Defense [*Immune*]. Seasonal changes can be quite stressful to the body. That's why it is important to support your immune system. Seasonal Defense combines andrographis with other immune-supporting herbs, including *Citrus aurantium* (6% synephrine extract), thyme, oregano and eleuthero root.

Andrographis has been used for centuries by many cultures. It is used widely in Ayurvedic medicine. Andrographis supports the immune system by promoting both specific and non-specific immune-response functions. Synephrine may help maintain the mucous membrane of the respiratory tract. Thyme, oregano and eleuthero root also have beneficial properties for the immune and respiratory systems.

Take 1 capsule with a meal three times daily.

Stock No. 806-6 (90) Ko

Senna Combination [*Intestinal*] supports the intestinal system and liver. Senna encourages intestinal contraction and supports proper waste elimination. It contains:

  Senna leaves
  Fennel seed
  Ginger rhizome
  Catnip leaves

NOTE: This product contains senna. See your health care provider prior to use if you are pregnant or nursing, any medical condition exists or when taking any medication. Read and follow recommendation carefully. Do not use if diarrhea, loose stools or abdominal pain are present or develop. Use of this product may worsen these conditions and be harmful to your health. Chronic diarrhea can result in serious illness.

Take 4 capsules before bedtime. To be taken only occasionally.

Stock No. 650-5 (100) Ko

7-Keto™ [Weight Management, Immune]

is a safe, natural metabolite of dehydroepiandrosterone (DHEA). Supplementing with 7-Keto may increase the production of T3, a thyroid hormone. The thyroid hormones play a role in determining the body's basal metabolic rate.

7-Keto also supports the body's immune system efforts by enhancing the function of white blood cells. It can also help the body's efforts to maintain overall health.

It is important to note that, unlike other metabolites of DHEA, 7-Keto is not converted to sex hormones (either androgens or estrogens).

Each capsule of NSP 7-Keto contains 75 mg 7-Keto in a base of chickweed herb (*Stellaria media*).

CAUTION: Those with hyperthyroidism should consult their health care professional prior to use of 7-Keto capsules.

7-Keto is a trademark of Humanetics Corp., patent no. 5,296,481.

Take 1 capsule daily with a meal.

Stock No. 2922-4 (30)

SF® [Weight Loss]

is designed to help with weight loss as it supports the body's intestinal, urinary and digestive systems. SF contains:

  Cascara sagrada bark
  Hawthorn berries
  Papaya fruit
  Licorice root
  Safflower flowers
  Black walnut hulls
  Chickweed leaf extract
  Fennel seeds
  Parthenium root
  Gotu kola aerial parts
  Dandelion root

NOTE: This product contains cascara sagrada. See your health care provider prior to use if: pregnant or nursing, any medical condition exists, or when taking any medication. Read and follow recommendation carefully. Do not use if diarrhea, loose stools, or abdominal pain are present or develop. Not intended for prolonged use. Use of this product may worsen these conditions and be harmful to your health. Chronic diarrhea can result in serious illness.

Take 2 capsules 30 minutes before meals three times daily.

Stock No. 1067-5 (100) Ko

Silver Shield with Aqua Sol Technology [Immune]

provides 18 ppm of silver that stays suspended

S

in purified, deionized water. Silver products have become popular alternatives to other products on the market, and you can trust NSP to provide the highest-quality, safest products available. Just 1 teaspoonful provides a full 90 mcg of pure silver without heavy metal contamination. This product compares with herbal products like Golden Seal and VS-C®. It can also be used as an EPA-approved surface disinfectant.

Take 1 teaspoonful with a meal three times daily. NSP Silver Shield is gentle enough for application to the eyes, ears and nasal passages.

Silver Shield Gel with Aqua Sol Technology [*Immune*]

provides 24 ppm of silver in a clear gel that moisturizes. Silver Shield Gel is made with food-grade ingredients, contains no alcohol, and is safe for children. This product is manufactured with a patented process called Aqua Sol Technology. Silver Shield Gel is completely non-toxic, safe and effective without the risk of heavy metal contamination.

Apply a small amount of gel to skin as needed.

Sinus [*Respiratory*] is a natural

homeopathic medicine for the relief of stuffy nose, runny nose and headache due to common sinusitis.

Take 10–15 drops under the tongue every 10–15 minutes or as needed until symptoms improve. Then decrease to hourly, then to

four times daily until symptoms are relieved. For children under 12, consult your health care professional.

Sinus Support EF® [*Respiratory*].

This ephedra-free formula supplies nutrients that may support nasal passages and proper respiratory function. It contains burdock root, immature orange peel (synephrine), capsicum fruit, golden seal root, parsley herb, horehound herb, althea root and yerba santa herb.

Take 2 capsules with a meal three times daily.

Skeletal Strength® [*Structural*]

is the key product formulated to provide nutrients necessary for proper structural system function. Skeletal Strength provides materials that the body uses to manufacture bones, muscles, ligaments, tendons and skin.

	Amount per 2 Tablets	% DV	Amount per 4 Tablets	% DV
Vitamin A (beta-carotene, contains soy)	250 IU	5	500 IU	10
Vitamin C	75 mg	125	150 mg	250
Vitamin D	100 IU	25	200 IU	50
Vitamin B6 (pyridoxine HCl)	2.5 mg	125	5 mg	250
Vitamin B12 (cyanocobalamin)	15 mcg	250	30 mcg	500
Calcium	300 mg	30	600 mg	60
Iron (ferrous gluconate)	1.5 mg	8.5	3 mg	17
Phosphorus	47 mg	5	94 mg	10
Magnesium	300 mg	75	600 mg	150
Zinc	7.5 mg	50	15 mg	100
Copper	1 mg	50	2 mg	100
Manganese	0.5 mg	25	1 mg	50

Potassium	50 mg	*	100 mg	*
Boron	0.5 mg	*	1 mg	*

*Daily Value not established

All of these are contained in a base of:

Horsetail herb
Betaine HCl
Papaya fruit
Parsley herb
Pineapple fruit
Valerian root
Licorice root

Take 2 tablets with a meal twice daily.

Stock No. 1806-7 (150)

Slippery Elm [*Digestive, Intestinal*]

is also known by the names Red Elm, Moose Elm and Indian Elm. It may help to relieve occasional digestive discomfort and provides mucilage, which may soothe the throat and digestive tract. Mucilage is an easily digestible long chain of sugars (polysaccharides) that make a slippery substance when combined with water. Historically, early American settlers used slippery elm as a survival food; George Washington and his troops survived for several days on slippery elm gruel during the bitter winter at Valley Forge. It may also be used externally as a poultice for the skin. Each capsule contains 360 mg slippery elm bark.

Take 2 capsules with a meal twice daily. Bulk: Mix 1 or 2 heaping teaspoon(s) in 8 oz. of pure water or juice.

Stock No. 670-7 (100) Ko
Stock No. 1391-2 (7 oz., 200 g) Ko
25 servings per container

Small Intestine Detox [*Digestive*]

supports the digestive system. Marshmallow has a high mucilage content, which may help to soothe digestive tract tissues. Pepsin is produced naturally in the body to help digest protein.

Take 2 capsules with a meal three times daily. For best results, use with Bowel Detox.

Stock No. 848-2 (100)

SnorEase® [*Respiratory*]

helps reduce the tendency to snore. Its unique formulation features three key ingredients: immature bitter orange, bromelain and Co-Q10. These components work together to promote air flow through the nasal passages. Immature bitter orange contains natural synephrine. Bromelain, an enzyme derived from pineapple, may help to break down mucus, which can help to facilitate respiration. Co-Q10, an antioxidant, helps support the circulatory system.

Take 1–3 capsules daily 30 minutes before bedtime. Do not use during pregnancy.

Stock No. 1815-4 (60)

SOD with Gliadin [*Structural, Immune, Nervous*].

SOD (superoxide dismutase) is an enzyme that also functions as an antioxidant. Every cell in the body uses SOD to combat damaging free radicals produced by normal cellular reactions. As we age, our bodies produce less SOD, which may contribute to the natural aging process. Gliadin protects SOD from digestion until it reaches the intestinal

S

tract, where it can be absorbed. SOD with Gliadin may benefit joint structure and function; the respiratory and cardiovascular systems; and cellular activity. Two capsules provide 300 mg SOD.

Take 1 capsule twice daily on an empty stomach.

Stock No. 1893-8 (60)

Sore Throat/Laryngitis

[*Immune*] is a natural homeopathic medicine for the relief of sore throats, hoarseness and laryngitis.

CAUTION: If sore throat pain is severe, persists for more than two days, or is accompanied or followed by fever, headache, rash, nausea or vomiting, consult your health care professional.

Take 10–15 drops under the tongue every 10–15 minutes or as needed until symptoms improve. Then decrease to every one or two hours, then to four times daily until symptoms are relieved. For children under 12, consult your health care professional.

Stock No. 8795-0 (1 fl. oz.)

Spirulina [*Nervous*] is a blue-green algae that grows in warm, alkaline fresh waters around the world. Spirulina naturally contains protein representing all eight essential amino acids, as well as chelated minerals, natural plant sugars, trace minerals and enzymes. Spirulina is easily assimilated by the body. It also provides naturally occurring chlorophyll. Spirulina can be used as a pre-meal supplement. It is one of the few plant sources of vitamin B12. Each capsule contains 400 mg of 100 percent blue-green microalgae.

Take 2 capsules with a meal three times daily.

Stock No. 681-1 (100) Ko

Spleen Activator, Chinese

[*Digestive*] is a Chinese combination of 17 herbs that, according to Traditional Chinese Medicine, may nutritionally act as a digestive system tonic and provide energy to a tired body. The Chinese call this formula *wen zhong*, which can be translated to mean "warm the center." According to TCM, this formula is designed to strengthen a "weak" earth element, nourish spleen function and support the pancreas. It may help provide relief from occasional nighttime leg cramps. Its primary herbs—ginseng, licorice and atractylodes—may help to provide energy and strengthen the digestive system. It contains:

Panax ginseng root
Astragalus root
Atractylodes rhizome
Hoelen sclerotium
Dioscorea rhizome
Lotus seed
Chaenomeles fruit
Citrus peel
Galangal rhizome
Ginger rhizome
Hyacinth bean
Licorice root
Magnolia bark
Tang-kuei root
Typhonium rhizome
Cardamon fruit
Zanthoxylum hull of seed

Take 3 capsules with a meal three times daily.

Stock No. 1880-8 (100)

Spleen Activator TCM Concentrate, Chinese [*Digestive*] contains the same herbs found in Chinese Spleen Activator but in a highly concentrated blend. This combination of 17 Chinese herbs, according to Traditional Chinese Medicine, may nutritionally act as a digestive system tonic and provide energy to a tired body. The Chinese call this formula *wen zhong*, which can be translated to mean "warm the center." According to TCM, this formula is designed to strengthen a "weak" earth element, nourish spleen function and support the pancreas. It may help provide relief from occasional nighttime leg cramps. Its primary herbs—ginseng, licorice and atractylodes—may help to provide energy and strengthen the digestive system. It contains:

> *Panax ginseng* root
> Astragalus root
> Atractylodes rhizome
> Hoelen sclerotium
> Dioscorea rhizome
> Lotus seed
> Chaenomeles fruit
> Citrus peel
> Galangal rhizome
> Ginger rhizome
> Hyacinth bean
> Licorice root
> Magnolia bark
> Tang-kuei root
> Typhonium rhizome
> Cardamon fruit
> Zanthoxylum hull of seed

NOTE: Pregnant or lactating women should consult their health care provider prior to taking this supplement.

Take 1 or 2 capsules with a meal daily. Each capsule is equivalent to 6 capsules of regular Chinese Spleen Activator.

Stock No. 1070-5 (30)

Sprains & Pulls [*Structural*] is a natural homeopathic medicine for the relief of pain, stiffness and inflammation caused by muscle or tendon strains, tennis elbow and overexertion during sports activities or workouts.

Take 10–15 drops under the tongue every one to two hours following overexertion or appearance of symptoms. Then decrease to three or four times daily until symptoms disappear. For children under 12, contact your health care professional. If symptoms persist, see your health care provider.

Stock No. 8970-7 (1 fl. oz.)

Stevia Powder Extract. NSP Stevia Powder Extract is made from an unusually sweet herb called stevia (*Stevia rebaudiana*) Glycosides present in the plant, such as stevioside and rebaudioside, give the plant its unique characteristics.

Fill scoop to line (approximately 1/4 teaspoon) and use as desired as a dietary supplement. Also available in convenient .7 gram packets. Each box contains 50 two-serving packets of stevia powder extract. These small packets slip easily into your wallet or purse, ready for use anytime, anywhere. Approximately two 1/4 teaspoon servings per packet.

Stock No. 1386-7 (1.26 oz.) Ko
Stock No. 1381-6
(50 2-serving packets) Ko

S

137

Stomach Comfort [*Digestive*]. This formula provides natural ingredients to help nutritionally support digestion in times of occasional stomach upset. It contains calcium carbonate, alginic acid (from kelp), wintergreen oil, papaya fruit, slippery elm bark, licorice root concentrate and ginger rhizome, all of which may help to protect the mucous lining of the esophagus, aid and promote digestion, and soothe the digestive tract. Stomach Comfort may help normal body processes in soothing occasional acid indigestion, heartburn or gas.

Chew 1 or 2 tablets up to three times daily for quick, temporary stomach relief. Chew 1–2 tablets between meals for pH balancing. Remember that digestive problems may be a sign of more serious health concerns.

Stock No. 1820-0 (60)
**Stock No. 2489-1
(20 retail packets)**

Stress-J [*Nervous*]. This anti-stress formula provides nutrients to help facilitate proper function of the nervous system. The formula contains one of the most favored herbs of Europe, chamomile, which is known for its calming effects. This combination is designed for occasional stress relief.

Complementary products include B-complex vitamins, bee pollen and vitamin C. It contains:
Passion flower aerial parts
Fennel seeds
Feverfew aerial parts
Hops flowers

Chamomile flowers extract
Marshmallow root extract
Available in capsule and liquid glycerin form.

Take 2–3 capsules with a meal three times daily. Liquid: Take 15–30 drops in water every four hours. Children: Take 10–20 drops in water every four hours. One ml is approximately equal to 2 capsules.

Stock No. 1084-1 (100) Ko
Stock No. 3163-3 (2 fl. oz.) Ko
4 Kids Too!

Stress Pack [*Nervous*]. When exposed to physical stress, the body uses more of certain nutrients like the B vitamins and vitamin C. That's why Stress Pack contains Nutri-Calm®, a supplement rich in both of these nutrients. Stress Pack combines herbs and vitamins to nourish the body under physical stress.

Each packet contains:

Stress-J (2 capsules): Contains passion flowers, fennel seeds, feverfew herb, hops flowers, chamomile flowers and marshmallow root.

SUMA Combination (2 capsules): Contains echinacea aerial parts, suma bark, astragalus root, eleuthero root, ginkgo leaves and gotu kola root and rhizome.

Nutri-Calm (1 tablet): Contains vitamin C, B1, B2, B6, B12, folic acid, biotin, niacinamide and pantothenic acid in a base of schizandra fruit, choline bitartrate, PABA, wheat germ, bee pollen, valerian root, passion flower, inositol, hops flowers and citrus bioflavonoids.

Hops Concentrate (1 capsule): Standardized to 5% alpha bitter acid.

Each capsule contains hops flowers concentrate.

Take the contents of 1 packet with a meal; use 1–3 packets per day based on individual need.

Stock No. 3022-1 (30 packets)

Stress Relief, Chinese [*Nervous*]

is a combination of 14 herbs and natural substances used in Traditional Chinese Medicine to support emotional balance and calm a stressed fire constitution. The Chinese call this formula *an shen*, which can be translated to mean "to pacify the spirit." These herbs may help to nourish the nervous system and subsequently help improve gastric function and strengthen the urinary system. Its primary nutrients—polygonatum, oyster shell, haliotis shell and fushen—may help support both mental function and the cardiovascular system. Stress Relief contains:

Oyster shell
Albizzia bark
Polygonatum rhizome
Haliotis shell
Fushen sclerotium with root
Acorus rhizome
Curcuma root tuber
Panax ginseng root
Jujuba seed
Polygala root
Coptis rhizome
Cinnamon twig
Ginger rhizome
Licorice root

This formula is commonly used in conjunction with vitamin B-complex, vitamin C, passion flower herb, chamomile flowers and hops flowers.

Take 4 capsules with a meal twice daily. For best results, use with Suma Combination.

Stock No. 1863-5 (100)

Stress Relief TCM Concentrate, Chinese [*Nervous*]

contains the same herbs found in Chinese Stress Relief but in a highly concentrated blend. This combination of 14 herbs and natural substances is used in Traditional Chinese Medicine to support emotional balance and calm a stressed fire constitution. The Chinese call this formula *an shen*, which can be translated to mean "to pacify the spirit." These herbs may help to nourish the nervous system and subsequently help improve gastric function and strengthen the urinary system. Its primary nutrients—polygonatum, oyster shell, haliotis shell and fushen—may help support both mental function and the cardiovascular system. Stress Relief TCM contains:

Oyster shell
Albizzia bark
Polygonatum rhizome
Haliotis shell
Fushen sclerotium with root
Acorus rhizome
Curcuma root tuber
Panax ginseng root
Jujuba seed
Polygala root
Coptis rhizome
Cinnamon twig
Ginger rhizome
Licorice root

NOTE: Pregnant or lactating women should consult their health care provider prior to taking this

S

supplement.

Take 1 capsule with a meal daily. For best results, use with Suma Combination. Each capsule is equivalent to 7 capsules of regular Chinese Stress Relief.

Stock No. 1033-5 (30)

SugarReg® [*Glandular*] is a formulation of eight nutrients that support proper glandular function. Specifically, this combination helps support the body's effort to maintain blood sugar levels that are already within the normal range. Many of the herbs in this formula (banaba, gymnema, nopal and bitter melon) have a history of successful use in supporting the glandular system. Newly added cinnamon extract has, according to studies, a positive effect on blood glucose levels. Chromium, a trace mineral, plays a role in maintaining blood sugar levels already within the normal range. SugarReg contains:

   Chromium
   Vanadium
   Cinnamon bark extract
   Fenugreek seeds
   Bitter melon fruit
   Gymnema leaves extract
   Nopal leaves
   Banaba leaf (standardized to
     18% corosolic acid)

Take 1 capsule with a meal three times daily.

Stock No. 927-1 (60)

SUMA Combination [*Immune*] supplies nutrients that support the body's regenerative functions. It is a blend of six powerful adaptogenic herbs that bolster the immune system and provide energy and emotional support. Suma root is referred to as *para todo* in South America, meaning "for everything." Suma is not a true ginseng, but it shares many of ginseng's properties. Astragalus root is a Chinese herb that also shares many properties of ginseng and is known as an energy-booster. Suma Combination contains:

   Echinacea aerial parts
   Suma bark
   Astragalus root
   Eleuthero root
   Ginkgo leaves
   Gotu kola root and rhizome
   NOTE: Pregnant or lactating women should consult their health care professional prior to taking this supplement.

Take 2–3 capsules with a meal three times daily.

Stock No. 1088-5 (100) Ko

Sunshine Brite Toothpaste

[*Structural*] features hydrated silica powder, calcium carbonate and sodium bicarbonate to help remove stains and polish teeth without damaging tooth enamel. Sunshine Brite also contains soothing aloe vera gel, golden seal, myrrh, Icelandic moss, astragalus, green tea and elderberry for natural oral health care. Sunshine Brite is naturally flavored with real mint. It contains no fluoride, which can be dangerous to children. Enjoy its fresh Mint Tingle sensation as you brush.

Brush teeth at least twice daily after meals. See your dentist regularly. For maximum gum health, let toothpaste foam remain in mouth for one minute before rinsing.

Stock No. 2851-6 (3.5 oz.)

Sunshine Concentrate.

This all-purpose, concentrated cleaner is tough on dirt, grease and grime, yet it won't harm the environment or your family because it contains no phosphates, borates or acids. Its biodegradable cleaning and sudsing agents break down easily, helping to prevent foaming in lakes and streams.
USES:

Kitchen—clean appliances, sinks, refrigerators, counters, wood surfaces, walls, floors, dishes (even finc china), pots and pans, silverware, copper and brass. Works in automatic dishwashers. Cleans ovens, grills, griddles, thermoses and plastic containers. Works as a fruit/vegetable wash.

Laundry—pre-spot stains, spots, grimy collars and cuffs. Pre-soak diapers. Hand-wash silks, fine woolens, sweaters and other delicate fabrics in cool or cold water.

Outdoors—clean tools, air filters, battery terminals, grease on concrete driveways, interior/exterior of cars/boats. Safe for lawns, gardens and farming. Excellent insect repellant. Great for shampooing the dog.

Indoors—clean windows, mirrors, shower, chrome, aquarium, rugs, tile, wallpaper, carpet, furniture, no-wax floors. Prevents mineral buildup in irons and humidifiers. Repels dust. Works as a shampoo and hand soap. Cleans shoes, handbags, eyeglasses, leather goods and more. Safe on house plants.

Bath—safe for bubble bath. Leaves no bathtub ring! Most soaps have a pH of 8 or higher. Sunshine Concentrate has a pH of 6.5, which is easier on your skin.

Safe for people, animals, plants and our environment. Biodegradable, non-polluting, chemical-free. Non-flammable. Save money. One bottle equals 200 gallons of window cleaner or 64 gallons of your average household cleaner.

Stock No. 1551-6 (32 fl. oz.) Ko
Stock No. 2601-5 Decanter pump

Super Algae

[*Vital Nutrition, Immune*] packs all the benefits of the three most popular algae supplements on the market today. Algae is a super-food, rich in easily assimilable nutrients. Spirulina is often added to food for its nutritional value. Chlorella is a freshwater green algae noted for its chlorophyll content. Klamath Lake in Oregon is a pristine source of Klamath Lake blue-green algae. Super Algae maximizes protein, amino acid, chlorophyll and carotenoid content of each algae species, providing a balanced, nutritional formula. Super Algae also supports the immune system.

Take 2–4 capsules with a meal three times daily.

Stock No. 1056-5 (100)

Super Antioxidant

[*Vital Nutrition*] is an exclusive formulation of several powerful antioxidants that help neutralize damaging free radicals inside the body and maintain

S

the structure and integrity of cellular makeup. This formula combines tocotrienols (scavenge free radicals within circulating lipoproteins), lycopene (a carotenoid antioxidant) and alpha lipoic acid (is both fat- and water-soluble to provide antioxidant protection throughout the body) in a base of rose hips fruit (a natural source of vitamin C, carotenoids and flavonoids), milk thistle seed (protects liver from toxins) and turmeric root (protects liver tissue).

Take 1 capsule with a meal twice daily.

Stock No. 1825-8 (60)

Super GLA Oil Blend

[*Glandular*] provides generous amounts of essential Omega-6 fatty acids (both linoleic and gamma-linolenic acid) from evening primrose, black currant and borage oils. In the body, these can be converted into eicosanoids. Three important eicosanoids are prostaglandins, thromboxanes and leukotrienes. This group of hormone-like compounds regulates many important bodily functions and processes. These compounds may affect circulatory system health, skin and joint health, immunity and nerve function.

Super GLA provides nutritional support to the female reproductive system, particularly before menstruation when normal conditions of mild mood changes, breast tenderness, cramps and swelling can occur.

Each capsule contains 130 mg of gamma-linolenic acid from evening primrose, black currant and borage oils.

Take 1 capsule with a meal three times daily.

Stock No. 1844-5 (90)

Super Omega-3 EPA

[*Circulatory*]. Omega-3 fatty acids are one of four basic fats that the body derives from foods. While many of the other fats are harmful, omega-3s benefit the body and are especially good for the heart. Super Omega-3 EPA is a source of two fatty acids, EPA and DHA. Supportive but not conclusive research shows that the consumption of EPA and DHA omega-3 fatty acids may reduce the risk of coronary heart disease. The body uses omega-3 fatty acids as one of the primary components of cell membranes. Omega-3s are also beneficial to the structural system and to the skin. Super Omega-3 EPA softgels contain approximately 1,000 mg fish oil, with a ratio of 33:16 EPA to DHA (380 mg EPA, 190 mg DHA) per softgel. It also contains lemon to significantly reduce the aftertaste from fish oil and to reduce gas.

Take 1 softgel with a meal three times daily.

Stock No. 1515-7 (60)

Super Supplemental Vitamins & Minerals [*Vital Nutrition*]

augments any diet. Balanced nutrients are often in short supply during periods of physical stress or convalescence, or in a diet consisting of mostly processed foods. Supplementing your diet with Super Supplemental can help fill the void. Each four tablets contain:

	Amount	% DV
Vitamin A*	16,000 IU	320
Vitamin C	500 mg	830
(ascorbic acid)		
Vitamin D	600 IU	150
Vitamin E	100 IU	330
(d-alpha tocopherol from soy)		
Vitamin Bl	25 mg	1,670
(thiamine)		
Vitamin B2	20 mg	1,180
(riboflavin)		
Niacin	60 mg	300
(niacinamide)		
Vitamin B6	30 mg	1,500
(pyridoxine)		
Folic acid	400 mcg	100
Vitamin B12	100 mcg	1,670
(cyanocobalamin)		
Biotin	300 mcg	100
Pantothenic acid	150 mg	1,500
Calcium	400 mg	40
(di-calcium phosphate, citrate, amino acid chelate, bone meal)		
Iron (gluconate)	30 mg	170
Phosphorus	200 mg	20
Iodine	200 mcg	130
(potassium iodide)		
Magnesium	400 mg	100
Zinc (gluconate)	30 mg	200
Selenium	100 mcg	140
(amino acid chelate)		
Copper	2 mg	100
(gluconate)		
Manganese	3 mg	150
Chromium	100 mcg	80
(amino acid chelate)		
Potassium	100 mg	*
(citrate)		
Inositol	50 mg	*
p-Aminobenzoic Acid (PABA)	25 mg	*
Choline (bitartrate)	50 mg	*
Lycopene	1 mg	*

*Daily Value not established

* Beta-carotene, palmitate. 8,000 IU from beta-carotene, 8,000 IU from palmitate; contains soy.

Other ingredients: cellulose, stearic acid, magnesium stearate, lutein, silicon dioxide, alfalfa herb, asparagus stem, barley grass juice, broccoli powder, cabbage powder, hesperidin, lemon bioflavonoids, rutin, rose hips concentrate and kelp plant.

Take 4 tablets with a meal. These can be taken all at once with a meal, or one at a time with each meal and at bedtime.

Stock No. 1792-7 (120)
Stock No. 1809-0 (120) without iron
Stock No. 2488-3
(20 retail sample packets)

Super Trio [*Vital Nutrition*] provides powerful, effective levels of three potent Nature's Sunshine formulas. Taken together, these proprietary blends offer a nutritious combination of essential fatty acids, vitamins, minerals and antioxidants— each an important component of daily nutrition, vitality and longevity. Every packet contains 1 each of the following:

• Super ORAC capsule. The antioxidants contained in Super ORAC help neutralize oxidation and the destructive effects of free radicals. ORAC, short for oxygen radical absorbance capacity, is used to determine the antioxidant value of foods or supplements. Two capsules provide 150 mg polyphenols in a proprietary blend of green tea leaves extract, mangosteen pericarp extract, turmeric root extract, quercetin, resveratrol, apple extract, açai berry extract and selenium.

• Super Omega-3 EPA softgel. Consumption of omega-3 fatty acids like eicosapentaenoic acid (EPA) and docosahexaenoic acid

S

(DHA)—found in fish oil—may help reduce the risk of coronary heart disease. Each Super Omega-3 EPA softgel contains approximately 1,000 mg fish oil with a ratio of approximately 2:1 EPA to DHA, plus natural lemon oil to drastically reduce the aftertaste of fish oil.

• Super Supplemental Vitamin and Minerals (without Iron) tablet. Super Supplemental provides 100% of the recommended daily value of 10 essential nutrients plus helpful amounts of 10 more, and two carotenoid antioxidants: lutein and lycopene. This formulation boasts extra amounts of B-vitamins (depleted by physical stress) for energy.

Take the contents of 2 packets daily with meals. This represents a 30-day program.

Stock No. 20-5 (30 day)

SynerProTein® [*Vital Nutrition*]
is a low-fat, balanced protein supplement providing essential amino acids, vitamins and minerals, and a great vanilla flavor. This improved formulation contains more protein and no longer contains canola oil.

SynerProTein is a blend of soy protein isolates from non-genetically modified (non-GMO) soybeans. SynerProTein also contains the exclusive SynerPro Concentrate, which provides a rich and wholesome base of fruits and cruciferous vegetables with antioxidant benefits.

Just 25 grams of soy protein a day, as part of a diet low in saturated fat and cholesterol, may reduce the risk of heart disease. One serving of SynerProTein supplies 20 grams of soy protein.

Mix 1 level scoop of SynerProTein with 8 oz. water, juice or skim milk.

Stock No. 2920-5 (12 oz.) Ko

T

Target Endurance Formula
[*Vital Nutrition, Structural*] is a caffeine-free nutritional supplement to support the physiological needs of the body during strenuous activity. Organic target minerals are chelated to specific amino acids, aiding absorption by the body. In this formula, copper and zinc are chelated to the amino acids arginine, leucine and glycine, which play roles in energy production. Copper and zinc are balanced for optimal use in the body. Zinc is stored in rather large amounts in the bones and muscles. It appears to be easily utilized and is important for many enzyme functions.

The target minerals have been combined with a unique blend of bee pollen, eleuthero root, gotu kola herb, capsicum fruit, licorice root, glutamine and choline bitartrate.

	Amount per 2 Capsules	% DV	Amount per 4 Capsules	% DV
Vitamin C	30 mg	50	60 mg	100
Niacin	8 mg	40	16 mg	80
Vitamin B6	6 mg	300	12 mg	600
Folic acid	50 mcg	12.5	100 mcg	25
Vitamin B12	10 mcg	170	20 mcg	340
Pantothenic acid	8 mg	80	16 mg	160
Calcium	25 mg	2.5	50 mg	5
Phosphorus	11 mg	1	22 mg	2
Iodine	21 mcg	15	42 mcg	30
Zinc	1.45 mg	10	2.9 mg	20
Copper	0.6 mg	30	1.2 mg	60

Potassium   25 mg   *   50 mg   *
* Daily Value not established
*Take 1–2 capsules with a meal
three times daily.*

Stock No. 2809-8 (90)

Target P-14 Formula [*Digestive*]

combines nutrients to support proper pancreatic function. Target minerals (chromium and zinc) are chelated to specific amino acids (glutamine, leucine and lysine) and are readily absorbed. Chromium is part of the glucose tolerance factor (GTF), which helps maintain blood glucose levels already within the normal range. It works with the body's natural production of insulin in the pancreas. Zinc is a companion mineral involved in maintaining blood sugar levels already within the normal range. It also supports the function of B vitamins.

These two minerals are combined within a unique blend of 14 herbs:

Golden seal root
Juniper berries
Uva ursi leaves
Rose hips
Mullein leaves
Garlic bulb
Yarrow flowers
Slippery elm bark
Capsicum fruit
Dandelion root
Marshmallow root
Nettle leaves
White oak bark
Licorice root

Each capsule provides:

	Amount	% DV
Chromium	80 mcg	70
Zinc	15 mg	100

Take 1 capsule with a meal three times daily.

Stock No. 2810-1 (90)

Target TS II Formula [*Glandular*]

is designed to help meet the nutritional needs of the glandular system—the pituitary, thyroid and hypothalamus glands in particular. Target minerals zinc and manganese are chelated to the amino acids glutamine, proline and histidine to aid absorption. Cell growth and repair are highly dependent on zinc, which is also key to enzyme reactions. The herbs in this formula also provide trace amounts of minerals that support proper thyroid function.

Each capsule provides:

	Amount	% DV
Manganese	5 mg	250
Zinc	15 mg	100

These minerals are combined with a unique blend of hops flowers, parsley herb, capsicum fruit, Irish moss plant and kelp plant.

Take 2 capsules before breakfast and 1 before lunch daily.

Stock No. 2815-7 (90)

Tea Tree Oil [*Skin*]

has been referred to as "the wonder from Down Under." It comes from the melaleuca tree, which is native to Australia and has long been used by the Aborigines. Legend has it the tree was first introduced to Europeans by Captain Cook, who made tea from the leaves while on a voyage to Australia. The oil is extracted from the tree's leaves through a special distillation process. The trees do not need to be harvested in order for their oil to be extracted; in fact, some trees have provided oil for over 60 years. Tea tree's beneficial properties make it a popular ingredient in

T

shampoos, creams, skin cleansers and other external cosmetic applications. The compounds in tea tree oil benefit the skin and are non-irritating.
The oil contains several important compounds, including terpines, cymones, pinines, terpinen-4-ol, sesqui-terpenes and sesquiterpene alcohols.

Tea tree oil is recommended for external use only in poultices and other skin-cleansing applications.

Stock No. 1777-1 (0.5 fl. oz.)

Teething, Herbasaurs®
(see Herbasaurs, Teething)

Tei Fu® Essential Oils *[Nervous]*
was developed and perfected by a Chinese herbalist several decades ago. He created it using an ancient formula that was passed down in his family for more than 1,000 years. His secret formula was not for sale—a trait typical of older-generation Chinese. This descendant realized the benefits of his family secret and decided it was too good to keep from others. Thus Nature's Sunshine became the beneficiary of thousands of years of Chinese wisdom and herbal knowledge. Tei Fu Oils contain safflower oil, wintergreen oil, menthol, camphor, clove, eucalyptus and lavender essential oils.

Tei Fu oils can be used for a wide variety of applications, especially where the refreshing, invigorating properties of essential oils are desired. Avoid contact with eyes, nose and other sensitive areas.

Apply 1–4 drops to desired area and rub in as an aid in conditioning skin.

Stock No. 1618-7 (.17 fl. oz.)

Tei Fu® Massage Lotion
[Structural] provides all of the benefits of Tei Fu Essential Oils but in a creamy lotion form. It's especially designed for broad skin application. It also leaves the skin smooth and supple. Contains essential oils of menthol, wintergreen, camphor, eucalyptus and clove. Now packaged in a tube for easy application and improved stability.

Apply to painful muscles and joints and massage into the skin. Avoid contact with eyes and nose. For external use only.

Stock No. 3538-5 (4 fl. oz.)

Thai-Go® *[Vital Nutrition, Immune]* is a blend of the most healthful fruits and nutritional supplements from all over the world. Thai-Go is replete with xanthones, bioflavonoids and powerful antioxidants. Bioflavonoids contribute to the bright colors of fruits and vegetables. In the body, bioflavonoids enhance vitamin C absorption and help maintain collagen and capillary walls. They also aid in the body's immune–defense system.

Antioxidants scavenge the free radicals that the body accumulates as a byproduct of energy production as well as through pollution, tobacco smoke, ultraviolet light and radiation. Antioxidants benefit virtually every organ and body system because they mop up damaging free radicals. Thai-Go delivers a punch of anti-oxidant potential with a very high ORAC value.

Brunswick Laboratories, the

leading commercial laboratory specializing in the science of antioxidants and oxidative stress, recently studied Thai-Go on a batch basis to certify its exceptional product quality. The Brunswick Lab's ORAC certification seal verifies that every bottle of Thai-Go delivers unparalleled antioxidant protection.

Among Thai-Go's key ingredients is mangosteen, a tasty fruit found in eastern tropical nations, such as Thailand. Mangosteen contains the greatest known supply of compounds called xanthones. Xanthones offer powerful immune and cardiovascular support. Other ingredients in this nutritious juice include wolfberry/gogi fruit, sea buckthorn, red grapes, grape seeds, grape skins, raspberries, blueberries, apple extract and green tea.

Take 1 ounce (2 tablespoons) twice daily.

Stock No. 4095-1 (2, 25 fl. oz. ea.)

THIM-J [*Immune*] supports the immune system and may aid thymus gland function and response. This formula contains antioxidants to neutralize dangerous free radicals and provides herbal sources of many trace minerals. It contains:

   Rose hips
   Beta-carotene (2,000 IU)
   Broccoli powder
   Cabbage powder
   Eleuthero root
   Parsley herb
   Red clover flowers
   Wheat grass powder
   Horseradish root
   Take 2 capsules with a meal three times daily.

Stock No. 1089-8 (100) Ko

Thyme Linalol BIO Pure Essential Oil (*see Essential Oils*)

Thyroid Activator® [*Glandular*] contains herbs to support the thyroid gland. It also contains trace minerals that may be lacking in the diet. Thyroid Activator contains:

   Irish moss plant
   Kelp plant
   Black walnut hulls
   Parsley herb
   Watercress herb
   Sarsaparilla root
   Take 2 capsules with a meal three times daily.

Stock No. 1224-0 (100)

Thyroid Support [*Glandular*] is a blend of nutritional and herbal supplements specially designed to nourish the thyroid gland and to support the actions of the thyroid hormones. The thyroid hormones regulate many body functions, including oxygen use, basal metabolic rate, cellular metabolism, growth and development, and body temperature.   Each capsule contains l-tyrosine, kelp, zinc, copper citrate, pyridoxal-5-phosphate, protease, stinging nettle, manganese, and thyroid and brain (anterior pituitary and hypothalamus) glandular substances from certified BSE-free cows from New Zealand.

   Take 1 capsule with a meal twice daily.

Stock No. 1228-6 (60)

T

Tiao He Cleanse®, Chinese

[*Intestinal*] is a 15-day nutritional program designed to help the body achieve *tiao he*—balance and harmony. It combines Chinese nutritional and Western herbal experience. The Tiao He Cleanse is designed to support the cleansing mechanisms of the body by targeting the intestinal and digestive systems. Each packet contains 1 capsule each of Chinese Liver Balance TCM Concentrate (digestive support), All Cell Detox, LBS II® (intestinal support), Psyllium Hulls (bulking agent), Burdock Root (intestinal system) and Black Walnut Hulls (digestive system).

NOTE: This product contains cascara sagrada, buckthorn, Turkey rhubarb and ginseng. See your health care provider prior to use if: pregnant or nursing, any medical condition exists or when taking any medication. Read and follow recommendation carefully. Do not use if diarrhea, loose stools or abdominal pain are present or develop. Not intended for prolonged use. Use of this product may worsen these conditions and be harmful to your health. Chronic diarrhea can result in serious illness. May cause allergic reaction in persons sensitive to inhaled or ingested psyllium.

Take the contents of 1 packet 15 minutes before meals up to two times daily (for 15 days) with 8 oz. water, followed by another 8 oz. water. This should produce two or three bowel movements daily. If stools become too loose, reduce the number of packets you
use. Continue the program until you have used all 30 packets. Not recommended for children.

Stock No. 4092-2 (30 packets)

Tobacco Detox

[*Nervous*] is a natural homeopathic medicine for relief of symptoms related to withdrawal from tobacco use, including nausea, cough and nervous tension. It aids detoxification.

NOTE: Not recommended for children under 12.

Take 10–15 drops under the tongue every one or two hours or as needed, then take four times daily until symptoms are relieved. Tablets: Dissolve 1 tablet in the mouth every 1–2 hours or as needed until symptoms improve. Then take four times daily until symptoms are relieved.

Stock No. 8712-5 (1 fl. oz.)
Stock No. 8721-6 (60 tablets)

Tofu Moo

[*Vital Nutrition*] drink mix comes from tofu, a soybean product that originated in the Orient. Soybeans are known for their many health benefits. Tofu Moo (powdered tofu) tastes similar to milk but contains no lactose—good news for the estimated 70 percent of the world's population that is lactose-intolerant.

Tofu Moo is low-fat, cholesterol-free and low in sodium. One 8-ounce serving contains 50% of the Daily Value for calcium. Tofu Moo also contains phosphorus and potassium. In addition, Tofu Moo Carob contains vitamins A and D. Tofu Moo is a healthful addition to the daily diet. It can be mixed with water for a tasty drink, substituted for milk or added to recipes. Carob Tofu Moo contains no hydrogenated oils.

NOTE: Not to be used as an infant formula.

For single serving: Add 1 scoop of powder to 6 oz. of hot or cold water. Stir briskly until dissolved, then add enough water to make 8 ounces.

Stock No. 1703-0 (22.5 oz.) Natural

Stock No. 3207-9 (25.9 oz.) Carob

Trace Mineral Maintenance

[*Vital Nutrition*] contains 70 plant-derived trace minerals that are chelated by nature for better absorption. The body uses even tiny amounts of various minerals, some of which were previously thought to be insignificant to the body. Minerals activate enzymes, which power thousands of necessary reactions in the body. The form the mineral takes is also important. For example, trace amounts of aluminum are commonly found in foods, but it is harmless in the natural form when eaten in moderation. Elemental aluminum can be toxic.

Trace Mineral Maintenance contains varying amounts of the following minerals: aluminum, antimony, barium, beryllium, bismuth, boron, bromine, cadmium, calcium, cerium, cesium, chlorine, chromium, cobalt, copper, dysprosium, erbium, europium, fluorine, gadolinium, gallium, germanium, gold, hafnium, holmium, indium, iodine, iridium, iron, lanthanum, lithium, lutetium, magnesium, manganese, molybdenum, neodymium, nickel, niobium, osmium, palladium, phosphorus, platinum, potassium, praseodymium, rhenium, rhodium, rubidium, ruthenium, samarium, scandium, selenium, silicon, silver, sodium, sulfur, tantalum, tellurium, terbium, thallium, thorium, thulium, tin, titanium, tungsten, uranium, vanadium, ytterbium, yttrium, zinc and zirconium. Six tablets contain 1,800 mg of Montmorillonite from an ancient ocean deposit and 16 mg of iron from ferrous gluconate, equivalent to 89 percent of the Daily Value.

Take 2 tablets with a meal three times daily.

Stock No. 1672-1 (450) Ko

Trigger Immune®, Chinese

[*Immune*] is a combination of 18 herbs designed to support natural immunity. According to Traditional Chinese Medicine, this formula is designed to strengthen a weakened energy constitution. Its Chinese name *sheng mai* can be translated to mean "generate the pulse." Trigger Immune is considered a general tonic formula. Its key herbs—schizandra, astragalus, dang gui, ginseng and ganoderma—build the immune system and promote energy. It contains:

Astragalus root
Panax ginseng root
Dang gui root
Epimedium leaf
Eucommia bark
Ganoderma plant

T

Lycium fruit
Rehmannia root
Achyranthes root
Atractylodes rhizome
Citrus peel
Hoelen plant
Ligustrum fruit
Ophiopogon root
Peony root
Polygala root
Schizandra fruit
Licorice root
Take 3 capsules with a meal three times daily.

Trigger Immune TCM Concentrate, Chinese [*Immune*]

contains the same herbs found in Chinese Trigger Immune but in a highly concentrated blend. This combination of 18 herbs is designed to support natural immunity. According to Traditional Chinese Medicine, this formula is designed to strengthen a weakened energy constitution. Its Chinese name *sheng mai* can be translated to mean "generate the pulse." Trigger Immune TCM is considered a general tonic formula. Its key herbs—schizandra, astragalus, dang gui, ginseng and ganoderma—build the immune system and promote energy. It contains:

Astragalus root
Panax ginseng root
Dang gui root
Epimedium leaf
Eucommia bark
Ganoderma plant
Lycium fruit
Rehmannia root tuber

Achyranthes root
Atractylodes rhizome
Citrus peel
Hoelen sclerotium
Ligustrum fruit
Ophiopogon root tuber
Peony root without bark
Polygala root
Schizandra fruit
Licorice root
NOTE: Pregnant or lactating women should consult their health care provider prior to taking this supplement.
Take 2 capsules with a meal daily. Each capsule is equivalent to 5 capsules of regular Chinese Trigger Immune.

Triple Relief® [*Structural*] is a

blend of herbs that have been used traditionally to help soothe minor muscle pain due to exercise or overexertion. It provides three natural sources of compounds that inhibit processes involved in minor muscle pain. Nexrutine™ is a natural plant extract that has been found to relieve muscle pain following exercise. Willow bark provides compounds (including salicin) long used in traditional herbology for the relief of minor muscle pain. Boswellia has been used traditionally for hundreds of years in Ayurveda for similar purposes.

Two capsules of Triple Relief provide 250 mg Nexrutine, 250 mg boswellia (standardized to 20% boswellic acid) and 120 mg willow bark extract (standardized to 15% salicylic acid).

Take 2 capsules with a meal two or three times daily.

Stock No. 1851-3 (90)

Stock No. 2786-3

(20 retail packets)

TS II [*Glandular*] contains herbs to support proper thyroid function and may help maintain balance in the thyroid gland. It contains:

Kelp plant
Irish moss plant
Parsley herb
Hops flowers
Capsicum fruit

Take 2 capsules with a meal twice daily.

Stock No. 1092-0 (100)

U

Ultimate GreenZone® [*Vital Nutrition*]. By combining wholesome ingredients like amaranth seeds, brown rice, millet and spirulina, with nutritional food stuffs, including carrots, broccoli, acerola fruit and lemon bioflavonoids, NSP has created Ultimate GreenZone—a beverage mix that is easily absorbed and metabolized for a great feeling of energy. Ultimate GreenZone is perfect for the young, the aged, the invalid and the very active. It offers a complement to a meal and provides additional nutrients and energy for people who are always on the go. Ultimate GreenZone is easily metabolized into energy and helps promote proper bodily functions, including waste elimination and immune capability.

Powder: Mix 1 scoop (10.5 g) in 8–12 oz. of water or juice. (May start with 1/2 scoop and gradually increase to 1 scoop.) Capsules: Take 4 capsules three or four times daily with a meal.

Stock No. 1098-3 (483 g)

Stock No. 1099-1 capsules (360)

1104-4

Uña de Gato (Cat's Claw)

[*Immune*] is found in the South American rainforest. It is particularly beneficial to the immune and structural systems, offering support to the joints. The inner bark of this vine provides beneficial alkaloids that provide immunostimulatory properties. Each capsule contains 300 mg of uña de gato combined with astragalus and echinacea, which support immune function.

Take 1 capsule daily with a meal.

Stock No. 175-0 (100) Ko

Urinary Maintenance [*Urinary*]

Urinary system function is important to the whole body. This formula contains herbs to support the urinary system organs and help maintain the body's delicate fluid and mineral balance controlled by the kidneys.

Uva ursi, hydrangea and hops help support kidney health and function. Many herbs in this formula help promote urine flow. Eleuthero and schizandra are adaptogens and help the body adapt to stress. Urinary Maintenance may also help sanitize the urinary tract and boost the immune system. This key product for the urinary system incorporates the benefits of asparagus stem, dandelion leaf, parsley leaves,

U

cornsilk, watermelon seed, dong quai root, horsetail stems and strobilus, hydrangea root, uva ursi leaves, eleuthero root and schizandra fruit.

Take 1 capsule with a meal three times daily.

Stock No. 2884-4 (120)

Uva Ursi [*Urinary*].

The leaves of this mountain bush have been used traditionally to aid the urinary system. Each capsule contains 440 mg uva ursi leaves. Do not take with Cranberry & Buchu concentrate.

Take 1 capsule with a meal twice daily.

Stock No. 710-9 (100) Ko

V

Vaccination Detox [*Nervous*]

is a natural homeopathic medicine for relief of vaccination side effects, including restlessness, fever and headaches.

Adults and children 12 and older: Take 15–20 drops under the tongue every one–two hours until symptoms are improved or relieved. Children and infants over 4 months: Take three–five drops under the tongue every 15–20 minutes until symptoms improve, then every two–four hours until they are relieved. Administer to children under 4 months only on the advice of a health care professional.

Stock No. 8980-0 (1 fl. oz.)

Valerian Root [*Nervous*]

comes from the Latin *valere*, which means "to be in good health." Records of valerian's use go back more than 1,000 years. Modern herbalists use the root primarily to support special needs of the central nervous system. Valerian root aids in relaxing the body and providing gentle sleep support. Each capsule contains 410 mg valerian root.

Take 1 capsule with a meal twice daily.

Stock No. 720-0 (100) Ko

Valerian, Time-Release

[*Nervous*]. This herb has been used as a sleep aid for over 1,000 years. Its ability to help relax the central nervous system, promote feelings of calm, decrease levels of anxiety and stress, and enhance restful sleep are known to millions the world over. Valerian is not known to cause morning grogginess. Each chlorophyll-coated tablet of NSP Time-Release Valerian contains 520 mg of the finest valerian root extract, concentrated and standardized to 0.8 percent valerenic acid. Time-release technology offers a steady release of valerian for 6–8 hours, ensuring better, more restful sleep.

Take 1–2 tablets one hour before bedtime for continuous, time-release benefits during the night.

Stock No. 721-1 (60)

Vari-Gone® [*Circulatory*]

is a combination of seven powerful herbs and nutrients that work together to fortify and nourish the overall health, strength and resilience of veins. This formula not only may improve appearance, but may also support optimal blood flow to the heart and legs. Its nutrients may improve the strength, tone and function of veins. Continued use may minimize the appearance of varicose and spider veins.

Vari-Gone contains:
Standardized extract of Horse chestnut
Standardized extract of Butcher's broom
Rutin
Hesperidin
Lemon bioflavonoids
Ascorbic acid
Fenugreek seeds
NOTE: Individuals who are taking prescription anti-coagulant medicines should consult their health care providers before using this product. Pregnant or lactating women should consult their health care professional prior to taking this supplement.

Take 1 or 2 capsules twice daily with a meal.

Stock No. 999-9 (90) Ko

Vari-Gone Cream® [*Skin Care, Circulatory*]

contains extracts of horse chestnut (helps tone the skin), butcher's broom (helps improve the look of saggy veins), aloe vera (used to improve the appearance of stretch marks and weeping skin) and yellow sweet clover (promotes skin health and appearance). Combined in a base of natural skin-conditioning ingredients, these botanical extracts promote improved appearance of unsightly varicose veins and spider veins while hydrating the skin and improving softness.

NOTE: Some of the ingredients in Vari-Gone Cream may promote blood thinning if taken internally. Individuals who are taking prescription anti-coagulant medicines should consult their health care providers before using this product.

Apply the cream to leg, calf and thigh. Apply in the early morning and again at bedtime.

Stock No. 4947-5 (2 oz.)

Viral Recovery [*Immune*]

is a natural homeopathic medicine that assists the body in detoxifying and regaining strength and vitality following viral infections.

Take 10–15 drops under the tongue two–six times daily, depending upon the severity of the symptoms. For children under 12, consult your health care professional. If symptoms persist or change, see health care provider.

Stock No. 8850-8 (1 fl. oz.)

Vita Lemon [*Vital Nutrition*]

makes use of one of nature's finest (and most tart) creations. Vita Lemon contains a healthful amount of fiber, including guar gum, microcrystalline cellulose, citrus pectin and xanthan gum. Fiber has been directly linked to colon health.

A one-scoop serving of Vita Lemon provides at least 10 percent of the Daily Value of vitamins A, C, D, B6, B12, thiamine, riboflavin, niacin, folic acid, biotin and pantothenic acid. Use it as part of a weight-control program.

For a refreshing pick-me-up: Mix one scoop of powder in 8 oz. of water. Stir briskly or blend in electric blender. Drink immediately.

In addition to your diet program:

V

Before eating in the morning, add 1/2 scoop of powder to 4 oz. of hot Nature's Spring water. Stir briskly or blend in electric blender. Drink immediately.

Stock No. 2932-7 (25 oz.)

VITAMINS

Vitamin A & D [*Vital Nutrition*].

Vitamin A was the first vitamin to be discovered. It is essential in maintaining good vision and promoting normal growth. It occurs in animal tissues as retinol but in plants as carotene, a precursor of vitamin A. This vitamin is necessary for the health of epithelial cells and the immune system. It is also required for the digestion of protein. It is essential for lactation, reproduction and the formation of steroid hormones. It is used to form the cells lining the digestive, respiratory, reproductive and urinary tracts and in all tissue linings of the body. It is also vital for healthy skin and is a famous antioxidant. It is best absorbed when taken with oil or fat. Each capsule contains 10,000 IU of vitamin A derived from fish oils, or 200% of the Daily Value.

Vitamin D works synergistically with vitamin A. It plays a role in absorbing and regulating calcium and phosphorus. This vitamin helps the body synthesize protein and helps build strong bones, teeth and skin. It is vital to the health of the nervous system and kidneys. It can be derived from the sun's action on oils secreted and reabsorbed by the skin. But if skin is tan or older, it is less capable of producing vitamin D.

Each capsule of Vitamin A & D contains 400 IU of vitamin D, which is 100% of the Daily Value.

CAUTION: If pregnant or planning pregnancy, daily vitamin A intake should not exceed 5,000 IU. Quantities in excess of 10,000 IU may result in reproductive hazards or birth defects.

Take 1 capsule daily with a meal.

Stock No. 4065-3 (100)

Vitamin B-Complex [*Vital Nutrition*].

Many different vitamin B compounds are grouped under the name B-complex. These vitamins are easily lost in refining and cooking; they also can be washed from the body by coffee, tea, alcohol and heavy perspiration. Physically stressful conditions can also deplete the body of B vitamins.

B vitamins are particularly important for the nervous system. They are also vital for good digestive function and enzyme reactions that control energy, circulation, hormones and overall health. Their actions are interdependent, so for greatest efficiency the complex should be taken together.

	Amount per 1 Capsule	% DV	Amount per 3 Capsules	% DV
Vitamin B1 (thiamine)	33 mg	2,200	100 mg	6,600
Vitamin B2 (riboflavin)	33 mg	1960	100 mg	5,880
Niacinamide (B3)	33 mg	167	100 mg	500
Vitamin B6 (pyridoxine)	33 mg	1667	100 mg	5,000
Folic Acid	133 mcg	33	400 mcg	100
Vitamin B12	33 mcg	550	100 mcg	1,650
Biotin	100 mcg	33	300 mcg	100
Pantothenic Acid	33 mg	333	100 mg	1,000

Choline (bitartrate)	33 mg	*	100 mg	*

*Daily Value not established

These vitamins are found in a base of acerola, inositol, lemon bioflavonoids, PABA, rose hips, rutin and wheat germ.

Take 1 capsule with a meal three times daily.

Stock No. 1778-9 (100)

Vitamin B-Complex, Balanced

[*Vital Nutrition*] is suitable for vegetarians both because of its high level of B12 and because no animal byproducts are used. Since the same amount of each B vitamin is not necessarily needed by the body, this formula is balanced to assist B12 absorption. Tablets are coated to preserve freshness. They contain no sugar, starch, artificial colorings or flavorings and are yeast-free. One tablet supplies:

	Amount	% DV
Vitamin B1	5 mg	330
Vitamin B2	6 mg	350
Niacin	50 mg	250
Vitamin B6	9 mg	450
Folic Acid	400 mcg	100
Vitamin B12	50 mcg	830
Biotin	100 mcg	30
Pantothenic Acid	45 mg	450
Calcium	120 mg	10
Phosphorus	90 mg	10

These come in a unique base of inositol, choline, PABA, wild lettuce, watercress leaves, cabbage leaves and rice bran polish.

Take 1 tablet daily with a meal.

Stock No. 1625-4 (120)

Vitamin B6 [*Vital Nutrition*] is

a cofactor that helps activate over 100 different enzymes involved in hundreds of biochemical tasks in the body. It is used to metabolize amino acids (protein management) as well as lipids (fats) and nucleic acids. As protein intake increases, so does the need for B6. This vitamin may help affect homocysteine levels, a factor in cardiovascular health. Vitamin B6 is important for the production of energy and for proper nervous system function. Each tablet provides 50 mg of vitamin B6 (pyridoxine hydrochloride), which is 2,500% of the Daily Value. It comes in a base of wheat germ flour and contains no animal byproducts (suitable for vegetarians).

Take 1 tablet daily with a meal.

Stock No. 1626-6 (120) Ko

Vitamin B12 Complete, Liquid
(see Liquid B12 Complete)

Vitamin C

Vitamin C is an antioxidant, and it performs many functions involving the immune system and tissue development. It is involved in iron absorption and in the synthesis of enzymes, hormones and proteins. The adrenal glands need large amounts of this nutrient. Vitamin C is water-soluble and is easily washed from the body if unused. It needs to be replaced constantly. Without vitamin C, the body cannot make collagen, the substance that holds the body's cells together. It works best with attending bioflavonoids. Timed-release formulations offer the advantage of a more consistent and efficient use of the vitamin by the body. NSP offers a variety of vitamin C supplements.

V

Vitamin C Ascorbates [*Vital Nutrition*].

America's favorite vitamin is available in a convenient, powdered, non-acidic form from Nature's Sunshine. Unsweetened Vitamin C Ascorbates may be mixed with water or other beverages for a pleasant-tasting, easy-to-prepare beverage. Each 1-teaspoon serving contains 2,000 mg vitamin C with three types of ascorbates: calcium, potassium and magnesium. Plus, the non-acidic, sugar-free formula is easy on the stomach. Vitamin C Ascorbates contains 57 servings per bottle at 10 calories per serving.

Add approximately 1 slightly rounded teaspoon (4.5 grams) to a glass of liquid and stir vigorously.

Stock No. 1606-3 (9 oz.)

Vitamin C, Chewable [*Vital Nutrition*]

comes in chewable wafers made with Vitamin C and whole orange juice, freeze-dried to preserve natural nutrients. It is mixed with orange, rose hips and natural lemon-lime flavor. It contains no artificial flavors, colors or sweeteners. Instead, it is sweetened with fructose (corn-derived). Each wafer supplies 410% of the Daily Value. Due to the moisture-absorbing ability of freeze-dried orange and fructose, small dehydrated particles have been enclosed in each bottle to help keep the product fresh and dry. (Close lid tightly after each use.)

Adults: Chew 2 tablets with meals twice daily. Children: Chew 1 tablet with meals twice daily.

Stock No. 1633-8 (120) Ko
4 Kids Too!

Vitamin C, Citrus Bioflavonoids

[*Vital Nutrition*] are nutritional compounds found together in nature. Bioflavonoids help protect the body from free radical damage. They are combined in a unique base containing lemon bioflavonoids, orange bioflavonoids, grapefruit bioflavonoids, hesperidin complex, rutin and rose hips extract. One tablet contains 500 mg of vitamin C or 835% of the Daily Value. Contains no starch, sugar, artificial flavors or colors.

Take 1–2 tablets with a meal three times daily.

Stock No. 1646-4 (90) Ko

Vitamin C, Time-Release [*Vital Nutrition*]

allows more efficient use of this vitamin by slowly releasing it into the body. Each tablet is designed with a special coating to release its contents only after reaching the intestine. This specially formulated product mixes 1,000 mg vitamin C in a base of lemon bioflavonoids, hesperidin complex derived from natural sources, rutin, acerola extract and rose hips extract. Each tablet provides 1,670% of the Daily Value of vitamin C. This product contains no sugar, starch, artificial colorings or flavorings.

Take 1 tablet daily with a meal.

Stock No. 1635-5 (60) Ko
Stock No. 1636-0 (180) Ko

Vitamins, Children's Chewable

(*see Herbasaurs Chewable Multiple Vitamins Plus Iron*)

Vitamin D (*see Vitamin A & D*)

Vitamin D3 [*Skeletal, Immune*].

The body manufactures Vitamin D through sun exposure, which makes it difficult to obtain adequate amounts of vitamin D during cloudy or winter months. Vitamin D comes in two forms, D2 and D3. Of the two, D3 is more bioactive. In the body, vitamin D is responsible for maintaining normal blood levels of calcium and phosphorus and for helping to build strong bones. Vitamin D works with other vitamins, minerals and hormones to promote bone mineralization. Additionally, research shows that vitamin D may help support a healthy immune system.

NSP Vitamin D3 contains 2,000 IU natural vitamin D3 derived from lanolin harvested from the wool fat of sheep from New Zealand and Australia. These animals are certified BSE-free.

Take 1–2 tablets daily with a meal.
Stock No. 1155-1 (60) Ko

Vitamin E [*Vital Nutrition*] is a

fat-soluble antioxidant that helps prevent fats and oils from becoming rancid. It is the most common vitamin found in nature and is often lacking in processed foods. This vitamin helps to maintain the fluidity of the blood and is necessary for maintenance of the skeletal, cardiac and smooth muscle membranes. It helps maintain and increase the storage of vitamin A and iron in the body. This vitamin exists in several chemical forms, the most active being d-alpha tocopherol. The "dl" form is synthetic and is not sold by Nature's Sunshine. Rather, vegetable sources that contain other naturally occurring tocopherols are used to ensure full potency of the entire vitamin E complex. Each hermetically sealed capsule of vitamin E comes in a base of cold-pressed soybean oil.

Take 1 capsule (100 IU) daily with a meal.
Stock No. 1650-6 (180)

Vitamin E Complete with Selenium [*Vital Nutrition, Circulatory*] offers the cardio-

protective and antioxidant benefits of vitamin E and the glandular and cellular benefits of the trace mineral selenium in a complete vitamin E formulation. This antioxidant formula may quench free radicals before they can damage cells.

Tocopherols and tocotrienols are two families of active compounds that we know as vitamin E. Many vitamin E products on the market contain only one or two of these compounds. This product contains all eight! The delta tocotrienol has been the subject of much research for maintaining cholesterol levels within the normal range and for supporting arterial health. Tocotrienols have also been studied for their support of the immune system. Each softgel provides 400 IU natural vitamin E (from soy), including 30 mg tocopherols (alpha, beta, delta and gamma) plus 5 mg mixed tocotrienols (alpha, beta, delta and gamma), and 25 mcg selenium in a base of annato/soybean oil.

Take 1 softgel daily with a meal.
Stock No. 1509-8 (60)
Stock No. 1508-5 (200)

V

VitaWave [*Vital Nutrition*]. A number of people today do not get optimal levels of essential vitamins and minerals. NSP VitaWave provides 100% or more of the Daily Value of 17 important vitamins and minerals. It is flavored with natural black raspberry, which also offers strong antioxidant protection. The 17 essential vitamins and minerals are found in a base of healthful herbs, an amino acid blend, plant-derived trace minerals and a body-supporting blend of healthful nutrients like lutein and lycopene, two proven antioxidants. Each serving of VitaWave contains:

	Amount	% DV
Vitamin A	10,000 IU	200
(50% retinyl palmitate, 50% beta-carotene)		
Vitamin E	100 IU	330
(d-alpha tocopheryl acetate)		
Vitamin K	80 mcg	100
(as menedione)		
Thiamine	50 mg	3,330
(vitamin B1 as thiamine hydrochloride)		
Riboflavin	50 mg	2,941
(vitamin B2)		
Niacin	50 mg	250
(niacinamide and nicotinic acid)		
Vitamin B6	50 mg	2,500
(pyridoxine hydrochloride)		
Vitamin B12	240 mcg	4,000
(cyanocobalamin)		
Biotin	300 mcg	100
Pantothenic Acid	50 mg	500
(d-calcium pantothenate)		
Calcium	250 mg	25
(calcium lactate)		
Iodine	150 mcg	100
(potassium iodide)		
Magnesium	100 mg	25
(magnesium gluconate)		
Zinc	10 mg	70
(zinc sulfate)		
Selenium	100 mcg	140
(sodium selenate)		
Copper	2 mg	100
(copper gluconate)		
Manganese	2 mg	100
(manganese gluconate)		
Chromium	120 mcg	100
(chromium chloride)		
Molybdenum	75 mcg	100
(sodium molybdate)		

The Herbal Blend contains 320 mg Asian ginseng root, damiana leaf, oat straw aerial parts, stevia leaves, saw palmetto fruit, stinging nettle leaf, green tea leaf extract, bilberry fruit extract and grape seed extract.

The Amino Acid Blend contains 220 mg taurine, alanine, arginine, aspartic acid, cysteine, glutamic acid, glycine, histidine, isoleucine, leucine, lysine, methionine, phenylalanine, proline, serine, threonine, tyrosine, valine.

The Body Support Blend contains 95 mg Vitamin C (ascorbic acid), alpha-lipoic acid, citrus bioflavonoids, inositol, p-aminobenzoic acid, choline bitartrate, lutein, lycopene (from tomato powder), vitamin D3 (cholecalciferol) and folic acid; plus Dead Sea salt, plant-derived trace minerals (10 mg) and boron (from boric acid) (2 mg).

Other ingredients include purified water, natural fruit flavoring (blackberry, raspberry, orange and mango), citric acid, potassium benzoate and potassium sorbate as preservatives, xanthan gum and natural coloring.

Adults: Take 2 tablespoons (1 oz.) daily with a meal. Children: Take 1 tablespoon (1/2 oz.) daily with a meal.

Stock No. 3332-3 (32 fl. oz.)

VS-C®, Chinese [*Immune*]. This immune-supporting formula is a combination that Chinese herbalists would describe as a "metal-enhancing" formula. These herbs create a favorable environment for microbial balance and overall health, support detoxification and promote a healthy respiratory tract. Originally developed by Dr. Wenwei Xie, VS-C is exclusive to Nature's Sunshine. It contains the following time-honored botanicals:

Dandelion root
Purslane herb
Indigo leaves and root
Thlaspi herb
Bupleurum root
Typhonium rhizome
Scute root
Cinnamon twig
Licorice root
Ginseng root

VS-C is also available in liquid form, with the components of its dried counterpart extracted and preserved in a glycerin base.

NOTE: Pregnant or lactating women should consult their health care professional prior to taking this supplement.

Adults: Take 4 capsules two–four times daily; liquid, take 30–40 drops two–four times daily. Children: Use half the adult recommendation.

Stock No. 937-7 (100)
Stock No. 3167-6 (2 fl. oz.) Ko
Liquid Herb, 4 Kids Too!

VS-C® TCM Concentrate, Chinese [*Immune*] contains the

same herbs found in VS-C but in a highly concentrated blend. This immune-supporting formula is a combination that Chinese herbalists would describe as "metal-enhancing." These herbs create a favorable environment for microbial balance and overall health, support detoxification and promote a healthy respiratory tract. It contains the following time-honored botanicals:

Dandelion whole plant
Purslane tops
Indigo leaves and root
Thlaspi whole plant
Bupleurum root
Typhonium rhizome
Scute root
Cinnamon twig
Licorice root
Panax ginseng root

NOTE: Pregnant or lactating women should consult their health care provider prior to taking this supplement.

Take 1 or 2 capsules with a meal daily. Each capsule is equivalent to 5 or 6 capsules of regular Chinese VS-C.

Stock No. 949-2 (30)

V-X [*Glandular*]. This herbal formula helps cleanse and nourish the female glandular/reproductive system and maintain female reproductive health. It contains

Squaw vine herb
Chickweed herb
Golden seal root
Marshmallow root
Mullein leaves
Plantain herb
Slippery elm bark

V

Yellow dock root
Take 3 capsules with a meal twice daily.
Stock No. 1382-4 (100)

W

White Oak Bark [*Immune*] is rich in tannin. Tannins give white oak bark its bitter and astringent qualities and may have an astringent effect on tissues. This herb is commonly used for supporting skin health. Each capsule contains 460 mg white oak bark.
Take 2 capsules with a meal three times daily.
Stock No. 730-7 (100) Ko

Wild Oregano Pure Essential Oil (*see Essential Oils*)

Wild Yam [*Glandular*] has been used for centuries by women seeking nutritional support and optimal balance for the glandular system. Wild yam contains diosgenin, a steroidal saponin that is used commercially to produce steroid hormones. Wild yam is used widely to address menopausal concerns. Each preservative-free capsule contains 375 mg of the finest wild yam root.
Take 1–2 capsules with a meal twice daily.
Stock No. 745-2 (100)

Wild Yam/Chaste Tree Combination [*Glandular*]. Wild yam is a great nourisher of the female reproductive system. It is widely used today to supply nutrients essential for optimal glandular function. It was

commonly called colic root 100 years ago in the U.S. It is also famous in Chinese herbology.
Chaste tree, also known as vitex, was called monk's pepper during the Middle Ages and was used by monks who wished to maintain their vows of celibacy. It is commonly used to address menopausal concerns.
Take 1–2 capsules with a meal twice daily. Drink one glass (8 oz.) of water with the capsules.
Stock No. 1108-7 (100) Ko

Women's X-Action® (*see X-Action, Women's*)

Wood Betony [*Nervous*] supports the nervous system, promoting relaxation and calmness. It has nervine, astringent and bitter tonic properties. Each capsule contains 325 mg wood betony herb (*Betonica officinalis*).
Take 1 capsule with a meal twice daily.
Stock No. 740-6 (100) Ko

X

X-A® [*Glandular*] is a natural source of minerals necessary for prostate function and a key to the production of male hormones. A proper balance of nutrients supports prostate function. X-A supports the prostate gland and boosts energy levels. It contains:
Eleuthero root
Saw palmetto fruit
Garlic bulb
Gotu kola aerial parts

Damiana leaves
Sarsaparilla root
Horsetail stems and strobilus
Capsicum fruit
Chickweed aerial parts
Parthenium root
*Take 1 capsule with a meal three
times daily.*

Stock No. 1130-2 (100) Ko

X-Action® Gel [*Glandular,
Nervous*]. A woman's sensuality can
influence her personal relationships
and her self-esteem. X-Action Gel
is a topical gel that can contribute
to a more pleasurable intimate
experience. This unique formula
combines l-arginine with menthol
and the herbal extracts of red clover
flower, *Panax ginseng* root, dulse
plant, green tea, black cohosh root,
saw palmetto fruit, red raspberry
fruit and dong quai root for better
lubrication and sensitivity. It is
used to lubricate vaginal tissues to
help enhance intimacy, arousal and
sensitivity.

*Apply topically as needed to
enhance the sensuality of intimate
pleasure.*

Stock No. 4937-6 (15 ml)
Available while supplies last.

X-Action®, Men's [*Glandular,
Nervous*] is formulated to enhance
male vitality levels. Its unique
herbal combination supports and
nourishes male reproductive health
and promotes prostate health.
Revitalize and energize yourself with
X-Action. It features Muira puama
(*Ptychopetalum olacoides*) stem
concentrate, Yohimbe (*Pausinystalia

yohimbe) bark, Epimedium extract
powder (also called Horny Goat
Weed) and l-arginine in a unique
herbal base containing:
Damiana leaves
Oat straw leaves concentrate
Saw palmetto berries
DHEA is also added to provide
valuable nutritional factors.

CAUTION: This product is not
intended for use by women, children
or those taking any prescription
medication. NOT FOR USE BY
INDIVIDUALS UNDER THE
AGE OF 18 YEARS. DO NOT USE
IF PREGNANT OR NURSING.
Consult a physician or licensed
qualified health care professional
before using the product if you have,
or have a family history of, prostate
cancer, prostate enlargement, heart
disease, low "good" cholesterol
(HDL), or if you are using any other
dietary supplement, prescription
drug or over-the-counter drug. Do
not exceed recommended serving
as this may cause serious, adverse
health effects. Possible side effects
include acne, hair loss, hair growth on
the face (in women), aggressiveness,
irritability and increased levels of
estrogen. Discontinue use and call a
physician or licensed qualified health
care professional immediately if you
experience rapid heartbeat, dizziness,
blurred vision or other similar
symptoms. KEEP OUT OF REACH
OF CHILDREN.

*Take 1 capsule with a meal three
times daily, or as directed by your
health care provider following
DHEA level assessment.*

Stock No. 1113-7 (100)

W
X

X-Action®, Women's [*Glandular, Nervous*] is especially designed to support the emotional, energy and vitality levels of women. It contains these carefully selected herbs and nutrients:

Maca tuber root
L-arginine
Eleuthero root
Oat straw concentrate
Red raspberry leaves
Damiana leaves
Licorice root
Sarsaparilla root

L-arginine helps facilitate blood flow to the reproductive area and promotes circulation.

Take 2 capsules with a meal three times daily. For best results, use with DHEA-F and Vitamin E.

Stock No. 1121-6 (100) Ko

Y

Yang pack. This (positive) package includes one each of the following Chinese TCM Concentrates: Anti-Gas, IF-C, Kidney Activator, Liver Balance, Stress Relief, Mood Elevator and Breathe EZ.

Stock No. 13343-2

Yarrow [*Respiratory, Digestive*]. Legend has it that yarrow's unique virtues were discovered by Achilles. Yarrow contains an alkaloid principle called achillein, as well as flavonoids, volatile oils, potassium and calcium salts, and tannin. Its effects are mostly astringent, which make yarrow helpful for firming and tightening tissues. Yarrow nutritionally supports the mucous membranes and has a soothing effect on the digestive system. It is closely related to chamomile, both botanically and chemically. Each capsule contains 300 mg yarrow.

Take 1 capsule with a meal twice daily.

Stock No. 750-2 (100) Ko

Yeast/Fungal Detox [*Intestinal*]. A healthy body is host to a delicate balance of yeasts and friendly microflora. That balance is affected by poor diet and certain other factors, which can influence the immune, digestive and urinary systems. Yeast/Fungal Detox helps the body detoxify itself and promotes optimal balance in microflora levels. This formula helps maintain the balance of microorganisms and supports the immune, digestive and urinary systems to promote optimal health.

Yeast/Fungal Detox contains Echinacea root, caprylic acid, sodium propionate, sorbic acid, pau d'arco, garlic bulb, oregano, selenium and zinc.

CAUTION: Do not exceed recommended dose. If symptoms of headache, nausea or diarrhea develop, reduce dosage and see your health care practitioner.

Take 1 capsule three times daily with a meal.

Stock No. 508-9 (90)

Yellow Dock [*Urinary, Intestinal*], a member of the buckwheat family, grows abundantly throughout the U.S. Pioneers used it for nutritional support of the urinary system. Its active principles include anthraquinones and tannins, the former are responsible for yellow dock's mild colon-stimulating activity. Yellow dock promotes proper elimination and colon health. It also supports liver function. Each capsule contains 460 mg yellow dock.

Take 2 capsules with a meal twice daily.

Stock No. 760-1 (100) Ko

Yin pack. This (negative) package includes one each of the following Chinese TCM Concentrates: Lung Support, Blood Build, IIY-C, KB-C, Nervous Fatigue, Spleen Activator and Trigger Immune.

Stock No. 13344-8

Ylang Ylang Complete BIO Pure Essential Oil
(*see Essential Oils*)

Yucca [*Structural*] grows abundantly in the southwestern U.S. and Mexico. The plant is also called soap root, with the reference to soap coming from a long historical use of the plant's roots as a foaming cleanser. Yucca contains large amounts of the steroid saponin, which accounts for its lathering ability. Saponins also support structural health due to their influence on joint health and function. The plant provides powerful nutritional support to the structural system. Each capsule contains 490 mg yucca.

Take 1 capsule with a meal twice daily.

Stock No. 770-3 (100)

Z

Zinc [*Immune*]. This trace mineral is extremely important to overall health. More zinc is found in the body than any other trace element except for iron. Relatively large amounts are found in bone and muscle. It's also prevalent in the prostate and retina.

Zinc is involved in hundreds of important functions in the body, including sugar metabolism, DNA formation, protein metabolism and energy production. It is also needed for the growth and development of bones. Pregnant and lactating women require extra zinc. This mineral supports immune functions, and its deficiency results in a compromised immune system.

This product is derived from zinc gluconate for more efficient absorption. For maximum benefit, it is combined in a rich, natural base of kelp leaves and stem, alfalfa aerial parts and thyme leaves. Each tablet contains 25 mg of zinc, which is 166% of the Daily Value.

Take 1 tablet daily with a meal.

Stock No. 1657-9 (150) Ko

Zinc Lozenges [*Immune, Respiratory, Glandular*]. For many people, seasonal changes often stress the respiratory and immune systems. NSP Zinc Lozenges can help support the immune system in times of seasonal stress. Each lozenge contains a blend of beneficial ingredients that help support the respiratory and immune systems: vitamin C (ascorbic acid), sodium ascorbate, echinacea root, slippery elm bark, zinc citrate, licorice root concentrate, eucalyptus oil and menthol. Zinc Lozenges also contain the natural sweetener xylitol and natural orange, peach and spearmint flavors for a great taste. Each lozenge provides 5 mg of zinc (33% of the Daily Value) and 100 mg of vitamin C (160% of the Daily Value).

Take 1 lozenge each hour or as needed. Allow lozenge to dissolve slowly in the mouth. Do not use more than 6 lozenges in a 24-hour period.

Stock No. 1596-8 (96)

NOTE:
*TCM Concentrates. These whole-herb, powdered extracts are identical in formula to our Chinese products and remain true to Traditional Chinese Medicine in philosophy and effect. In the extraction process, the entire herb formula is percolated at a temperature low enough to minimize evaporation and the breakdown of active constituents, but high enough to allow the synergistic interaction to occur. In TCM, the entire formula of Chinese herbs is extracted as a whole. Resulting products are highly potent. Our TCM concentrates are four to nine times as potent as their complementary original Chinese product!

Federal and state laws and regulations preclude Nature's Sunshine Products from making specific medicinal or drug claims for its nutritional supplements. Any disease or other symptom mentioned in this guide refers only to the homeopathic product line. However, many products provide essential substances that affect bodily functions that may be influenced by poor dietary practices. Nature's Sunshine's nutritional supplements are designed to provide nutritional support for the body as it works to maintain a healthy condition.

These statements have not been evaluated by the Food and Drug Administration. These products are not intended to diagnose, treat, cure or prevent any disease. For counsel on injuries or disease, Nature's Sunshine recommends that you see a health professional who can help you make responsible decisions concerning your specific health concerns.

164

Glossary
of
Terms

Glossary of Terms

Amino Acids: Amino acids are 22 nitrogen-containing acids that are basic building blocks of proteins. Essential amino acids must come from the diet or supplements. Our bodies cannot manufacture them. Non-essential amino acids are made by the body.

ATC (*Ancient Traditional Concept*): These products are air-dried and are concentrated 4 to 1.

Ayurvedic: The ancient Ayurvedic natural health system comes from India. This "science of life" methodology considers the complete human—body, mind and spirit—with the goal of integrating all parts into one harmonious whole. Ayurvedic practice strives to nourish the body at a cellular level, trusting the body to do what only it can to optimize itself to wholeness and harmony. The selection of herbs, growth conditions, processing, concentrating and standardizing of NSP's line of Ayurvedic products are supervised by a world-renowned Ayurvedic practitioner in India. NSP Ayurvedic products combine the best of both worlds: ancient theory and modern processing technology to preserve nutritional freshness.

B-Vitamin Processing: NSP's vitamins, hormones and other organic compounds from plants, animals and/or microbes are all natural. Most B vitamins and folic acid are isolated from microbial fermentation (yeast). We isolate the B vitamins from the yeast and get rid of all the excess yeast. Most fat-soluble vitamins come from natural vegetable or fish oils. The components used in NSP vitamin products are carefully selected and analyzed by our QA/R&D departments to be sure that they are true, natural materials.

Binders: Binders help hold a tablet together. Nature's Sunshine uses only plant cellulose in the production of its tableted products. One of these is vegetable stearate, which acts as a natural lubricant and keeps the tablet from sticking to the tablet press. NSP uses no animal products as binders in the tableted products.

Buffered: Buffering usually involves mixing an acid with its conjugate base salt. This is done so when a supplement goes into solution (like in the stomach), any changes in pH that would normally occur in the presence of acid or alkali are reduced. Buffering helps keep the pH of the blood and body fluids at a virtually constant level.

Bulk Products: These products come in a powder form and need to be mixed with water, juice or milk.

Capsules: Capsules are made of 100 percent bovine (beef) gelatin.

CU: Cellulase units, or the amount of cellulase digested.

Chelated: Most minerals are better-absorbed when bound to certain compounds. This binding is called "chelation." The best chelates differ for each mineral. Amino acid chelates have been found to be the most effective.

Children: The Herbasaurs product line is designed for children 2 to 12. To calculate children's dosages for other products, the following formula can be used. Children's Rule: (for children 2 years and older) Age/(Age + 12) x Adult Dose. For example: 3.5 year old child to be given ALJ Liquid: Adult Dose = 20 drops with a meal three times a day 3.5/(15.5) x 20 drops = 4.5 drops with each meal three times a day.

NSP labels recommend that you consult a pediatrician before administering vitamins or herbs to any child age 4 or younger.

Disintegration: NSP follows pharmaceutical industry test standards for tablet and capsule disintegration as outlined in the United States Pharmacopoeia (USP). The disintegration testing requirements hold true for all capsules and tablets, except those that are timed-release (which follow a different set of requirements) or chewable (which begin dissolving at the time of chewing in the mouth).

DU: Digestive units, or the amount that is digested.

Enzymes: Digestive enzymes are essential for digestion as they help break down foods. Our bodies may lack or be low in necessary enzymes, and if we don't get them from the food we eat, supplementation is often helpful.

Equivalents: See chart on page 176.

Essential Oil Information:
AOC = Appelation d'Origine Contrôlée. This notation signifies that an essential oil has been certified of authentic origin.
BIO = NSP "BIO" essential oils are certified organic by Eco-Cert, a highly regarded European organic certifier.

Each 5 ml bottle has approximately 125 drops. For recommended usage, please consult the Essential Oils Guide.
Small Amber bottles: Our oils are packaged in 5 ml amber bottles. We use smaller bottles because every time the bottle is opened, air can get in and evaporate the oil. The small amber bottles are used to mix and store oils. The bottles are sold separately in 2 fl. oz. size.

Excipients: The nature of the manufacturing process requires that NSP use some excipients in its products. These include:
  Capsules [empty] (dosage delivery, containment)
  Cellulose & Modified Celluloses (compression aid, flow aid, disintegrant and coating film)
  Magnesium Stearate (dry lubricant, flow aid)

Stearic Acid (dry lubricant)
Silicon Dioxide (flow aid)
Maltodextrin (flow aid, compression aid)
Sorbitol (compression aid, sweetener)
Dicalcium Phosphate (binding agent)
Guar Gum (smoothing agent, extended release of tablets)
Acacia Gum (smoothing agent, extended release of tablets)

Homeopathics: Homeopathy is a safe, natural system of medicine that has been in use for well over 150 years. Through many "provings," Dr. Samuel Hahnemann devised a system of healing based on the body's symptoms. He called this system "homeopathy," from the Greek words *homeos* (similar) and *pathos* (suffering). These remedies are designed to help resolve deep problems that are causing symptoms to appear. Homeopathic remedies may be used in conjunction with (but at separate times of the day as) orthodox and other medical treatments. All of these products are made in accordance with the Homeopathic Pharmacopoeia of the United States (HPUS) and are recognized as legal and safe by the FDA. These products are highly diluted in pure solutions that are recognized as medicines.

HUT: Hemoglobin units on tyrosine (amino acid) basis. This test evaluates the activity of the enzyme based on how much tryrosine it gets out of hemoglobin in a certain amount of time.

IU: International unit. The conversion of IU to mg depends on the vitamin.

Kosher Certified: Products marked kosher (a small   on the label) are certified kosher by Rabbi David Novoseller of Kosher Service, Philadelphia, Pa. He periodically examines NSP's manufacturing plant and oversees the mixing and manufacturing processes to ensure the kosher status of these products. Offering kosher products makes NSP supplements available to more people worldwide.

Liquid Herbs and Extracts: An herb is extracted with a solution of water and alcohol. After the herb material is extracted, the alcohol and water are evaporated from the extract, and vegetable glycerin is added to the herbs.

Polyethylene Plastic Bottles: These are designated as number 2 for recycling purposes and are recycled in most areas. Polyethylene is less fragile and provides a better moisture barrier. Polyethylene has been tested extensively and is approved safe for use as a food container. No gases are released from the plastic once it has cooled.

Preservatives: We use sodium benzoate that is found in natural benzoin gum. Other preservatives used in the products include methyl paraben and propyl paraben. These two parabens work best when they are used together and require less than one-tenth of one percent in a combined form. The parabens and sodium benzoate are derived from benzoic acid. Benzoic acid is found naturally in benzoin, Peru and tolu balsams, and several other balsamic substances. The only way to produce plant products without using some preservatives is to irradiate or heat the product and require refrigeration after opening.

Probiotics:
Probiotics are "friendly" bacteria that populate the intestinal tract. Probiotics help keep harmful microorganisms in check, enhance digestion and improve elimination. NSP Acidophilus, Bifidophilus Flora Force, L. Reuteri and Probiotic Eleven are probiotic products.

Product Combination Key:
X = Dr. Christopher
A = Paavo Airola
J = Jeanne Burgess
W = Dr. Eugene Watcliff

Proprietary Formulas:
Many of our herbal combinations are proprietary formulas, and the amount of milligrams of any particular ingredient cannot be disclosed. Each label lists all of the ingredients in a formula from the highest to the lowest amounts.

Softgel Capsules:
These capsules are made of glycerin, gelatin (from either porcine or bovine sources) and water. Our softgel capsules are sealed to hold the liquid or gel inside.

Standardization:
Standardization applies to a whole herb or, more frequently, to an extract made from a whole herb. Because plant content can differ depending on the time of year plants are harvested and the amount of sunshine, rainfall and variation in temperature the plants experience, different amounts of active ingredients can be present in the plants. In order to ensure that our customers receive the same product time after time, we analyze plant material for active ingredients. Then we analyze each batch of herb to ensure the same levels of active ingredients. We assay and adjust our concentrates. Too much of a particular active ingredient may result in illness; not enough active ingredient could result in an ineffective product. For example: ginkgo biloba is standardized to 24% ginkgo flavone glycosides and 6% terpene lactones.

Sweeteners:
Vitamins and minerals have a very unpalatable taste. NSP uses natural sweeteners in its chewable products. Many sweeteners such as molasses and syrups contain sucrose that cause tooth decay. NSP uses sorbitol, which occurs naturally in berries, cherries, plums, apples and blackstrap molasses and is very safe. It is 60 percent as sweet as sugar. We use 500 mcg (0.005 g) or less in each tablet. Mannitol, another sweetener, is found in pineapples, olives, asparagus, carrots, seaweed and grasses.

SynerPro®: Syner is short for synergy, and that's what the dynamic SynerPro vitamin/herb/mineral line is all about. Each combination comes in a natural herb base consisting of dehydrated broccoli, carrot, red beet, rosemary, tomato, turmeric, cabbage, Chinese cabbage, grapefruit and lemon bioflavonoids, and hesperidin.

USP Alcohol: USP (United States Pharmacopoeia) is a scientific body with the object of "establishing one uniform standard and guide for the use of those engaged in the practice of medicine and pharmacy in the United States whereby the identity, strength and purity of all such medicines and drugs may be accurately determined." Hence, a material (such as alcohol) with a USP rating is guaranteed to be of the purest standard (no deadly contaminants, high level of activity, etc.).

Vegitabs: These are 7/8" round (or small oval) coated tablets. These tablets are vegetarian, including the coating, which is plant cellulose. Vegitabs contain 10% more herbal ingredient than capsules.

Vitamin Coating: A special coating enhances the life of the tablet and makes them easier to package and to swallow. We use a water solution containing a vegetable fiber base. Tablets are loaded into the coater. They are then tumble-heated, and four spray guns inside the machine spray the water-based solution onto the tablets.

Sales Aids & Supplies

Sales Aids & Supplies

Chewable/Lozenge Tablet Refillable Tube. This plastic carrying tube can be used to carry all chewable tablets, including Stomach Comfort, Papaya Mints, Herbasaurs products and Chewable Vitamin C.

Stock No. 2689-3

Cholestrak® Home Cholesterol Test Kit.

High cholesterol can have serious and even lethal effects on the body. With the help of NSP's Cholestrak test kit, you can measure your cholesterol level quickly, simply and conveniently in your own home. This kit contains everything you need to obtain one accurate cholesterol reading:

- 1 test device
- 1 cholesterol result chart
- 1 finger stick device (lancet)
- 1 gauze pad
- 1 bandage
- 1 brochure
- 1 questions & answers brochure
- With the easy-to-use

Cholestrak, you will know in minutes if you have a healthy cholesterol level, if you should modify your lifestyle and work to decrease other risk factors, or if you should consult a physician. Not for use by hemophiliacs or those taking blood-thinning medications.

Stock No. 2916-1 (1 kit)

Cleanse/Detox Brochure.

Promote natural cleansing and detoxification through the use of herbal supplements with this informative, full-color brochure. Spotlights CleanStart, Tiao He Cleanse, Para-Cleanse, Enviro-Detox, Heavy Metal Detox and Yeast/Fungal Detox.

Stock No. 1997-3 (English, 10)
Stock No. 1996-2 (Spanish, 10)

Customer Bag.

Professionalize your business image with these tan-colored, plastic customer bags embossed with the NSP logo. Available in two sizes, 12 x 9-1/2"and 12 x 16-1/2". 25 bags per order

Stock No. 2696-1 (12 x 16-1/2)
Stock No. 2697-2 (12 x 9-1/2)

Customer Price List/Order Form.

A complete listing of NSP products, broken down alphabetically in categories, with stock numbers, suggested retail prices and ordering information makes it easy for your customer to order NSP products at a glance. (Note: Lists only retail prices.)

Stock No. 2060-4 (Bilingual)

Customer Receipt Pad.

This standard receipt pad is customized for the needs of an NSP independent distributor and embossed with the company logo. Helps you keep track of payment method, taxable and non-taxable items, shipping costs, sponsor/Manager and QV month. Measures 6 x 4", three-part NCR. 50 pages per pad.

Stock No. 2049-2 (English)
Stock No. 2307-2 (Spanish)

Enzyme Brochure.

This three-panel, full-color brochure features NSP enzyme products—Proactazyme® Plus, Food Enzymes, PDA, Protease Plus, High Potency Protease, Lactase Plus and Hi

Lipase. It spells out the role that enzymes play in the digestive system and describes the specific benefits of each product.

Stock No. 1970-1 (English, 10)

Essential Oils Guide.
This comprehensive booklet provides a great introduction to aromatherapy and NSP's line of premium-quality essential oils and blends. It includes the history of essential oils, how these oils work in the body, a look at NSP's unsurpassed quality and a helpful guide to using essential oils.

Stock No. 2775-2 (English)
Stock No. 2776-8 (Spanish)

Health Analyzer.
Use this to determine which body systems are most in need of supplementation. Two-sided, colorful piece contains the analysis on one side and product information on the other. Pad of 50 sheets. 8.5x14".

Stock No. 2757-7 (English pad of 50)
Stock No. 2758-3 (Spanish pad of 50)

Herbal Solutions Catalog.
This full-color catalog is the perfect way to introduce family and friends to some of NSP's finest and best-selling products. Features 30 or so NSP products with compelling descriptions and lists both retail and wholesale prices. Put this very nice sales piece to work for you.

Stock No. 2740-4 (English, 10)
Stock No. 9760-4 (English, 100)
Stock No. 2742-5 (Spanish, 10)
Stock No. 9814-9 (Spanish, 100)

Introduction to NSP (Classic).
This colorfully illustrated booklet presents the company in full spectrum, from NSP's philosophy, to its products, to its quality control measures and more. It's a handy reference for those interested in learning more about NSP. This version features the Classic marketing plan and its benefits.

Stock No. 2853-1 (English, 10)
Stock No. 2854-9 (Spanish, 10)

Introduction to NSP (Legacy).
This colorfully illustrated booklet presents the company in full spectrum, from NSP's philosophy, to its products, to its quality control measures and more. It's sure to spark further questions about the company and products. This version features the Legacy marketing plan and its benefits.

Stock No. 5244-4 (English, 10)
Stock No. 5245-8 (Spanish, 10)

Master Price List.
Lists the stock number, suggested retail price, QV, direct cost and Member to Member cost for virtually all NSP products and sales aids. Products are listed in categories in alphabetical order (single herbs, combinations, homeopathics, etc.).

Stock No. 2070-2 (Bilingual)

Natria® Product Catalog.
This 29-page, full-color catalog introduces you to the exclusive ingredient complexes found in Natria products. Then it walks you through the steps of essential skin nutrition and care and the products that provide that care. It also provides detailed information on custom care products,

body care products and hair care products. Includes a comprehensive ingredient glossary.

Stock No. 6201-3 (English)
Stock No. 6202-7 (Spanish)

Natria Skin Analysis Kit.
For use with Natria skin nutrition products. This kit contains two tests. Use Skin Type Analysis customized tabs to determine your skin type and discover which Natria products best suit your needs. Use Dryness customized tabs to reveal the degree of dryness present on the surface of your skin. Use tabs in your own before-and-after test to see how Irish Moss Hand and Body Lotion replenishes and helps maintain your skin's vital moisture.

Stock No. 6205-6 (bilingual)
(5 cards and tester tabs for each test)

Natural Health Solutions Catalog.
This beautiful 78-page catalog features over 100 top-selling NSP products, grouped by category (herbal formulas, singles, liquids, body systems, etc.). It's chock full of informative tidbits and testimonials. Includes pages on NSP history, scientific expertise, opportunities, rewards, travel and more. It's a great way to introduce NSP products to new people. Includes price list for catalog.

Stock No. 12750-8 (English, 1)
Stock No. 12752-1 (English, 10)
Stock No. 12566-4 (English, 100)
Stock No. 12751-9 (Spanish, 1)
Stock No. 12753-3 (Spanish, 10)
Stock No. 12567-0 (Spanish, 100)

Nature's Noni® Brochure.
This colorful brochure explains the many wonderful health benefits of noni juice and encapsulated herb. Includes scientific information and user testimonials.

Stock No. 2311-4 (English, 10)
Stock No. 2314-2 (Spanish, 10)

Nature Seal Brochure.
Good health begins with healthy food preparation. NatureSeal is top-of-the-line cookware. This four-page, 5-1/2 x 8-1/2" brochure describes the complete line of NatureSeal cookware and includes photos of all cookware. It details the five enemies of healthy food preparation and explains how NatureSeal cookware overcomes these enemies.

Stock No. 2659-7 (Bilingual, 10)

NSP from A to Z with Sales Aids and Supplies and Systems Guide.
Newly updated, this is the definitive listing of all NSP products in alphabetical order, from Acidophilus to Zinc Lozenges. Features detailed product descriptions, stock numbers, recommended usage, glossary of terms and more. It also includes a comprehensive listing of all NSP sales aids and supplies and information from the systems guide.

Stock No. 2720-7 (English)
Stock No. 2722-2 (Spanish)

NSP Logo Posters.
Set of five posters that have NSP Independent Distributor logo. 16 x 14 1/2".

Stock No. 2207-4 (bilingual)

NSP Power Shaker.
Mix up your NSP drinks with this handy, clear, plastic shaker cup. Special wire whisk ball helps to thoroughly mix your powder drinks. Graduated

markings let you see how much you're drinking. Includes green domed twist-on lid with drinking spout. Holds 20 fl. oz.

Stock No. 2877-5

pH Balancing Simplified Brochure.
Get a quick education on pH and how it affects health with this 16-page booklet. Find out the difference between acidity and alkalinity. Discover what you don't know about the dangers of high acidity and high alkalinity. You'll find a complete supplement program for both acidic and alkaline conditions plus other helpful hints, including a chart of the effects of common foods on pH balance.

Stock No. 2836-1 (English, 10)

pH Test Strips.
Test your salivary and urinary pH levels at home with these convenient test strips.

Stock No. 2918-8 (100)

pH Test Card Charts.
Share your pH knowledge with your customers. Give them a test card chart with several test strips and a brochure so they can monitor their pH levels.

Stock No. 2843-8 (25)

Phone-In/Mail-In Order Form.
This order form features a complete listing of all NSP products and sales aids with stock numbers, QV and direct cost. Alphabetized in categories such as single herbs, combinations, homeopathics, etc. Includes ordering instructions and Customer Service/Order Sales phone numbers.

Stock No. 2000-7 (Bilingual)

Policies & Procedures Manual.
Get answers to your NSP questions here. Includes information on rank advancement, membership benefits, account questions, compensation plans, NSP events and trips, shipping, ordering and payment options, distribution centers and much more.

Stock No. 1999-5 (English)
Stock No. 1998-7 (Spanish)

Quality Assurance Booklet.
All products are not created equal. This is the best reference tool to have on hand when a customer asks, "Why should I pay more for your products?" Learn all about the rigorous testing NSP products and raw materials undergo in this booklet, including HPLC, GC/MS, FTIR, ICP–MS, Dissolution, Ash testing, Microbiological testing and much more.

Stock No. 2305-9 (English, 10)
Available while supplies last

Retail Posters.
Promote some of your best-sellers with these colorful, informative posters. Each measures 20 x 24" and makes a nice addition to your display area. Set includes: Thai-Go, Food Enzymes, Super Omega-3 EPA, Super Supplemental, Bifidophilus Flora Force, Liquid Chlorophyll, Nutri-Calm, EverFlex, Everybody's Fiber and Liquid Cleanse.

Stock No. 5321-9 (English, 10)

Retail Trial Packs.
Allow customers to sample your products by offering retail trial packs. Each bag contains 20 trial packs (one serving per pack) packaged matchbook

style, with product information and recommended use. Choose from:

Stock No.
Carbo Grabbers 2789-9
Fat Grabbers 2485-4
Food Enzymes 2494-1
LBS II 2497-0
Nature's Hoodia 3019-9
Nutri-Calm 2493-9
Stomach Comfort 2489-1
Super Supplemental 2488-3
Triple Relief 2786-3

RG-Max Brochure.
This full-color, one-fold brochure outlines the health benefits of RG-Max amino acid drink mix, providing specific details on each ingredient in the unique formula. It also includes a few testimonials.

Stock No. 5275-3 (English, 10)
Stock No. 5276-7 (Spanish, 10)

Sales Receipt Book.
Keep track of sales, and provide your customer with a receipt of purchase with this sales receipt book designed especially for the needs of the NSP distributor. 8-1/2 x 4", two-part NCR. 50 pages per pad.

Stock No. 2040-8

Sign-up Application.
Use this standard, one-page form to sign up an NSP Distributor or Member. Instructions are included on the form. Simply fill out and return to NSP Home Office. Two-page, self-carbon. Shrink-wrapped in packs of 10.

Stock No. 2120-2 (English)
Stock No. 2119-3 (Spanish)

Small Shipping Box.
Heavy-duty cardboard folds out to a shipping box 4-1/2" deep, with sides 7-3/4 x 6-1/4".

Stock No. 2450-1 (10)

Super Trio Brochure.
This full-color brochure features NSP's Super Trio supplement program. Product information on Super ORAC, Super Omega-3 EPA and Super Supplemental Vitamins and Minerals (without iron) along with health information on antioxidants and vitamin supplementation promote Super Trio as a basic health program.

Stock No. 5270-5 (English, 10)
Stock No. 5271-6 (Spanish, 10)

Thai-Go brochure.
Our best-selling product shines in this tri-fold brochure, which promotes the antioxidant and immunostimulatory benefits of Thai-Go herbal supplement. Includes a chart that correlates Thai-Go's 11 ingredients with the body systems they support. Also includes user testimonials.

Stock No. 5241-1 (English)
Stock No. 5242-9 (Spanish)

Vitamin/Herb Pocket Pack.
This sturdy, beige, plastic, pocket-size nutritional supplement carrier is divided into six sections so you can carry your supplements with you wherever you go. Measures 3-1/2 x 2-1/4 x 3/4" deep. Easy to carry to work, school or on vacation in your purse or pocket.

Stock No. 2692-5

Women's Product Booklet.

Health & Nutrition for Today's Woman features the line of NSP products designed especially to support women's health. It addresses important topics in women's health, from PMS, to weight management, to pregnancy and nursing, to menopause. Find out which products help support various women's health concerns.

Stock No. 2841-4 (English, 10)

Xylitol Product Brochure. This

colorful booklet introduces the reader to xylitol natural sweetener and describes our Nature's Sweet Life products: dark chocolate bars, chewing gum, mints, mouthwash and bulk xylitol. The health benefits of xylitol are provided, including oral health benefits, blood-sugar impact and lower calorie/carb count benefits.

Stock No. 5190-3 (English, 10)
Stock No. 5191-4 (Spanish 10)

Volume Measurement Equivalents

1/4 teaspoon	= 15–20 drops		= 1 ml
1 teaspoon	= 1/3 Tablespoon		= 5 ml
1 tablespoon	= 3 teaspoons	= 1/2 fl. oz.	= 15 ml
2 tablespoons	= 1/8 cup	= 1 fl. oz.	= 30 ml
4 tablespoons	= 1/4 cup	= 2 fl. oz.	= 59 ml
1/2 quart	= 1 pint	= 16 fl. oz.	= 473 ml
1 quart	= 2 pints	= 32 fl. oz.	= 946 ml

Weight Measurement Equivalents

1 gram	= 1000 mg	= .035 oz.
1 milligram	= .001 gram	= 1000 mcg
1 ounce	= 28.35 grams	

Concentrations

| 1 ppm | = 1 ml/L | = .001 g/L | =.0038 g/gallon |

Some abbreviations commonly used on product labels

fl. oz.	= fluid ounce (volume)
oz.	= ounce (weight)
g, gm	= gram
mg	= milligram
mcg	= microgram
l	= liter
ml	= milliliter
ppm	= parts per million

The Body Systems Guide to Natural Health

The Nature's Sunshine philosophy

Throughout history, health care trends and fads have risen and receded like tides of the ocean. However, along the way some undeniable truths have emerged. Perhaps the most important of these is the notion that food plays a significant role in the human condition.

Mankind must have always understood—at least at some level—the importance of supplementing the diet with particular foods when health becomes a concern. Stone and papyrus records dating back to 4,000 B.C. extol the virtues of special foods in relation to certain health conditions. In the Orient, food has been a standard part of health care procedure for more than 5,000 years.

According to Irwin Ziment, M.D., a professor of medicine at the University of California at Los Angeles (UCLA) College of Medicine, "The use of food as a drug had always been important until the modern drug industry arose in the 19th century."

Indeed, prior to World War II many herbs were listed side-by-side with chemical drugs in the U.S. Pharmacopoeia, the official listing of accepted medicines. Even now, nearly 50 percent of the most commonly used and prescribed drugs are either derived from a plant source or contain chemical imitations of a plant compound.

Only recently has society scoffed at relying upon nutrition as a means to improve health. For several decades in this century, people believed that laboratories and man-made materials—not nature—were the source of all necessary answers.

Times have changed. Today science tells us that most of the health issues people face can be traced to lifestyle and diet. It tells us, too, that what we eat and breathe and how we live affects how we feel and how our bodies function.

Nature's Sunshine was established on the premise that natural foods—herbs, in particular—are beneficial for health. It has always been NSP's goal to make herbs available in the purest, most effective form possible. As NSP matured, its list of product offerings grew to include vitamins, minerals, Chinese formulations, homeopathic remedies and other health-related items. Nevertheless, the company's focus remains constant—promoting and supporting optimal health through quality nutritional supplements.

A vital key to health: good nutrition

Although there are many principles of good health, one of the most important is proper nutrition. Wise food selection is critical to good health.

What is true health and well-being? To be truly healthy is to be whole. The word health even comes from the same root as the word whole. Unfortunately, many people equate health with merely the absence of disease, and these individuals hardly consider their health...until after they have lost it.

Health involves three important concepts: balance, harmony and joy. A truly healthy person possesses all these elements. When we are whole, our bodies are in balance and our spirits are in harmony with our surroundings. The result is a wonderful feeling of well-being. Health isn't just the absence of disease; it goes beyond just feeling "normal." To be truly healthy is to have a zest for life and the ability to enjoy the activities you love.

The wonderful machine

More than 100 years ago, American herbalist Samuel Thomson compared the body to a furnace that needs both air and fuel to function. The furnace burns air and fuel to create energy. In the process, it eliminates the smoke while the residue, or ash, falls away. If high-quality fuel and sufficient oxygen are used in the furnace, it burns clean and hot with minimal waste. However, if poor fuel or too little air is present, the fuel smolders and produces a great deal of ash and smoke.

Actually, one could also compare the human body to a high-performance machine made to burn high-performance fuel and produce large amounts of energy. The body can't work efficiently if we throw in low-grade fuel such as junk foods. When people complain that they are tired and don't have enough energy, they should take a close look at what they're eating. Many times they are using low-quality fuel, resulting in their internal furnaces burning poorly?

Eliminating waste

Natural health care seeks not only to provide the body with a nutritious diet, but also to open up the eliminative channels to keep the internal furnace hot and clean.

Why?

The ability to absorb dietary nutrients is only part of being healthy. To keep its internal furnace functioning properly, the body also needs to eliminate toxic waste. In fact, healthy elimination is a part of good nutrition. Hippocrates, the father of medicine, taught that illness results from man's inability to properly digest his food and eliminate waste.

This view is the foundation of every modern natural health philosophy.

Healthful changes

What kind of dietary changes should people make if their goal is optimal health? They can begin by limiting or avoiding the four whites: refined sugar, refined flour, salt and shortening (or highly hydrogenated and saturated fats). One should gradually replace them with healthier substitutes. Of course, individuals should also avoid smoking and excessive alcohol consumption.

Eat plenty of fresh fruits and vegetables, whole grains, nuts, seeds, legumes; consume meat sparingly. In general, the closer foods are to their natural state, the better they are for us.

When basic concepts of natural health are applied on a consistent basis, the body can usually take care of its natural processes with amazing efficiency. Almost anyone can understand and follow these simple, tried-and-true principles of health.

Beyond the basics: herbs and health

Millions of people use herbs regularly in the belief that they are a good source of important elements either missing or greatly diminished in modern diets. People usually take the herbs in the form of encapsulated powders, concentrated liquids or teas.

However, in the past, many herbs were used as foods. At one time dandelions, burdock, marshmallow, comfrey leaves and alfalfa were served at mealtime. Unfortunately, many of these wonderful plants have lost favor in the eyes of modern people whose tastes became accustomed to an unwholesome, highly refined regimen.

Edward Shook, an herbalist and biochemist who lived in the early 20th century, is one of the few researchers who based his work mainly on the nutritional value of herbs. In his *Advanced Treatise of Herbology,* Dr. Shook argued eloquently that herbs are sources of organic compounds (or foods) that body tissues can use to build, repair and maintain themselves. His premise was that herbs are sources of nutrients (especially minerals) vital to maintaining health.

In an effort to add to the research that has been done on the nutritional value of herbs, a few years ago Nature's Sunshine Products undertook studies to verify the longstanding historical belief in herbal nutrition. For example, our scientists found that alfalfa is a source of many trace minerals. The plant naturally contains potassium, calcium and magnesium with smaller quantities of phosphorus, sulfur, copper, cobalt, molybdenum, iron, boron, sodium, fluorine, chlorine and strontium. Alfalfa naturally contains vitamin K, vitamin D, vitamin C, vitamin E, beta-carotene, folic acid, thiamine, riboflavin, pantothenic acid and niacin. Pyridoxine and choline are also present in varying amounts. That's not all. Alfalfa contains flavonoids, lipids, chlorophyll, volatile oils, proteins, sugars, starches, organic acids, alkaloids and saponins. Every one of these elements is processed in the human body, even if the required amount is minute.

Understanding the body

Trillions of living organisms called cells make up the body. Each cell requires a constant supply of oxygen, nutrients, pure water and the right temperature to survive. Waste must be removed. If cells are not supported in all of these ways, they will die.

It is impossible for each cell to supply its own needs. In order to perform specialized functions, each type of cell is organized in a beautiful system of interdependence that works for the good of the whole. Some cells are grouped to specialize in supplying food to the whole body (the digestive system). Others are adapted to coordinate the pumping of fresh air into the body and the removal of stale air (the respiratory system).

Because of the specialized nature of these cells, their nutritional needs may be different, depending on their activities. For example, the structural system needs more calcium, while the kidneys' filtering system requires more sodium and potassium. If the various specialized systems aren't supplied with correct elements, they can't perform their unique functions, which affects the entire body. Once the body's balance breaks down, various symptoms may appear. These symptoms are commonly called disease, meaning "the lack of ease."

Chinese herbal formulas

Nature's Sunshine recognizes the unique benefits of both Eastern and Western health care philosophies. The primary intent of Chinese herbal formulas is to provide nutritional support for harmony and balance in the body. For more than five millennia, Chinese herbalists have carefully observed the nutritional advantages of herbs and learned how to blend them carefully to meet the needs of people according to their constitutional differences.

Based on the principles of yin and yang, the Chinese herbal system is one major example of how ancient ideals are being recognized by modern scientific research— particularly the concept of treating each person as unique, rather than assuming that good results for one person will apply to everyone else the same way.

Another Chinese concept gaining attention in the West is the idea of treating the whole person, not just some of his/her manifestations. This includes taking a look at seemingly unrelated issues and emotional makeup.

NSP is proud to bring the expertise and success of Chinese experience to the West. Nature's Sunshine has a number of Chinese herbal formulas. In addition, many of Nature's Sunshine's exclusive formulas incorporate the time-honored principles of Chinese herbology.

The body system(s) that each product nutritionally supports is/are listed after the product name. This will help you think of our products as foods, to be used for the special needs of various body systems.

Get Well—Keep Well™ homeopathic remedies

Nature's Sunshine's Get Well—Keep Well line of homepathic remedies was born in 1991. Each remedy offers a time-tested approach to health care. Such an approach meets the needs of modern consumers who want to take greater responsibility for their well-being.

In accordance with guideline regulations, each Get Well—Keep Well homeopathic remedy is labeled with information about the minor disease symptoms for which the remedy is intended. The label also includes complete, easy-to-follow instructions.

NSP homeopathic medicines are formulated in strict accordance with traditional guidelines and methods. Only the highest quality ingredients are used. Get Well—Keep

Well homeopathics are an ideal addition to the Nature's Sunshine line of products designed to achieve better health, naturally—and to be consistent with our systems approach to health care.

It is vitally important to distinguish between the nature of our homeopathic remedies and that of our non-drug supplements, which are designed to nourish and strengthen body systems. This distinction allows customers to alleviate minor disease symptoms with safe and effective homeopathic remedies. They can then take advantage of the additional benefit of nutritionally strengthening the body systems involved by using other NSP products.

Safety and Efficacy— Homeopathics

All of Nature's Sunshine's homeopathic products are made in accordance with the Homeopathic Pharmacopoeia of the United States (HPUS), recognized as the official legal compendium of homeopathic active ingredients. They are also handmade and potentized as required by the methods and provings of Samuel Hahnemann, father of homeopathy. Because of our state-of-the-art packaging and insistence on Good Manufacturing Practices (GMP) standards, you may rest assured that Nature's Sunshine offers safe, excellent quality medicines for various ailments requiring an over-the-counter remedy.

For more information on the history of the company, our Quality Assurance, Research & Development, Manufacturing, Educational offerings or our product guarantee, visit our website at www.naturessunshine.com.

The Body Systems

The Circulatory System

The role of the circulatory system is twofold: it delivers oxygen and nutrients to all parts of the body while picking up waste and toxic materials that need to be eliminated. It accomplishes this monumental task through a network of nearly 60,000 miles of blood vessels and a fist-sized organ, the heart, which pumps more than 2,000 gallons of blood through its chambers each day.

Transporting your life blood

Blood vessels are divided into three main categories: arteries, veins and capillaries. Arteries are thick-walled vessels that carry blood from the heart to all parts of the body. Each time a person's heart beats, the elastic walls of the arteries swell to make room for the blood that is forced into them. The muscles inside the walls contract slowly, in effect squeezing the blood and forcing it to move along the arteries toward the capillaries. If arteries lose their elasticity—known as arteriosclerosis (hardening of the arteries)—the heart has to work much harder to keep the blood circulating. Like a machine, if the heart is overworked and not properly maintained, it cannot function optimally.

The lymphatic system

In addition to moving the blood along, the squeezing process forces fat globules, tiny protein particles and other nutrients to go outside of vessel walls. Once these things are out, due to their size, they cannot re-enter. Instead, they are collected along with other cellular debris lying between cells.

The lymphatic system picks up these particles and mixes them with plasma, which forms lymph. The lymph is then purified, recycled in the lymph nodes, and added back to the blood. This process, which is vital to the circulatory system, is also essential to the success of the immune system.

The return trip

Veins are thin-walled blood vessels. Their purpose is to return the blood from the body to the heart. Many larger veins have valves to prevent a back-flow of blood. If these valves experience prolonged or excessive pressure, veins can become overstretched, and the valves may be destroyed or rendered incompetent. This results in problems like varicose veins.

Capillaries are the smallest blood vessels in the body. They serve as intermediaries, connecting arteries with veins. Since capillaries are extremely small and have permeable walls, it's possible for capillaries to reach nearly every cell in the body and to transfer substances, including important nutrients, to and from the tissues.

The heart

The heart is made up primarily of muscles that facilitate its pumping action. This most vital of organs consists of four compartments or chambers. The upper two are referred to as the atria, and the lower two as ventricles. Oxygen-poor blood enters the right atrium and moves through it to the right ventricle. From there, blood is sent via the pulmonary arteries to the lungs so that it can pick up a fresh supply of oxygen. Once it has taken on a supply of oxygen, blood moves through the pulmonary veins—first to the left atrium and then to the left ventricle.

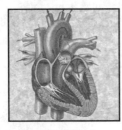 The heartbeat is sustained by the sinoatrial (SA) node, which functions as a pacemaker. A healthy heart has a regular beat, although the rate can vary depending on several factors including age, sex, physical activity and emotion.

Health factors

For the circulatory system to function properly, the heart must be strong, the vessels capable of safely transporting optimal amounts of blood, and the blood itself must be healthy. Serious problems can arise when these conditions are not met. Each year approximately 25 percent of all deaths in the U.S. occur from heart attacks, and the majority of these are attributable to hardening of the arteries. In addition to heart attacks, a poor circulatory system can lead to strokes, kidney disease, varicose veins, blood clots and a variety of other conditions that can kill or severely limit the enjoyment of life.

Three major factors that contribute to circulatory problems are hypertension (high blood pressure), high levels of triglycerides and cholesterol in the bloodstream, and smoking. Nutrition has been linked directly to hypertension and high levels of triglycerides and cholesterol. Other factors include obesity, heredity and emotional stress. Unfortunately, the threat of problems increases significantly when more than one factor is present. That means that when a person has three risk factors, his chances for disease are six times greater than when only one is present.

How can you maintain a healthy circulatory system? Most experts agree that the keys are 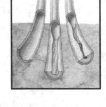 to avoid smoking, monitor your diet, exercise regularly and manage stress.

The Digestive System

The digestive system is the means by which the body transforms food into the energy it needs to build, repair and fuel itself. On average, an adult body processes roughly 2-1/2 gallons of digested food, liquids and digestive secretions each day.

Digestion begins in the mouth, where food is chewed by the teeth and mixed with saliva. The saliva

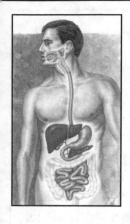

helps lubricate both the mouth and the food and dissolves food particles to enhance taste and facilitate swallowing. Saliva also cleanses the mouth.

Chewing is important because as food is ground into increasingly fine particles, digestive juices containing enzymes mix with it. The more thoroughly food is chewed, the more complete the digestive functions are that occur at this point.

Once food is swallowed, it travels through the throat or pharynx to the esophagus. Both the pharynx and the esophagus are muscular tubes that work through a series of contractions to move the food along and eventually empty it into the stomach. The stomach then churns it into a paste called chyme, which is easier to digest. Some of the components of the food, such as water and sugar, are absorbed directly from the stomach into the bloodstream.

The next stop is the pyloric sphincter, which serves as the gateway to the small intestines. The digestion of starches, proteins and fat occurs in the small intestine with the help of secretions that originate in the pancreas, liver and intestinal villi.

How different nutrients are digested

Carbohydrates (starches and sugars), proteins and fats are made up of extremely complex molecules that must be broken down or digested in order to be useful to the body. The process of digestion changes starches and complex sugars into simple sugars, proteins into amino acids, and fats into fatty acids and glycerin. In these forms the nutrients can finally be absorbed into the bloodstream.

The digestion of carbohydrates begins in the mouth. Saliva contains the enzyme ptyalin, which changes some of the starches into sugar and makes them available to the bloodstream. The process continues in the stomach.

Proteins begin the digestive process only after reaching the stomach. This is due to the presence of hydrochloric acid and another enzyme called pepsin. Only a small amount of absorption occurs between the stomach and the bloodstream; most of it takes place after the contents have moved on to the small intestine, where it is met by pancreatic secretions that contain the enzymes amylase, trypsin and lipase. Amylase works to change starch into simple sugars, trypsin breaks down partially digested proteins, and lipase splits fats into fatty acids and glycerin.

In addition to these fluids, the intestinal walls produce secretions that, while milder than pancreatic juices, perform similar functions. Bile, which is produced in the liver and stored in the gall bladder, also flows into the small intestine through the bile duct. Bile helps to further digest and absorb fats. In addition to producing bile, the liver stores fats, carbohydrates, proteins and vitamins. It also absorbs poisons and toxic substances before neutralizing them.

About 90 percent of absorption takes place in the small intestine. Food is digested when it has been broken down into particles small enough to be absorbed by the tiny blood and lymph capillaries located in the walls of the small intestine. From there the nourishment is circulated to all the cells in the body.

Factors in digestive health

There are many ways to abuse and weaken the digestive system. Overeating, constant snacking and diluting digestive secretions with

What Are Enzymes?

Enzymes are complex organic substances produced in plants and animals that catalyze (speed up) chemical reactions in cells and organs. The digestive enzymes work with the body fluids to break down large chemical chains into smaller particles. The body is then able to absorb and utilize these smaller food particles.

Digestive Enzymes & Their Work

Region	Time	Enzymes	Action
Mouth	minutes	ptyalin	starch to malt sugar
Pharynx	seconds		
Esophagus	5-10 seconds for solids; 1 second for liquids		
Stomach	2-6 hours	pepsin	proteins to peptones acts on milk protein
Small intestine	5-6 hours	various enzymes acting on carbohydrates	maltose to simple sugars, mainly glucose
From pancreas		trypsin, amylase, lipase	turns proteins into amino acids, starch to maltose, and fats to fatty acids and glycerol
From liver/gallbladder		bile	makes fats water-soluble

liquids can all place undue stress on digestive organs. Eating too fast, or feelings of emotional stress may adversely affect digestion. In addition, as people age, the amount of hydrochloric acid (HCl) their bodies produce decreases. The decrease starts between ages 35–45. By age 55, almost everyone has reduced levels of HCl.

Heredity may also be a factor in digestive health. Some people begin life with digestive organs predisposed to problems. Of course, when this is the case, any kind of abuse only compounds the problem.

The importance of enzymes

Enzymes are the catalysts of all chemical changes that occur in the body. They are found in both the food we eat and in our bodies. Without enzymes, body functions would be too slow to sustain life. Unfortunately, although they are absolutely essential, each person is born with a limited potential for enzymes. That's why maintaining an adequate supply of enzymes plays such an important role in supporting the health of the body.

When the enzymes that exist naturally in foods are destroyed by heat, wilting or other abuse prior to digestion, the body must create new ones before it can properly digest the food. One of the best ways to help maintain a healthy supply of enzymes in the digestive system is to eat fresh, raw fruits and vegetables as often as possible. In addition to the enzymes these foods contain, fruits and vegetables are a rich source of the vital coenzymes (vitamins) needed by the body on a constant basis.

After food leaves the small intestine, it moves into the large intestine or colon, a muscular tube—about five feet in length and approximately two inches in diameter—coiled into a frame around the convoluted small intestine. Waste material is forced through the colon by the action of the muscles. It then exits the body through the rectum.

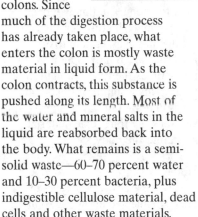

The colon has three main parts: the ascending, transverse and descending colons. Since much of the digestion process has already taken place, what enters the colon is mostly waste material in liquid form. As the colon contracts, this substance is pushed along its length. Most of the water and mineral salts in the liquid are reabsorbed back into the body. What remains is a semi-solid waste—60–70 percent water and 10–30 percent bacteria, plus indigestible cellulose material, dead cells and other waste materials.

The process of elimination takes anywhere from 12–24 hours or longer. Generally, the shorter the time, the better. Unfortunately, modern diets and health habits sometimes result in greatly increased transit times. As transit time increases, the stool becomes increasingly hardened and difficult to pass due to dehydration.

Systems Guide

Moreover, as the body reabsorbs the fluid content of the feces, it also absorbs many soluble toxins.

Factors in colon health

People whose diets are high in refined foods (including sugar and white flour) and low in fiber content are especially susceptible to intestinal problems. In fact, colon and rectal disorders are much more common in America than Africa, where the average diet contains seven times as much fiber as in the U.S.

The colon works best when it is moderately full. Dietary fiber fills this need. Although it contains no nutrients, fiber helps promote good health by providing the necessary bulk to encourage timely movement of fecal material through the colon. As this happens, certain toxic materials are removed along with many times the fiber's weight in water. This is important because it helps maintain bowel regularity and shortens the time toxic materials remain in the body.

Fiber

There are two basic types of fiber: soluble and insoluble. Soluble fiber includes pectin, gums and some hemicellulose. Fruits, vegetables, seeds, brown rice, barley and oats are sources of soluble fiber. Soluble fiber works mainly by helping to produce a softer stool. It also chemically reduces the absorption of certain substances into the bloodstream.

Insoluble fiber includes cellulose, some hemicellulose and lignin. Whole grains and the outside of seeds, fruits, legumes and other foods are the main sources for insoluble fiber, which works like a sponge, absorbing many times its weight in water and swelling up inside the intestines. The result is more efficient elimination.

When extra fiber is added to the diet, it is important that extra fluids also be added. If not, the beneficial effects can be diminished as the added fiber actually slows down or even blocks proper intestinal elimination. Spreading out fiber intake is also suggested to help ease any unpleasant side effects that may occur at the start of a new, fiber-rich dietary regimen.

Exercise also plays a role in the health of the intestinal system. Without sufficient exercise, bowel action may slow and normal circulation within the digestive system may be reduced.

Beneficial bacteria

In addition to eating sufficient amounts of fiber, it is important to maintain a good supply of beneficial bacteria, such as *Lactobacillus acidophilus*. Unlike bacteria that cause disease, *L. acidophilus* is extremely helpful. It produces digestive enzymes and assists in the final processing of food. It also produces important vitamins such as vitamin K and the B vitamins (B12, thiamine and riboflavin), and helps inhibit the growth of harmful bacteria. Unfortunately, naturally occurring lactobacillus can be destroyed by a course of antibiotic treatment.

The Brain & the Nervous System

Together, the brain and nervous system are responsible for processing and storing information, thinking, sleeping, perceiving pain, breathing, contracting muscles, glandular secretions, maintaining body temperature and more. In short, they provide a vital communication link between our internal and external worlds. This happens because the sensory organs of the nervous system receive external information and relay it to the brain. There it is sorted, prioritized and passed to organs, tissues and cells so that they can adapt to changes in both environments.

The nervous system has two parts, the central and the peripheral systems. The central system consists of the brain and spinal cord, both made up of nerve fibers. The peripheral system is the network of nerves located throughout the body.

The brain has three main parts: the cerebrum, cerebellum and brain stem. The cerebrum receives information, thinks about it, processes it and then sends it out. The cerebellum is essential for balance and coordination. The brain stem connects the cerebrum to the spinal cord and is responsible for regulating such functions as respiration, heart rate and blood flow, eye movements and pupil size, and neck and head movement.

The peripheral system penetrates every tissue of the body just as the circulatory system does. It is composed of 28 billion neurons, or nerve cells that transmit messages by means of electrical impulses, or signals, to organs. When the impulses arrive at an "end organ" or effector, they cause activity. If the effector is a muscle, the activity is contraction. But if it is a gland cluster connected with the digestive tract, the action is the release of digestive enzymes.

The communication process and stress

The nervous system communicates two basic types of messages: one is to activate, the other is to relax. Some of its actions are automatic (e.g. the heartbeat, breathing and digestion) and some are voluntary (e.g. eating, drinking and walking).

In addition to influencing the physical functions of the body, the nervous system also influences how it acts or reacts to stress. The fight-or-flight response is a good example. This is a hormonally stimulated state that prepares the body for an upcoming challenge.

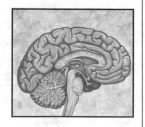

191

Stress is a factor in every life, and the degree to which it affects us negatively is largely determined by how we react to stimuli around us. We need to supply the nervous system with good food so that our nerves can accurately communicate and handle the various stresses to which they are constantly exposed.

Even though everyday hassles may seem minor, researcher Dr. Richard Lazarus has found that in combination they can have an even bigger impact on our health than traumatic events such as death, major illness or financial difficulties.

It seems that our nervous system doesn't differentiate between a physical threat and an emotional one. Thus, crying children, a critical boss, unpaid bills, traffic jams, missed deadlines and a host of other mental/emotional crises can be perceived by our nervous system as a form of danger, and may even evoke our fight-or-flight response. This defense mechanism can actually damage our

The nervous system works electrochemically. Tiny impulses, or currents, pass along the fibers without the fiber moving, changing color or altering its appearance in any manner. The current is generated through millisecond exchanges of charged potassium and sodium particles across nerve cell membranes.

health if it is evoked constantly and unnecessarily and the energy released by it is not dispelled through fighting or fleeing.

Prolonged emotional stress can lead to a breakdown of health. Evidence shows that many of us may not handle stress well. In fact, it has been estimated that one-half of those going to see a doctor have symptoms that can be traced to psychological stress.

Of course, emotional stress is not the only factor involved in illness and disease, nor is it necessarily the primary cause. It is, however, one of the risk factors associated with poor health.

Stress management

Psychologist Donald A. Tubesing related stress to the tension on a violin string. He said we need "enough tension to make music but not so much that it snaps."

Fortunately, stress can be managed and its effects reduced. Exercise, meditation and relaxation techniques, attitude changes and improved nutrition are some effective ways to handle it.

Stress can also increase the need for certain nutrients since it alters our metabolic process. For example, an increased metabolic rate means an increase in the burning of carbohydrates. When larger than normal amounts of carbohydrates are metabolized, the need for thiamine and other members of the B-complex family may increase.

Stress is closely related to nutrition. The fight-or-flight response increases the metabolic process, which in turn increases the need for certain vitamins—particularly the water-soluble vitamins that must be replenished on a daily basis. This is why the B-complex and C vitamins arc the core of all anti-stress vitamin supplements.

Glandular System

The human body has two types of glands—exocrine glands that secrete fluids into a duct or a tube, and endocrine glands that release chemicals known as hormones into general 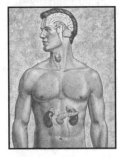 circulation. Endocrine glands include the pituitary, pineal, thyroid, parathyroids, thymus, pancreas, adrenals and sex glands (ovaries and testes). The hormones they release regulate basic drives and emotions while promoting growth and sexual identity and controlling body temperature. They also help to repair broken tissue and generate energy.

The amount of hormones released by the endocrine glands depends on the body's needs. Levels change in response to infection, stress and changes in the chemical composition of the blood. Hormones are regulated by control mechanisms within the body. The process is something like this: an endocrine gland secretes its hormone and then the hormone travels to receptors on cells located within a particular tissue or organ. The tissue or organ is then able to carry out its function. However, when the level of activity of the tissue or organ becomes too high, there is a "negative feedback" to the gland that tells it to cut back on production and secretion of this hormone.

Factors in glandular health

The endocrine system functions best when it has ample stores of minerals—particularly trace minerals. For example, the thyroid gland maintains proper metabolic rates and levels of body fluids when it has ample iodine. Similarly, the pancreas, which controls blood sugar levels, needs chromium.

Eating foods rich in trace minerals helps support the body's glandular functions. Unfortunately, many foods that are a mainstay of the modern dict are devoid of trace minerals. This is due in part to the depletion of soil and the effects of processing. For example, raw sugar loses 94 percent of its chromium and 89 percent of its manganese during processing. Likewise, as wheat is processed into white flour, it loses 50 percent of its chromium and 86 percent of its manganese.

Nutritional supplements rich in trace minerals, when taken with a well-balanced diet, help ensure the endocrine system gets the nutritional elements it needs to function properly.

Pituitary

The pituitary is roughly the size of a pea. The front lobe produces hormones that stimulate the thyroid, adrenals, testes and ovaries; encourage the growth of the body; and stimulate the secretion of milk in a mother's breasts. Growth hormone affects almost every tissue in the body by regulating the amount of nutrients taken into cells. Too much growth hormone results in gigantism in children, while too little causes dwarfism.

The intermediate part of the pituitary may be involved with melanin secretion, which affects skin color.

The back lobe produces a hormone that causes the uterus to contract during childbirth and then stimulates the production of milk in the mammary glands. It also produces another hormone that regulates the retention of water by the kidneys.

Pineal

Named for its pinecone shape, the pineal gland may function in hormonal regulation, menstruation and sex development. It secretes a large number of active chemicals, the most important of which is melatonin, a substance that is present in higher concentrations during the night. Melatonin plays a role in controlling the sleep cycle. It also inhibits the secretion of gonadotropins. This is why tumors of the pineal gland may slow down the development of sexual maturity or in some cases accelerate it.

Thyroid and parathyroid

The thyroid controls the body's metabolism and has the ability to concentrate iodine consumed with the diet. It also produces the hormone calcitonin, which helps to lower the level of calcium in the blood.

The parathyroid glands are small glands, usually four in number, embedded within the back of the thyroid. They produce the hormone parathormone, which regulates calcium and phosphorus metabolism. Calcium plays an important role in many metabolic processes. Too much calcium (hypercalcemia) or too little (tetany) can disrupt the normal function of the muscles and nerves. The body's cells are extremely sensitive to changing amounts of blood calcium.

Thymus

The thymus gland is central to the body's defense mechanisms. It is composed largely of developing lymphocytes, a special type of infection-fighting cells. Although its function is not fully understood, it is known that the thymus plays an important role in developing immunities against various diseases. This is especially true during the early years of life. After puberty the thymus begins to shrink in size. Researchers have speculated that the progressive shrinking of the thymus gland as age increases is one of the reasons older people are somewhat prone to infections.

Hypothalamus

The hypothalamus is actually a tiny cluster of nerve cells located at the base of the brain. It serves as a link between the autonomic nervous system and the endocrine system. It is responsible for many body functions because it integrates and ensures appropriate responses to stimuli. In addition, it regulates hunger, thirst, sleep and wakefulness and also plays an important role in the regulation of most of the involuntary mechanisms of the body including body temperature, sexual drive and the female menstrual cycle. Finally, it regulates the work of the pituitary gland.

Pancreas

The pancreas contains cells that secrete enzymes involved in the digestion of food, and other cells that produce the hormones insulin and glucagon. Insulin lowers the amount of sugar in the blood by facilitating its movement into the cells of the body. It is also important in the manufacture and storage of fats and proteins and in growth. Glucagon increases the amount of sugar present in the blood by causing the breakdown of fats and proteins. It tends to be secreted in times of stress.

Adrenal

The adrenal glands are essential for functions such as the body's chemical regulation of sodium and potassium; blood concentration; pulse rate; smooth muscle relaxation or contraction; and dilation of pupils. Although it appears to be one organ, it is actually two small glands. The outer cortex of each is essential for the body's chemical regulation. The adrenal cortex secretes two hormones, cortisol and aldosterone, which are known collectively as corticosteriods. They help the body reduce stress and are essential for life. Cortisol is an energy generator that regulates the conversion of carbohydrates into glucose and directs reserves to the liver. It also suppresses inflammation. Aldosterone regulates the mineral and water balance of the body. It prevents excessive loss of water through the kidneys and maintains the balance between sodium and potassium in the bloodstream. This balance is important to the contraction of muscles. The inner part, or medulla, secretes epinephrine and norepinephrine, two hormones that help the body reduce stress and are important in the fight-or-flight response.

Ovaries

The ovaries are located on each side of the abdomen. They have a dual function: producing and releasing ova (eggs), and secreting female sex hormones such as estrogen and progesterone. These hormones are responsible for the development of secondary sexual characteristics in girls after puberty and, along with others, are responsible for the regular bodily changes that accompany the menstrual cycle. Both of these functions cease at menopause.

Testes

Located in the scrotum, the testes produce sperm and secrete testosterone, which is responsible for the development of secondary sexual characteristics in boys after puberty, and for maintaining maleness throughout a man's adult life.

Immune System

According to one scientist, the immune system is the sixth sense; it recognizes viruses and bacteria the brain doesn't identify, and then converts that information into hormones that go to the brain to activate the immune process.

The immune system works in partnership with other protective body systems. For example, the skin forms a physical barrier against foreign materials, while the respiratory system utilizes cilia, mucus and coughing to rid the body of inhaled microbes and pollutants. In addition, acid in the stomach and enzymes in the pancreas and intestines destroy many harmful microorganisms.

If foreign materials overcome the body's other protective mechanisms, then the immune/defense system begins operating. This system is composed of lymph nodes, blood proteins (known as immunoglobulin) and specialized white blood cells such as lymphocytes, as well as the organs that produce these cells and the blood vessels that transport them.

Lymph nodes, or lymph glands as they are sometimes called, are usually small oval structures that are normally the size of small kidney beans. They are generally located in clusters near veins at strategic points along medium-sized lymph vessels at the knee, elbow, armpit, groin, neck, abdomen and chest.

The lymph nodes clean and filter blood. The also serve as a gathering place for germ-fighting cells during illness. The filtration process prevents bacteria, cancer cells and other infectious agents from entering the blood and circulating through the system. The lymph nodes are also centers for production and storage of some of the white blood cells, namely the lymphocytes and monocytes, which are important elements in the body's immune mechanism. During any kind of infection, the nodes become enlarged due to the multiplication of lymphocytes in the node.

All of the parts of the immune system are designed to react rapidly to disease-producing organisms and their toxins. If the disease gets past these defenses, the body produces a generalized fever, localized inflammations and other reactions designed to conquer unwelcome invaders.

Antibodies (immunoglobulin) are important for proper function of the immune system. These proteins distinguish between the body's own protein and foreign protein. When foreign protein is identified, antibodies can destroy it. It is estimated that there are 100 million different kinds of antibodies, each of which is custom-built.

The body constantly battles mutant (cancer) cells. Some immunologists believe that there are always malignancies in the body and that they are usually recognized and destroyed by the immune system.

Factors in immune system health

We live in a world of natural poisons and man-made pollutants. These environmental pollutants, along with improper diet and other harmful habits such as smoking and improper rest, can reduce the body's ability to protect itself from harmful bacteria, viruses, chemicals and other factors that can lead to disease.

Purdue University nutritionist Thomas Petro, Ph.D., wrote, "It's not that certain nutrients affect the immune system—it's that every nutrient affects the immune system." For that reason, a balanced diet is probably the most important consideration in maintaining a healthy immune system. In addition, when the body is deprived of some minerals, it is more likely to retain pollutants.

A great deal of focus has been directed at the antioxidant vitamins A, C and E because of their function in protecting the cells from damage caused by natural body processes, lifestyles, and environmental and chemical pollutants. These vitamins and other powerful antioxidant nutrients, along with the trace mineral selenium, help prevent important molecules and structures within the cell from reacting with oxygen, which often injures—literally burns—the cell structure. This process is called oxidation.

Respiratory System

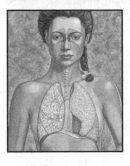

The lungs are the center of the respiratory system, which includes the nose, throat and trachea (windpipe). Air comes into the body through the nose and mouth and travels past the larynx (voice box) to the trachea, which branches into two main tubes or bronchi. From there, air moves into the inner recesses of the lungs, where the lungs transfer oxygen into the blood via small air sacs called alveoli. Each alveolus has extremely thin walls containing a network of capillaries involved in the exchange of oxygen and carbon dioxide.

Breathing, usually automatic and regulated in the medulla oblongata of the brain, takes place 10–15 times per minute. Inhaling occurs when a message is sent from the respiratory center of the brain to the diaphragm and certain rib muscles. These contract, pulling the lower surfaces of the lungs downward so they can fill with air. Stretch receptors in the lungs then send signals back to the brain, which causes the diaphragm and rib muscles to relax. This in turn causes the diaphragm to move upward, so that the air is exhaled.

Blood is responsible for carrying both food and oxygen to cells. The cells use the oxygen to convert carbohydrates and fats into energy. The byproduct of this process is carbon dioxide, which the body exhales.

It happens this way: The right side of the heart pumps blood with a high concentration of carbon dioxide into the lungs. There the carbon dioxide is replaced with oxygen, which causes the blood to change from a dark red to a bright red color. This indicates that hemoglobin has picked up the oxygen. The oxygen-enriched blood is then pumped through the left side of the heart, and next circulated throughout the body. Then the carbon dioxide is exhaled.

The respiratory system is sensitive to the amount of carbon dioxide present in the blood. If this amount rises, the breathing response will increase so that more oxygen is available for energy metabolism.

Factors in respiratory health

Most people start out with a pair of bright, healthy pink lungs. As they go through life, many individuals either knowingly or unknowingly abuse and weaken their lungs. The seriousness of this cannot be overemphasized. Remember, the respiratory system is responsible for supplying oxygen to the blood and expelling waste gases. Without life-giving oxygen, cells cannot utilize the energy resources that are available to them and so cannot function. If the efficiency of the respiratory system begins to diminish, any energy stored in the body has to be released at a slower rate.

Cigarette smoking is a major cause of lung damage. Of the more than 4,000 substances found in cigarette smoke, two of the most dangerous are nicotine and carbon monoxide. Nicotine, believed responsible for the addictive properties of cigarettes, causes the release of epinephrine, a hormone secreted by the body. This in turn produces an increase in blood pressure and heart rate. Carbon monoxide prevents the 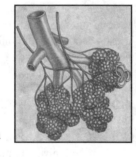 blood from carrying the full amount of oxygen, and over time this can be extremely harmful.

Cigarette smoke damages the lungs, bronchi, blood vessels, heart and other organs and tissues. In addition, it is associated with increased risks for all of the following conditions and diseases: coughing, breathing problems, respiratory infections, pneumonia, stroke, hardening of the arteries (arteriosclerosis), stomach and intestinal ulcers, and cancer of the mouth, throat, esophagus, kidneys, bladder and pancreas. Smoking during pregnancy increases the risk of miscarriage and fetal death. Even secondhand smoke has been reported to increase the risk of respiratory and middle ear infections in children and has been related to deaths due to lung cancer and heart disease.

Beyond smoking, the respiratory tract is especially vulnerable to particles floating in the air due to pollution. Professor Julius Comroe of the University of California has estimated that city dwellers may take in as much as 20 trillion particles of foreign matter per day.

The respiratory system has several ways of dealing with these particles. For example, the cough and the sneeze reflexes keep the passageways of the lungs clear of foreign matter. Cilia, the hairs in the nose, trap irritants, contaminants, bacteria, viruses, fungi, vehicle exhaust and other materials. But not all particles are trapped here.

There are also cells in the respiratory tract especially designed to engulf and rid the body of foreign particles. These particles irritate the tissues, causing them to swell and produce extra mucus. The lining of respiratory tract becomes uncomfortable and sore, and swelling and mucus eventually obstruct the passages. If particles are trapped further down in the tract, bronchitis and asthma may result.

Since oxygen is so vital to the energy needs of the body, it is essential that we maintain healthy lungs by breathing unpolluted air as much as possible and by supplying the body with good nutrition.

Urinary System

The urinary system consists of two kidneys, each having a ureter connecting it to the bladder. The bladder is then connected to the urethra, which ultimately leads to an opening out of the body. 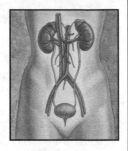 The function of the urinary system is to produce and remove a waste product called urine, and to regulate the amount, alkalinity or acidity, and consistency of body fluids.

Kidneys filter blood. Every minute, one-fourth of the blood in the body enters the kidneys, which are composed of about 2 million microscopic filters called nephrons. Nephrons are responsible for absorbing nutrients and eliminating toxins and other waste materials from the blood. In addition, the kidneys help regulate other bodily functions by secreting the hormones renin, erythropoietin and prostaglandin. Renin helps control blood pressure, while erythropoietin helps stimulate the body to produce more red blood cells.

Prostaglandin is not limited to the kidneys. In other tissues and situations, it causes smooth muscles to contract or relax, is involved in abnormal fluid collection in the body, is responsible for some types of fevers and pain, and is heavily involved in the process of inflam-

Systems Guide

mation. But in the kidneys, prostaglandin causes dilation of the veins and helps with the urine-making process.

The bladder is a sac-like organ located in the pelvis. Its function is to store urine until it is excreted. It is made up of three layers of involuntary muscles that provide it with the ability to expand and contract. When empty, the bladder shrivels up to the shape of a small prune, but it swells and stretches as needed to hold urine. Most people's bladders can hold about a pint of urine. Then, when the bladder is full, the walls expand and send impulses to the brain telling it to urinate.

Urine is 96 percent water. The other 4 percent includes a mix of urea, salt, sugar, proteins, fat, vitamins and coloring from bile pigments. Its color is usually clear or yellow, though this depends upon the diet and health of the individual. Urine has a distinct, ammonia-like smell that is primarily due to the nitrogenous wastes it contains.

Factors in urinary health

Kidneys are designed to keep the blood clean. They spend every minute of the day filtering out impurities. However, like any intricate structure, they have limitations. Even so, modern society seems to dictate that they must deal with more and more abuse. Drinking water frequently during the day can alleviate some potential problems by helping the kidneys flush toxins from the body.

Healthy cells need the proper concentration of salts. That's why potassium and sodium are crucial to the body's fluid balance. More than half of the water in the body is located inside the cells. The rest is mixed with salt—rather like diluted sea water—that bathes the cells.

The kidneys are the major regulating mechanism for maintaining proper sodium and potassium balance. They are designed to excrete extra potassium and save sodium. In times past, there was plenty of potassium in foods, but not as much sodium. Today, people eat more foods that contain sodium (mainly processed foods with added sodium) and not as many fresh foods with natural potassium.

Unfortunately, even with a high-sodium diet, the kidneys still save sodium and excrete potassium. Obviously, we can't change the way our kidneys function, but we can change our diet. Since food processing lowers the potassium content of foods, we should eat plenty of fresh foods.

Herbal supplements, vitamins and minerals can also help provide the urinary system with the nutrients it needs to effectively perform its delicate chemical balancing act.

Structural System

The structural system provides a framework for the body. Consisting of bones, muscles and connective tissues, it gives the body not only form, but also the ability to move.

When a baby is born, it has

about 350 bones, all soft because they are composed mostly of a watery substance called cartilage. As the baby grows, calcium phosphate permeates the bones, and they stiffen. This process is called calcification. Eventually calcified cartilage is replaced by true bone, made up largely of calcium phosphate, and some of the bones fuse together. A normal adult has between 206 and 209 bones in his body, depending upon whether he has one or two additional ribs and an extra bone in the coccyx (tailbone).

Calcium phosphate is deposited in bones in two ways. At the outer edge it takes the form of a solid, compact material covered by a membrane called the periosteum. Deeper inside, it becomes a honeycomb of sponge-like, porous material called cancellous bone. A soft material known as marrow fills the spaces inside the cancellous bone. Marrow is actually the manufacturing site of both red and white blood cells, and as such is tunneled with vessels that move freshly made red and white blood cells out and bring in red ones containing essential nutrients.

Although bones generally stop growing in length during mid-teens for girls and at around age 20 for boys,

they never really stop the growing process, because they are constantly rebuilding themselves.

Bones contain two types of cells, osteoblasts and osteoclasts. These work together to continually build new bone material on the outside and remove old, unneeded material from the inside. To sustain this growth, the body must have sufficient supplies of certain nutrients, including calcium, phosphorus and vitamin D. If there is a shortage of calcium in the bloodstream, the body will remove it from the bones without replacing it. This can eventually cause bones to become weak and porous. Unchecked, it can lead to a severely lifestyle-limiting, sometimes fatal condition known as osteoporosis.

Connections

Joints have been called masterpieces of engineering because they are designed to permit movement between bones that must meet, but not touch each other. Their role is to bind two or more bones firmly together while cushioning and lubricating them well enough to last through a lifetime of lifting, swinging, bending, walking, etc.

While their individual construction may vary, most joints are made up of the same elements. The joint is enclosed in a tough, fibrous capsule of connective tissue that secretes a liquid called synovial fluid. The synovial fluid lubricates the moving parts. Outside the capsule, fibrous anchors called ligaments surround the joint and link the bones. Ligaments protect the capsule and

Systems Guide

help keep all motion of the joint within safe limits. In places where muscle tissues, called tendons or sinews, pass next to large joints so that muscles on one side will be linked to bones on the other, small fluid-filled pouches, or bursae, also act as buffers.

Muscles

Bones and sinews may control the movements of the body, but muscles create them by converting chemical energy from food into mechanical energy.

Muscles perform their work by contracting. This means that they pull, never push, and because of this it takes a pair of them to make a range of movement possible. There are more than 600 muscles in the body consisting of three basic types: heart muscle, smooth muscle, and skeletal muscle. Each muscle is made up of innumerable tiny, string-like fibers, and each of these, in turn, is composed of bundles of infinitesimal filaments varying in length from half an inch to about a foot. Small muscles have just a few fibers, while large ones have a great many.

Muscles grow strong through use. The effort it takes to use muscles makes the heart supply them with more blood and nutrients. This stimulates the growth of new muscle fibers and blood vessels. In effect, exercise enlarges and strengthens muscles just as it does bones.

Factors in structural health

Regular, lifelong activity is essential to keeping bones and muscles functioning optimally. If a person is never very active, his/her bones won't be able to grow as dense as nature meant them to be. Likewise, if a person is active enough to develop the strongest skeleton possible, but then becomes inactive, the bone that is no longer needed will eventually be lost.

Diet is also extremely important. As mentioned earlier, a shortage of calcium over an extended period of time can spell disaster. In fact, the loss of calcium is the most serious nutritional problem experienced by older Americans. Bone loss appears to begin as early as age 35, and is particularly serious for women. As they approach menopause, their rate of bone loss accelerates greatly, partly because of a decreased secretion of the hormone estrogen, which helps maintain bone mass. An estimated 5 million women are affected by bone loss. Men, too, should be cautious, although the number of men experiencing serious loss is only about one-fifth that of women. The National Institutes

Although an adult's skeleton weighs only a little more than 20 lbs., it is capable of bearing incredible loads. This is largely due to the fact that bones are not only hard, but resilient. In fact, bone tissue is almost 20 times as resilient as steel.

of Health suggests that a daily calcium intake of at least 1,200 mg is required by adults. Because it is difficult to obtain that amount from food alone, and because some individuals may be allergic to the best dietary sources of calcium, supplementation is recommended.

Skin & Hair

A protective barrier against the elements, skin is the largest and most

 exposed organ of the body. It is a waterproof covering that shields more vulnerable organs and

protects the body from toxins, damage and infection. It does this while maintaining body temperature and helping to eliminate certain wastes.

Skin is composed of three basic layers: the outer epidermis, inner dermis and the inner subcutaneous layer. The epidermis can be further divided into two layers. The outermost is actually a covering of dead cells and a protein called keratin. Next to it is a layer containing melanin and keratin. Melanin determines skin color.

The dermis houses hair follicles, blood vessels, nerves, muscle tissue and sweat, oil and other glands. All of these components are loosely connected by collagen, a protein substance that is found not only in skin, but in tendons, bones and cartilage, too. Collagen works with elastin, another protein substance, to give the skin its tone and suppleness.

The subcutaneous layer is made up of connective tissue that specializes in the formation of fat. It helps prevent heat loss and cushions the body against injury.

Hair

Hair is an elastic filament made up of keratin. Only the root, which is located in the dermis, is alive. There are approximately 100,000–200,000 strands of hair on the average head, with the number varying, sometimes dramatically, from person to person. Individual hairs grow about 1/2 inch per month for two to six years, and then rest for about three months. (Eyebrows and eyelashes grow for 10 weeks and then rest for nine months.) At the end of the rest cycle, the hairs fall out. At any given time about 90 percent of the hairs on a head are growing, and 10 percent are resting. People normally shed anywhere from 30–200 hairs a day. However, emotional stress can boost the number to 500 per day, and extreme physical or emotional shock can also make hair fall out.

Each hair has three layers, with color forming in the middle. Its shape and texture is determined by the shape and size of the follicle from which it grows. Cross sections of hair show that straight hair tends to be round, while curly hair is flat or oval. The number of active follicles per square inch determines whether hair is thick or thin, while coarseness or fineness describes the width of the hair itself.

Systems Guide

Nails

Fingernails and toenails are a specialization of the epidermis that is formed by a hardened protein called keratin. Contrary to popular belief, nails have a very low calcium content. In fact, keratin has a high sulfur content. Nails have three major sections: the root, the body of the nail, and the free portion that extends over the tip of the finger or toe. Fingernails grow more slowly than hair, about 1/10 inch a month, and they grow about four times faster than toenails. For some reason, they seem to grow more slowly during infancy, old age and in the wintertime.

Fingernails have long been known as an indicator of health, and any dramatic changes in their texture, shape, color or growth rate may be a signal to see a health care professional.

Factors in skin, hair and nail health

Genetics are a major determining factor in the health of skin. Some people have naturally great skin, while others are troubled with a variety of conditions. Heredity isn't the only factor, however. Skin is also affected by diet, exercise, rest and stress. Even the climate in which a person lives can play a big role in his/her appearance. People who live in warm places inevitably get more exposure to the sun than those who live in colder areas. Skin cells absorb the sun's rays. These cells produce vitamin D as well as a healthy-looking tan. Unfortunately, excessive exposure to the sun can also cause skin cancer, especially among people who are very fair skinned. In addition, overexposure can cause signs of premature skin aging.

Internal skin care begins with proper nutrition, including whole grains and plenty of fresh fruits and vegetables. It also includes drinking plenty of fresh, pure water, which helps to hydrate skin from the inside out as it helps flush toxins out of the body.

Obesity can make an individual prone to eczema, rashes and fungal infections, largely because extreme weight makes people sweat too much. This generally interferes with the body's own systems of self-disinfection.

At the other extreme, a diet containing too few calories can give skin a withered, dry, rough, inelastic and even cold appearance. Adequate amounts of nutrients including the B-complex vitamins, vitamin C, vitamin A, vitamin K, essential fatty acids, the minerals zinc and iron, and protein are all important for healthy skin and hair—as are exercise and rest. Finally, stress has been called one of the biggest enemies of beautiful skin.

For external skin care, a good daily treatment regimen is vital. This can help maintain the skin's current state of health by nourishing and protecting it, as well as removing any oily buildup of debris that accumulates throughout the day.

Like skin, hair is affected by diet, cleanliness and stress. Proper nutrition is essential for healthy hair that looks its best, while thinning hair can sometimes signal anemia or a hormonal problem. One note: Although the skin on the head renews itself about once a month, occasionally the rate of this regeneration becomes unusually rapid. The result is flaky dead skin cells known as dandruff.

The health of nails can be affected by things as obvious and simple as exposing them to harsh chemicals (while cleaning, etc.) or continual moisture. Nutrition also plays an important role. In fact, whitening of the nails may indicate a protein-deficient diet, whereas spooning—when the nails become concave—may signal iron deficiency.

General Nutrition

It's probably an illusion that Americans are well-nourished. We may be overfed, but not with substantial nutrients. Chances are that most Americans are not getting all the nutritional support they need to maintain good health from their diets alone.

Dietary surveys indicate that 30–50 percent of the total caloric intake of the typical American is made up of highly processed, adulterated and nutrient-deficient foods. For example, white flour has been deprived of 60 percent of its original calcium, 71 percent of phosphorus, 75 percent of iron, 67 percent of copper and 85 percent of manganese. The loss of vitamins is similar.

The National Research Council's Committee on Diet and Health has stated, "A comprehensive review ... indicates that diet influences the risk of several major chronic diseases."

Studies show that health and longevity are increased by avoiding smoking, drinking moderate amounts of alcohol or none at all, controlling weight, reducing stress, exercising regularly and eating a well-balanced diet.

Learn to eat smart

The first step to eating smart is making sure your diet includes sufficient amounts of fiber and other essential nutrients, and restricting the amounts of fat and refined sugar and flour that you consume.

The American Cancer Society recognizes a relationship between certain types of cancer and the way people eat. Most people should eat as varied a diet as possible and become better acquainted with all kinds of fresh vegetables, fruits, fish, poultry, eggs, 100 percent whole grains, nuts and seeds.

The American Heart Association proposes that total fat intake should be less than 30 percent of total calories consumed. Saturated fat intake should be as low as possible, and polyunsaturated fat should be less than 10 percent. Amounts of monounsaturated fat can be as high as desired as long as it doesn't increase total fat intake to more than 30 percent of daily calories.

Nature's Sunshine provides products aimed at increasing the levels of general nutrition for all the systems in the body. Make sure that you are getting the nutrients you need.

Systems Guide

Index

Index by Body System or Category

Home/Household Products

Immune

Intestinal

Men's Products

Nature's Sweet Life

Nervous

212

Index

Vital Nutrition

Index

Weight Management

Women's Products

010841SL